Caring for Our Own:
A Portrait of Community Health Care

Caring for Our Own:
A Portrait of Community Health Care

By George Bellerose

Painter House Press

Middlebury, Vermont

Design: Futura Design, Shelburne, Vermont

Printing: Leahy Press, Montpelier, Vermont

ISBN: 0-615-13049-6

Library of Congress Control Number: 2005909304

COVER PHOTO: *Pediatrician Jack Mayer*

For the
Health Care Providers
of Addison County

CONTENTS

Preface

United Way of Addison County's mission since its formation in 1969 has been to improve the lives of everyone by mobilizing community resources. Today, the agency focuses its outreach, problem-solving, and fund-raising efforts in three areas: basic needs, services for children, youth, and families, and services for seniors.

In publishing *Caring For Our Own: A Portrait of Community Health Care* we hope that we can heighten everyone's awareness of the health care needs of rural communities everywhere. This portrait can help us appreciate what we are doing well and better understand the challenges that we face.

In *Caring For Our Own,* photojournalist George Bellerose has listened to the concerns of residents of Addison County. In 40-plus narratives, providers—an elementary school nurse, an emergency room doctor, an aide in a nursing home, the head of a community hospital—discuss the satisfactions and challenges in health care today. Health care recipients—a farm family

without health insurance, a daughter caring for an elderly parent, a teen parent—consider how the health care system in this rural county of 36,000 people is working for them.

Like the rest of the country, annual double-digit increases are placing health insurance beyond the reach of Vermont's small businesses, families, and individuals. At the same time, our health care system has become overwhelmingly complex and confusing. No one legislative study, commission report, or documentary can "fix" this system. But *Caring For Our Own* can help all of us clarify the core questions and values that must be at the heart of this discussion.

MaryEllen Mendl
Executive Director
United Way of Addison County

Foreword

By David Moats

Health care is easy to talk about and hard to understand. It's easy to talk about because all of us have experience with the health care system. We have all been sick, and we have all been to the doctor. Our loved ones have been sick, and some of them have died. We have cared for small children, worrying over ailments, major and minor. We have watched our elders enter their later years and have worried whether care they need will be there for them.

Health care is hard to understand because the health care system is really no system at all but a patchwork of services shaped by the chance of historical circumstance and by providers struggling to do the right thing. Thus, economic forces often beyond our understanding shape the care we get in ways we may not perceive.

We may have had an instructive and helpful conversation with our doctor about our cholesterol level, but we may have only the barest notion of why our conversation costs what it does, who is really paying for it, and why our heart medicine costs so much. And we can't fathom why a neighbor with a similar condition has been unable to receive adequate treatment.

Our understanding of the health care system is shaped as well by the people with whom we deal. We may be bursting with gratitude for the help and attentiveness of our physician. But a conversation with an insurance office may leave us seething with frustration. The nursing home staff may cause us to despair when they tell us nothing more can be done for a parent who has suffered a stroke. A visit from a home health nurse who outlines a plan of care will revive our faith that people want to do the right thing.

Caring for Our Own: A Portrait of Community Health Care displays the full complexity of the health care system and also the fundamental humanity that motivates caregivers. Addison County is a microcosm of the way health care workers in rural areas everywhere struggle to bring order to a complex array of services. Amidst this complexity there is a unifying theme in this portrait: People usually want to do the right thing.

It is sobering to realize that this book describes health care in a place where, relatively speaking, life is simple compared with densely populated urban areas. But even in a quiet place like Addison County, the health care system is an enormously complex web of people and services that is difficult to manage and coordinate.

Reading these chapters makes clear that the array of services available in Addison County is far from a system at all. There is a crucial and essential level of cooperation among the doctors, nurses, hospital, clinics, mental health, elderly, parent-child and other services that constitute the health care sector. But this cooperation is not grounded in a formal structure. Providers will this cooperation on an ad hoc basis as the only way to counter the centrifugal forces that drive them apart. Those forces are the result of competition, as organizations vie for limited resources, and the isolation of organizations pursuing varied missions. Thus, health care happens in Addison County despite these obstacles because dedicated providers insist that it must happen.

At this moment in our history, Americans aren't sure what to think about health care. The administration of President George W. Bush has advanced a view of society that places greater responsibility on individuals to take care of their own health care needs. It does this in the name of choice and responsibility. But the Bush program has raised alarms among many people because it seems to be an assault on the social compact by which society as a whole has accepted responsibility for caring for the elderly and the needy. For this reason, the Bush program has caused some people, like law professor Cass R. Sunstein, to think more deeply about the origins of that social compact.

In his book *The Second Bill of Rights: FDR's Unfinished Revolution and Why We Need It More Than Ever*, Sunstein explores the thinking behind Franklin Roosevelt's New Deal and the expanded New Deal that Roosevelt contemplated toward the end of his life. Roosevelt believed that people require a fundamental level of security in order to be free. Two of his Four Freedoms were freedom from want and freedom from fear. Social Security, the crowning achievement of the New Deal, was designed to diminish want and fear among the elderly. Destitution makes no one free. A society that guarantees a fundamental degree of security for its elderly grants them the blessing of freedom in their old age and also lifts an enormous burden off younger family members.

Roosevelt envisioned a Second Bill of Rights that would expand the guarantees of security. He believed people had a fundamental right to remunerative work and to adequate housing and health care. These freedoms would unleash the productive power of workers and cause our economy to expand.

He also believed that people wanted to work and provide for themselves, but that they were subject to the caprices of circumstance—a lost job, a health care emergency—and their own mistakes. And he believed that a safety net designed to rescue people from catastrophe and destitution was in the interest of everyone.

Providers and recipients of health care who describe their work and lives in these pages understand these fundamental principles. Whether they are a home health nurse, a hospice volunteer, or a daughter caring for her elderly stroke-ridden father, they are working from the unspoken premise that we have a responsibility for our neighbors. Neglect is not an option.

They patch together a system of services, grab resources where they can, forge alliances among themselves, all to further the freedom from fear and want that would otherwise oppress us. This is not a political act. It is the work of people acting out of ordinary compassion.

At the same time, those who have become aware of the growing economic and social dislocations caused by the inequities in our health care system have turned to politics in search of a remedy. "Politics is medicine writ large," says Dr. Jack Mayer in the final chapter of this book. Indeed, our approach to the health care system is likely to reflect our approach to politics.

Mayer, for example, argues that medicine is not a commodity, and his practice as a pediatrician has shown what he means. In his younger years he was the only pediatrician in rural Franklin County, and there were times when he might see 100 patients in a day. Social services were limited, and under President Reagan, they were cut back further. He was practicing what he called social medicine, which went far beyond the usual physical ailments. His work ran counter to every imperative of the marketplace, which had no mechanism for dealing with many of the people in the region.

Businessman Maynard McLaughlin, who served as chairman of a health care task force of the Vermont Business Roundtable in the late 1990s, offers another view. It is not the government's responsibility to provide health care, he says. People have to take responsibility for their own well-being. It is not possible to provide unlimited health care resources for people.

McLaughlin, who provides health care benefits for his employees, believes the only way the state will be able to begin an effective public dialogue about health care is by saying no and acknowledging the limits of our resources. The imperatives of the marketplace are something to which McLaughlin, a businessman, is sensitive.

At the same time, it is doubtful that most business people would advocate a system that callously disregards people's needs. Encouraging health-

ful behavior and individual responsibility is important. But there will always be some people with self-inflicted ailments—from smoking, drinking, drugs, or poor diet. Even if we understand the extent to which their own actions caused their illness, the state is unlikely to adopt policies that turn them away.

Ultimately, everyone needs medical care—for ordinary illness, injury, social pathology, or old age. At any one time, only a small percentage of us require care—it would be surprising indeed if most of us were sick at the same time. But we want the system to be there when we and our loved ones need it.

In the same way, we may spend a lifetime paying taxes to support the fire department. We may never need the service, but we know our towns are more prosperous and secure because the service is there.

The need to reconcile social obligation with individual responsibility and to marshal competing economic interests toward the common good has stymied health care reform for decades. In the early 1990s Gov. Howard Dean and the Vermont Legislature worked on a track parallel to the efforts of President Clinton to create a more rational system. But in Montpelier as in Washington, the competition of ideas and interests was never resolved. Now with costs skyrocketing and access becoming more difficult, Vermonters are demanding action again.

In 2005 the Vermont Legislature began the process of addressing these issues and asking fundamental questions. How do we guarantee health coverage to everyone? How do we pay for it? How do we improve the quality of care available to us? They address these questions, not as an academic exercise, but because they know failure to address them will worsen the problems of access, cost, and quality.

These questions are driven by our understanding that a growing number of Vermonters lack coverage and even more have inadequate coverage. People lacking coverage usually have access to emergency care, but they usually go without important routine care. The stories in these pages show that even for people with coverage it is often difficult to obtain high-quality care.

The Legislature, dominated by Democrats, was intent on pursuing system-wide reform. One of the principles underlying its effort was the idea of sharing the burden.

Gov. James Douglas, a Republican, was worried that the Legislature would adopt a system that would be too costly for the economy. The differences between Douglas and the Legislature could be seen in the competing proposals that emerged from the legislative session.

The Democrats in the Senate proposed taxing the payrolls of businesses that did not provide health care coverage to finance coverage for people lacking health insurance. It was a way of spreading the burden.

Douglas worried that a tax on businesses and their employees would be an economic burden. Instead, he proposed taxing the health care premiums of those who already had insurance, using the money to help provide access to those without it. Democrats countered that such a tax would add to the burden of those whose premiums already reflected the added the cost of covering those without insurance.

Douglas accused the Legislature of pursuing a single-payer, government-run system; legislative leaders denied it. At the same time, the legislators were impatient with the market-oriented approach advocated by Douglas.

The Legislature formed a special commission that began work in the summer of 2005 to develop a reform proposal; they were searching for a way to extend coverage and contain costs. During the fall, the special commission and the governor held separate forums around the state to listen to Vermonters.

Any reform plan faced unavoidable obstacles. About half of all Vermonters were covered by Medicare and Medicaid, and another sizable segment was covered by self-insurance plans that by federal law were protected from state regulation. With these segments of the population outside the reach of a state program, policymakers wondered how comprehensive a statewide program could be.

Yet the health care marketplace appeared to be spinning out of control. There was enormous waste in administrative costs; some estimates said a third of health care costs went to administration. There were enormous potential gains in streamlining the system and making system-wide changes, such as the establishment of sophisticated information technology.

As these pages make clear, the battle is not between government and the private sector. The health care system is intimately tied up with the government already. For many people health care is too costly to leave to the private sector; indeed, the private sector shuns people likely to prove too costly. More and more people understand now that there is an essential contradiction when the profit motive gets mixed up in health care. After all, insurance companies make money by denying care, not by paying for it.

Health care should not be about financial gain. It should be about service. Doctors and hospitals need to make money, but money cannot be their principal motive.

This understanding underlays Franklin Roosevelt's belief that health care was one of those essential needs, like education and employment, that are fundamental to our freedom and prosperity. Do we leave health care to the caprices of the marketplace in the belief that people are better off when they take responsibility?

With the establishment of Medicare and Medicaid we have already answered that question at least for the most vulnerable among us. These programs are meant to insulate the elderly and the needy from disaster. That leaves many others—working people, people between jobs, and others who fall outside the ordinary categories—vulnerable to the same burdens and disasters.

It doesn't have to be that way.

～

November 2005

Introduction

Addison County: Then and Now

In 1895, *The Middlebury Register* carried a boxed ad, "Castoria for Infants and Children," that promised relief for nearly every childhood ailment. Castoria destroyed worms, allayed feverishness, prevented vomiting of sour curd, cured diarrhea and wind colic, relieved teething troubles, and cured constipation and flatulence.

What peddlers of health care nostrums in the 19th century may have lacked in sophistication they made up for in certitude. Home remedies in fact often worked just as well as a poorly trained physician's all-purpose prescription—regulate secretions, extract blood, and promote perspiration, urination or defecation with cathartics to bring the body into balance—that reflected the limited understanding of the causes of disease. And doing nothing and letting the body heal itself was frequently the best course of all and far less painful than the bleeding, purging, blistering, induced vomiting and sweating essential to "throw off some noxious substance."

For much of the late 1700s and early 1800s, many mothers depended on the Dr. Spock of the day, Dr. William Buchan. His 400-page Bible of health care, *Domestic Medicine*, which went through 30-plus American printings, counseled that "every thing valuable in the practical part of medicine is within the reach of common sense."

"The man who pays proper attention to these (diet, exercise, and fresh air) will seldom need the physician, and he who does not will seldom enjoy health, let him employ as many physicians as he will," wrote the populist Buchan, who was not always popular with his colleagues in The Royal College of Physicians in Edinburgh.

The History of Addison County, Vermont recounts the all-purpose hydropathics treatments of Dr. Frederick Ford, Sr. that brought him a wide following and lucrative practice in the early 1800s:

Cold water he used in subduing fever in almost every form. Among his papers are found minute descriptions of its successful employment in numerous and some extremely critical cases of scarlet fever, puerperal fever, bilious fever, typhoid fever and even mumps. The use of the doctor's favorite remedy was often so prompt and sometimes so abundant as to meet the opposition of his medical brethren, and to awaken the fears of his patients and their friends. He tells us, in his written reports of these cases, of wrapping some of his patients in wet sheets frequently renewed, or of pouring upon them pailful after pailful of water; of immersing his patients in casks of cold water; and even once of laying a child upon a snow bank, wrapped in a wet cloth and there applying the water.

See a doctor in the 19th century? Only if you were desperate. Most "doctors" were poorly trained—there were no laws regulating the practice of medicine until 1876 and anyone could hang out a doctor's shingle after a short apprenticeship—and nearly all, including medical school graduates, struggled to make a living.

As one observer of mid-19th century medical science wrote, "...if all the various medicines used in the treatment of disease were immediately thrown into the sea it would be so much the better for mankind and so much the worse for the fishes." In fact, during the second half of the 19th century doctors abandoned many of their earlier practices—cupping, bleeding, and purging—in favor of bed rest and observation.

Self-reliance, family, friends, and home remedies

The Cost of Care in the 1840s

Per Visit Fee Schedule
Travel and Treatment

One-half mile	$.50
One-half to two miles	$1.00
Two to four miles	$1.50
Four to six miles	$2.50
Six to eight miles	$3.00
Eight to ten miles	$5.00

Fee Schedule for Office Visits

Advice and medicine	$.50
Venesection or tooth extraction	$.25
Reduction of a dislocated humerus	$2.00
Reduction of a dislocated femur	$5.00
(All other dislocations in proportion to difficulty.)	
Amputation of a lower limb	$20
Amputation of a superior limb	$15
Operation for hernia	$20
Operation for tracheotomy	$10
Operation for harelip	$10
Operation for trephining	$15
Paracentesis of abdomen	$5
Paracentesis of thorax	$10
Opening a difficult abscess	$2
Sutures	$1

made up the health care system for most people throughout the 1800s. Today's health care infrastructure—a network of doctors, hospitals, nursing homes, mental health services, and cradle-to-grave community health and social services—simply could not have been envisioned during much of the 19th century.

When Thomas Jefferson assumed the presidency at the turn of the century, there were but two hospitals in the country—one in New York, the other in Philadelphia. With the Civil War and the need to treat the war wounded, rudimentary military hospitals sprang up everywhere. However, hospitalization was often considered a death sentence, and twice as many soldiers died of disease and infection, many in hospitals, than from bullets. Vermont's military hospitals in Burlington, Brattleboro, and Montpelier had more the 2,000 beds among them—more beds than the state's 14 hospitals have today.

In 1875, there were fewer than 130 hospitals in the country. Vermont's first community hospital, 36 beds, was opened in Burlington in 1879. Addison County's Porter Hospital opened in 1925 with 22 beds.

Hospitals were not places of healing so much as charitable havens and a refuge for the homeless, very poor, and foreign born. Doctors were not paid by either the hospital or the patient, but valued hospital care "as an opportunity for clinical experience and as a chance to enhance their reputation with their middle-class patients."

We forget perhaps today, when childbirth is relatively routine, how life threatening it once was. Town clerks did not begin keeping vital statistics until the 1850s, but tombstones in town cemeteries attest to childbirth's toll on mother and infant in the 1700s and early 1800s. In 1900, about 120 infants per 1,000 live births did not survive their first year. Today, that figure is six.

But by the end of the century, some of the seeds of today's health care system had been planted, and the era of "therapeutic nihilism"—better to observe and do no harm—was coming to an end. With a growing understanding of the causes of disease, the medical community began developing effective vaccines and drugs to combat the great killers—smallpox, yellow fever, cholera, and diphtheria. Hygiene-conscious hospitals were beginning to control another great killer, hospital-incurred infections, which killed more patients than the afflictions that led to their admittance.

And with new technical resources, like X-ray machines, hospitals were on the road to becoming houses of science and technology rather than houses of mercy and charity. But much of the improvement in community well-being came from basic public health measures—clean water and better sewage treatment, vaccinations and uncontaminated food.

Reading accounts of community health care practices 100 and more years ago, one shakes one's head in wonder at how far we have come. We have moved from Model T to high-tech medicine in a lifetime and at a pace where questions arise far faster than answers.

For some, we are in the midst of a Golden Age of medicine where new drugs, therapies, and technologies are improving the quality of life and have nearly doubled life expectancy in a century.

For others, our health care system is in crisis; costs are out of control; millions have no insurance coverage; tests and technology have replaced compassion and caring and detailed knowledge of patients and their families.

No doubt, 100 years from now future generations will marvel at our practices and at how far they have come.

When future generations look at how we cared for our own, what will they see?

What will they think of our priorities and how we cared for the old, the troubled, and the less fortunate?

Will they find a society that was responsive to the needs, hopes, and fears of all its people?

How will they judge our efforts to balance the cost, accessibility, and quality of community care?

Will this era be seen as a time when communities and institutions worked together for a greater good or as a time when each institution protected its own?

"One of the most familiar sights in Middlebury during more than 50 years was our doctor driving at a slashing pace through the village after a round of out-of-town visits. His horses were celebrated for their courage and intelligence. His night calls were incessant and he often slept while driving. In that event, the horse was expected to attend to the details of the road and to bring him home safely. Mrs. Eddy used to tell of finding him asleep in his buggy in the barn after an all-night drive."

Obituary of Dr. M.H. Eddy, who died at the age of 100. Middlebury Register, March 9, 1933.

Addison County Today

On a gray, snowy morning in early December of 2001, 10 health and human services professionals gathered in Conference Room A at the Porter Medical Center for a "Visioning Session" on the needs of Addison County.

The discussion began with a one-idea-per-person circuit of the participants around the table: the president of Porter Hospital, the county's 45-bed community hospital; the administrator of the affiliated 105-bed nursing home; an obstetrician, whose practice—he had delivered nearly 5,000 babies—had touched many in the county; a family doctor from a neighboring community to the south; the branch manager from Social and Rehabilitative Services; the drug and alcohol abuse consultant from the regional Department of Health office; the head of the county counseling service; the director of the county's public transportation system; the director of a youth-oriented community program; the executive director of the county's United Way agency.

"More prevention and outreach."
"Multiple options to age in place."
"Ten units of low- to mid-income housing with a resident manager."
"Affordable drugs."
"Dentists and doctors who accept Medicaid."
"More education for parents of children, from birth through adolescence."
"Expanded public transportation so people can get to the doctors."
"Provide 90% of the health care services that residents need within the county."
"Integrate our services better. Reduce the shuffle and maze that our clients face."
"Affordable child care."
"A real dream. Simplified health insurance forms."
"Scarcity of quality staffing."
"Better connections among generations."
"Smoking cessation programs for all ages."
"A living wage."
"Share resources and infrastructure among health and human service organizations."
"Integrate alternative medicine with mainstream medicine."
"Pro bono legal counsel for non-profits."

"Nutritious food, available in homes and schools."

Within 45 minutes, the facilitator had magic-markered half a dozen easel-sized sheets of paper with comments and laments.

The World Health Organization defines health as "a state of complete physical, mental, and social well being and not merely the absence of disease or infirmity." This group of community leaders in its own ad hoc fashion had arrived at much the same definition.

There would be visioning sessions for other interest groups—agriculture, business and utilities, education, and finance/professions—and town conversations in the county's three major communities, Middlebury, Vergennes, and Bristol, and a group conversation for the county's 20 smaller communities. Ideally, within a year, the session's sponsor, the Addison County Economic Development Corporation—one of 12 regional private, non-profit development organizations in the state—would be able to develop a Comprehensive Economic Development Strategy. Once the federal Economic Development Administration approved this planning document, the county would be eligible for EDA funding for projects that addressed the region's most pressing needs.

Included in the morning's information packet was a three-page "Quick Facts" analysis of the county. All the participants at the morning's session had anecdotal evidence of the economic health of the county, but here were the cold-blooded numbers.

A magazine headline writer once referred to the county as "The Land of Milk and Honey," an editorial encomium that aptly described the county's rich agricultural heritage as the "Dairyland of Vermont" and postcard-perfect location between the Green Mountains on the East and Lake Champlain on the West. But Addison County was not way above average, at least by these numbers.

The county's 2000 census population, 35,974, ranked it in the middle—seventh most populous of the state's 14 counties. The county's three major communities—Middlebury, 8,200; Bristol, 3,800; and Vergennes, 2,700—and 20 smaller communities had grown 9.2% in the previous decade, a shade faster than the state. But this growth perhaps reflected in-migration of people drawn by job opportunities in adjacent Chittenden County, the state's most populous and prosperous county.

In per capita income, the county ranked a notch lower, eighth. Little change here. For the past 30 years, county incomes had lagged about 10% below the

Porter Hospital's Community Advisory Committee, seen here, met throughout 2004. Their priorities included a new birthing center, expanded smoking cessation programs, better integration of services for patients with chronic diseases, and exploration of short-term inpatient psychiatric care in the community.

state average, with the state lagging about 10% below the U.S. average.

The good news, for those who like open space, fields of corn, and herds of grazing Holsteins, was that Addison County continued to be the leading agricultural county in the state, producing approximately a quarter of the state's agricultural revenues. The bad news, the development corporation reported later in a longer economic analysis, was that even the most efficient of the county's dairy farms were struggling with record-low milk prices.

Manufacturing jobs had declined by 15% while service sector jobs had increased 35% during the past decade. Although job growth had been strong, many jobs were in services and retail, which were often part-time.

And because local wages tend to be about three-quarters of their national job equivalents, county residents were more dependent on government transfer payments (food stamps, aid to children, housing assistance) and a variety of part-time jobs. "The data point to underemployment in the region, as well as a less diverse economy than the state as a whole. The region tends to be more susceptible to downturns in the economy," "Quick Facts" concluded.

Although the fact sheet did not state it, this employment pattern often meant that manufacturing jobs with health insurance and good benefits were being replaced with service-sector and part-time jobs without health insurance and few benefits.

In an analysis of Addison County in the mid-1990s, a Middlebury College sociologist and University of Vermont colleague reviewed the county's economic history and starkly described a trend of "bad jobs" replacing "good jobs":

The loss of stable employment and the growth of bad jobs are now systemic features of economic prosperity. There is now a fundamental disconnect between what a significant portion of the working population are told they should be able to expect of themselves and what they can realistically attain.

We have found that the failure of the economy to provide these other benefits—long-term and stable employment, vacations and sick days, regular hours, assured pension plans and health insurance—is an equally (and perhaps even more) significant impediment to the capacity of households to get by and to recreate the so-called traditional household with its complement of gendered activities.

Session participants, no doubt, understood in their bones the significance of these developments. They all confronted the consequences of the county's two-tiered economy of relative haves and have nots every day.

"Quick Facts" did not inventory the community's health assets. If it had, there would have been many reasons for optimism. Unlike many underserved rural areas in Vermont and throughout the country, Addison County has been able to attract and retain health and social services professionals.

By most measures, these providers have stitched together a relatively seamless cradle-to-grave web of services. Community programs, from the Parent/Child Center at the beginning of life to Project Independence's adult day care center near the end of life, are national models. The community hospital and nursing home, the home health agency and counseling service are recognized throughout the state for the quality and breadth of their services. An appealing rural, small-town lifestyle, Middlebury College, and a sound educational system attract and keep a talented health and social services workforce.

At the same time, county providers, be they a home health nurse, a therapist at the counseling service, or an aide in a nursing home, are being pressed to do more, do it faster, and do it with less. Like the rest of the country, annual double-digit increases in premiums are placing health insurance beyond the reach of county small businesses and individuals. And ever-changing conditions and reimbursements are requiring agencies to reinvent themselves in a matter of months and to "compete" with each other for patients or face layoffs and closure.

Those are givens that health care professionals everywhere face today. So what was this group's vision for the county?

At the end of the hour-and-a-half session, the group had a rough working document with a goal:

All citizens of our community are supported to lead healthy and productive lives with an integrated, modern, affordable system of medical, mental, and substance abuse care that is available to all residents regardless of age or income.

How well is the county meeting that goal?

Community well-being is a shared responsibility. Do Addison County agencies, as many providers believe, work more collaboratively than most? If so, what can other communities learn from Addison County?

If not, how does a community create a collaborative and comprehensive safety net?

Shelves of statistics-fat reports with local, state, national, and international figures and comparisons can help us answer that question. But these benchmarks can be cold and distant and inadequately convey the human costs of our health care policies. And they rarely capture in any detail the ground-level perspectives of providers and recipients of service.

No one legislative study, commission report, or collection of community interviews can fully answer these questions. So how can we get our arms around the state of community care? We can start by being good listeners.

The following interviews are an attempt at just that. They are a report card with a human face on how Addison County, our national health care system writ small, is meeting the challenge of caring for its own.

Chapter 1

The Frontlines of Caregiving

Once a Nurse, Always a Nurse

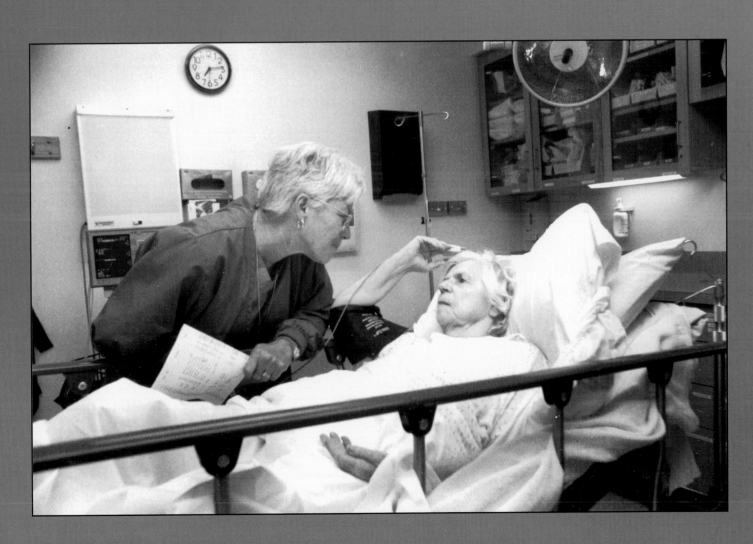

Nursing Today

There is good news. Most nurses never lose their belief that community caregiving is a fulfilling and rewarding life. At the end of a long discussion that concluded with a dispiriting listing of the pressures and frustrations in today's hospital, Diana Clark, when asked would she become a nurse again, unhesitatingly replied, "Absolutely!"

There are many Diana Clarks among the 80 registered nurses at Porter Hospital and the approximately 4,500 registered nurses practicing in Vermont.

But the bad news is that there are simply not enough nurses, especially in high-skill areas like intensive care units, emergency and operating rooms, and psychiatric and geriatric units.

As the Blue Ribbon Nursing Commission reported in 2001 in *A Call to Action: Addressing Vermont's Nursing Shortage*:

> Vermont is in the midst of a crisis. The number of nursing students has declined at the same time the number of working nurses who are retiring is increasing. The confluence of these two dynamics has created unacceptably high nursing vacancy rates in hospitals, nursing homes, and home health agencies.

This global perspective, translated to the Addison County ground level, has meant staffing pressures if not shortages in nearly every agency.

The nursing home has had to restrict admissions, at times, because of staffing shortages. The hospital has had to hire very expensive RN "temps" from out-of-state. The home health agency, which can offer Monday–Friday daytime-only shifts, has fared better, with little turnover and few vacancies.

Vermont's problems mirror what is happening throughout the country. In the short term, administrators have been reconfiguring work loads and assignments, state organizations have been offering a variety of incentives to attract people into the profession and to retain them, while recruiters have been hiring English-speaking nurses from Canada, Ireland, the Philippines, and most recently India.

In the long term, the U.S. Department of Health and Human Services forecasts that the nursing shortage will only get worse – by 2020 the country, with an aging population, will need an estimated 1.75 million RNs but only 635,000 will be available if current trends continue. Compounding the problem is a national shortage of faculty at nursing schools; 11,000 qualified applicants could not be accommodated in nursing programs in 2003.

Closer to home, three-quarters of Vermont's registered nurses are over 40. Their replacements, the 20 to 30 age group, make up only 7% of the nursing workforce. By 2010, the Office of Nursing, Workforce, Research, Planning, and Development at the University of Vermont College of Nursing and Health Sciences estimates that the state will face a shortfall of 500 full-time nurses even with a 100% increase in nursing school capacity. While the number of nursing students and graduates has increased since the 2001 Blue Ribbon study, there is little room for further expansion due to the lack of qualified faculty, an Office study reported in 2004.

This much is clear today. Fewer and fewer 17- and 18-year-old women – 95% of registered nurses are female – are interested in nursing. There are simply more career options today than for women 30 years ago. And those who choose nursing have more options within the field – doctors' offices, schools, health centers – which can be less demanding than work in vacancy-plagued hospitals, home health, and long-term care, which employ about two-thirds of all registered nurses.

So why would a 17-year-old want to become a nurse? In the four following interviews, three long-time nurses and one nursing aide offer some answers in discussing their life's work in community care.

PRECEDING PAGE: **Diana Clark, RN, Porter Hospital**

Leigh Smith, LNA

Helen Porter Rehabilitation and Healthcare Center

I've Been Told
That I Have a Knack

Labor-intensive nursing homes are facing the double challenge of very tight budgets and a nursing shortage throughout health care organizations. A rough staffing rule of thumb for nursing homes is that for every registered nurse (RN) you need two to three licensed practical nurses (LPN). For every LPN you need two or three licensed nursing assistants (LNA).

For a 100-bed nursing home like Helen Porter that translates to 30 to 35 nurses (RNs and LPNs) and 70 to 80 nurses' aides to cover three shifts—roughly a one-to-one staff-to-resident ratio.

Leigh Smith began as an aide at the newly opened Helen Porter Nursing Home in 1993 during relatively flush times. By 2001, Porter, like nursing homes everywhere, was struggling to find and retain help, especially nurses' aides, who provide the bulk of the hands-on care and feeding.

People ask me, "How can you work in a nursing home? It's so.... I could never do what you're doing."

And I say, "Yes, you could."

And they're like, "Oh, no. I could never do that."

And so maybe you couldn't. That's OK. I enjoy my job.

Don't get me wrong. We work hard. There's a lot of lifting. There's a lot of caregiving, and it's tough.

"Coming here is a big change. I try to understand residents' frustration, because I don't know how I would feel if somebody plucked me out of familiar surroundings and I lost control," says Smith.

I've been told that I have a knack, but I don't know where it comes from. Maybe it's because I'm comfortable around older people.

I was raised that what goes around comes around. I believe that very, very deeply. What you put out is what you get back. And if you put out something nice, it'll come back. Maybe not now, maybe later, maybe not to you but to a family member.

Coming here is a big change, and I try to understand residents' frustration, because I don't know how I would feel if somebody plucked me out of familiar surroundings and I lost control.

It's easy for me to sit here and talk about it, but if it ever happened to my parents I probably would try to do it all myself. I figure that nobody

can care for my parents as well as I can, but there comes a point when you have to sleep.

On the West Wing people come in for rehabilitation and therapy and get better and go home. On our East Wing we have Alzheimer's and special needs residents. Take a person who comes in with borderline Alzheimer's. You watch the deterioration, but you also build up a friendship.

If we know that someone's not doing well we'll tell each other, "If you want to go and say good-bye you need to do it today." I don't have a formal way of saying good-bye. Because certain ones I can't, especially if I have to work the rest of the day. I may just say, "It's OK. I'm here, and it's going to be OK."

It doesn't get easier with experience. The day

it doesn't affect you is the day you need another job.

I come in at 6:45. At the morning meeting, all the aides get a taped report from the night shift supervisor on who has had a good night or a bad night, who needs extra care or who has new orders. Right now we have about 47 residents on the East Wing.

After report we start bathing and dressing the residents. Some people get tubbed down and some get a bed bath, just a washing off and dressing.

We have three kinds of people to feed: people who can feed themselves in the dining room; people who are prone to choking or who can't feed themselves and require one-on-one feeding in the day room; and residents who eat in their rooms because they need the quiet or want to eat there.

Normally, we finish with breakfast by 9:45, sometimes by 10 o'clock. If we go past 10 o'clock, we're either really short-handed or it's one of those poopy kind of days where you have a lot of total care.

After breakfast we start taking our 15-minute breaks and giving baths and showers. On a good day, everybody will be out of bed, dressed, had breakfast and be in activities by quarter to eleven. Most of the time we're not finished until 11:15, 11:30.

On a perfect day residents' lunch begins at noon and is usually over by about 1:15, 1:30. And then we start toileting people again.

Our goal is to toilet every two hours. Some people can toilet on their own. Others you have to undress, and it can take two people. State regulations say you're supposed to turn people every two hours if they are unable to get out of bed. It gets rough when you don't have the staff.

On a good day we have everybody back in their rooms or at afternoon activities by 2:30.

Leigh Smith's non-stop day involves helping dress, feed, toilet, bathe, and move to activities or therapy half a dozen and more residents.

We will make up a nourishment cart and go around to everybody's room and see if they want an ice cream, soda, or cookie. By then it's quarter to three and we do our paperwork and answer bells. When the 3 to 11 shift comes out of report, we go home.

I leave at 3:15. It's overtime after that.

We've been working really shortstaffed most of the summer with four or five aides on the day shift, instead of seven. At one point, we had like 9 or 10 aides and that was nice. We could give extra baths, take more time with fingernails, toenails, and spend more time just talking with people.

A lot of people are burning out, because we can't keep help. People take the two-week LNA course here and get their license. Then they leave and go some place that pays more and where the work is not as hard.

Today, we have two aides who are staying to work a double shift because the wing is understaffed. I try not work a double shift more than once every two weeks because it just wipes me out.

You start at 3:15 and help with dinner and then get them to bed. If you stop for supper or breaks you won't finish until 9. But if you have a lot of energy left and don't take a break you can be done from 7:30 to 8:15. That's without anything going wrong.

All of us who have worked here for a long time know that we're not going to get rich from our job. Training class starts at $6.50 (2001). When you pass LNA certification and the three-month waiting period it goes to $7 or so. Senior people can make $9 to $10 an hour. We do it because we like it.

I've suggested to people that they come and work here. It's a day job for most of us, which is hard to find around here. The benefit package is good – I always push the benefit package – and they're very flexible in giving you time off when you need it.

You can't work here all year and not take a vacation. It's going to mess with you, physically and emotionally. You need a break, even if it's only a long weekend.

I'm going to get my LPN and have started a program this year through the Community College of Vermont. It would be a pay increase and a big change because LPNs give out medications, do feeds, and don't do the direct care. There wouldn't

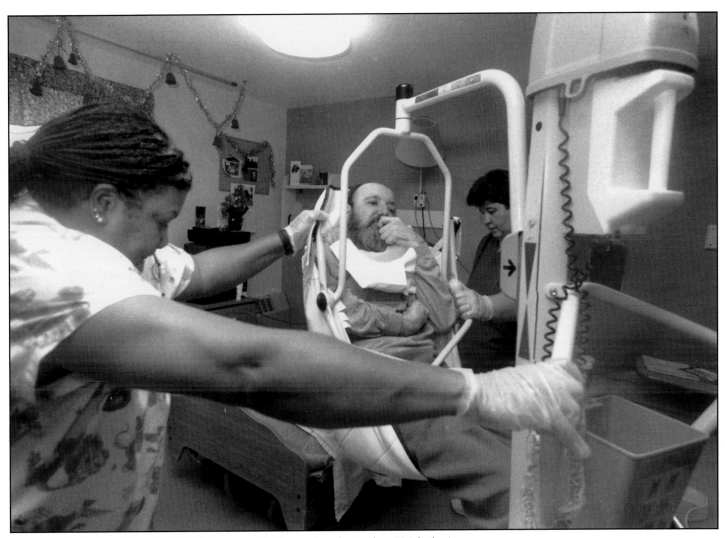

"Time goes by fast here," says Smith. "We have our calm days and our hectic days. Mainly they're hectic. With all the lifting I may not be able to do this until I'm 60."

To qualify for nursing home placement residents must require skilled nursing care, often following hospitalization. Alternatively, they must require 24-hour help with activities of daily life, such as eating and decision making.

be as much lifting either.

Being 51 and having had leukemia my energy level isn't what it used to be. And it probably never will be. Most of the other LNAs are in their 30s and some are in their 20s. So I will have to make my job easier.

Somebody just teased me, "Well, Leigh, when you become an LPN you'll just tell us what to do."

I laughed because it will take at least three years to take courses and do my clinical while I'm working here.

"You know I'm not going to be that way," I said.

But I have to be realistic about the lifting part. I may not be able to do that until I'm 60 or 70. I was hoping to retire at 62, but I may have to work longer.

I was mostly embarrassed after I came back when I was chosen employee of the quarter. Maybe people were just being nice. I had taken a break from Helen Porter and worked at International Paper for three years in Ti (Ticonderoga in New York). My daughter was going to Castleton (Castleton State College), and we had to come up with tuition and the pay is good there.

At the paper plant, I made $17 an hour when I analyzed the wastewater that went into the lake and time and a half when I stayed over. But there would be days when they would bounce me to maintenance, and I'd make $10 an hour. I was working all the time, and working around the big machines is dangerous.

Finally, I said the money's not worth it. After I came back in February of 1999, I found out that I had leukemia from the blood test from my physical. The leukemia wasn't diagnosed until the first part of April. Waiting was emotionally draining, but I kept working. When I was on chemo, I missed a couple days but I was able to keep working.

It was a nice surprise when I got the award. And it was nice to know that everybody was appreciative of me coming to work, even though they had to help me sometimes.

Everybody has been really super while I have waited for the results of the latest biopsies. I got the first good news over the Christmas (2000) holidays that the leukemia was 93% gone with this new drug. I think I was the first person in Vermont to be part of this trial study, and they're close to saying that this drug is a cure for CML (chronic myelogenous leukemia).

Everybody has been so happy for me. It's just a miracle, really. Every three months I have a bone marrow biopsy, and I have been in complete remission for six months.

My best friend asked me the other day, "Well, what's your goal now? What are you going to do if you get your LPN?"

And I said," You know, I'd really like to go into research."

That would be a little bit easier. I'd be interested in cancer research because of what I've been through. You can be a LPN and be part of a research study because the nurse that took care of me was a LPN.

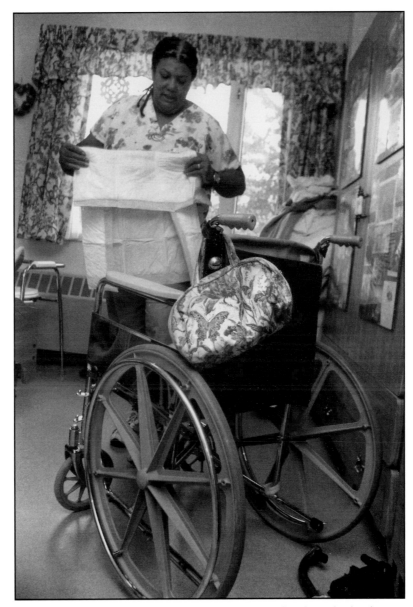

Only a handful of the Helen Porter's 100 residents can walk independently. About 40% require help eating. About 45% have some form of dementia. About 60% have bladder incontinence.

"I was raised that what goes around comes around. I believe that very, very deeply. What you put out is what you get back. And if you put out something nice, it'll come back," says Smith.

Diana Clark, RN
Porter Hospital

Today It's Boom!
In and Out!

During the course of a week, Diana Clark may wear several hats at Porter Hospital: floor nurse caring for four to six patients in the medical-surgery unit; charge nurse for the 32-bed unit, assessing patient needs and determining nursing coverage; and "supe," the supervising nurse who monitors the needs of the medical-surgery, maternity, emergency room, and special care units.

Clark, who began her nursing career in the late 1960s and started at Porter in 1977, has had a bedside seat during the transformation of American medicine.

With the constant financial pressure to reduce hospital stays, nurses have less and less time to understand and respond to patients' medical, emotional, and psychological concerns, says Clark.

When I started in 1977, Porter had the same number of beds, 45, that it does today. There were about 15 doctors on the medical staff. Today there are over 60. Helen Porter Nursing Home was full, and we had some patients with chronic illness who would be in the hospital for 90 days until they could find a nursing home bed.

We had really good relationships with the patients then because we got to know them medically and psychologically. We could almost anticipate what they needed. They were also healthier than the patients in Porter today. Today it's boom! In and out!

This change is very frustrating, and I go home these days feeling more inadequate than I did years ago. We have to give so much information to patients and their families and have very little time to do it when the average stay now is

slightly less than four days. Years ago someone with a colostomy would stay for 10 days. Now with a change in surgical techniques it's a couple days.

You have to teach patients how to protect their skin, put the bag on, empty it. You have to educate them on their diet and about skin care. During this time they don't have much energy because they have had major surgery. It's just wham, wham, wham.

Many patients are overwhelmed by this. I always tell patients that they will be able to rest when they get home, and that home health will show them how to take care of themselves, which is entirely different at home from being in a hospital.

People coming into the hospital today are much more educated and know more about their

bodies. Some have watched operations on TV on the Learning Channel or "Emergency Room," on the Discovery Channel. They may know somebody who has had the procedure.

But if a person hasn't been in a hospital before, our routine is an assault on the senses. There will be nurses, housekeepers, people from the lab to draw blood. There might be a dietitian and the discharge coordinator. You could have 15 people doing something directly with you. That's a lot of strangers, especially when you're feeling exhausted and uncomfortable.

The first thing that I tell a patient is, "If you don't know, ask. It's your right, your body." Uncertainty is worse than knowing what is going to happen.

Second, I describe the routines. I tell them

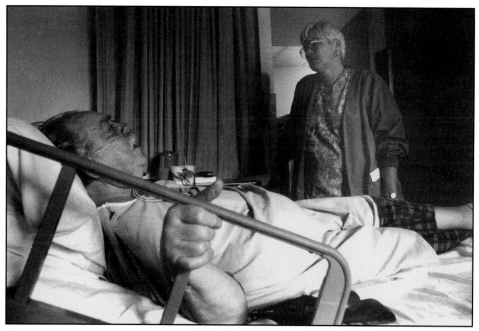

Nurses need to be part healer, social worker, psychologist, and teacher. Understanding these roles takes time, says Clark, but once you have it, it all makes sense.

that they will not get any sleep, because this is the way of the beast. If you're in the hospital that means you're sick and need to have your vital signs and blood pressure taken.

I also say that niceties stop at the front door. We're very interested in everything that goes into the body and everything that comes out. It's very difficult for a lot of people when you go in and say, "We have to measure your urine. We have to know when you pass flatus. We have to look at your bowel movements to see how your body is working."

We have always done this, but the time to explain and do it has been compressed.

Hospital stays started shrinking in the 1980s with Medicare's introduction of DRGs (Diagnosis-Related Groups). This was a code and criteria that

determined how much the government would pay for every disease and procedure. I realized then that agencies other than hospitals were having a major impact on how we treated patients.

Take somebody who has a heart attack with another underlying problem, such as a leg ulcer that won't heal. This delays the normal recovery and takes a lot of dressing changes, but the payment would often only cover the chest pain as the primary diagnosis and not the leg ulcer. If the norm for treating this is six days and the patient stays 10 days, the hospital will have to justify the additional time or it won't get reimbursed under the DRG system.

Medicare, HMO, OSHA regulations are in the back of your mind all the time. I don't know

who is sitting there at a desk making the regulations, but I would like them to spend two days with us to see what reality is.

Our daughter has said that she will never be a nurse. It's too hard. You have a life, but you really don't have a life.

Our days off are staggered. Everyone has to work holidays. For many years, Jim (her husband, a RN in the emergency room) worked evenings and I worked nights. We had no time off together when our kids were young. Now we have the same days off every other weekend.

You can't fix the schedule. It's part of the job.

For many years the pay was really very poor. Then in the 1980s during a nursing shortage there was an amazing jump. I've been in it for a long time so my salary is good. However, I know I will never make a big jump. It's like teaching. You know that you will go up gradually.

Better retirement and continuing education benefits would help. There are a couple LPNs who are going for their RNs. Porter does reimburse you for tuition if you have a certain average.

Another thing that would help would be more nurturing for new nurses and graduates. When I was in nursing school there was much more clinical work. You were in the hospital eight hours a day. You were incorporating into patient care what you were learning. Castleton (State College) loves to come here with nursing students, because we say, "This is how it really happens. This is reality."

The state is sponsoring workshops and Porter has sent six or seven experienced nurses to learn how to be better preceptors to new employees. It takes a while before new graduates get to that point where they say, "It makes sense." It used to be three months, six months, but now there is so

Today, only the very sick and patients recovering from major surgery are hospitalized. Updates on patients' condition are the first order of business at the change-of-shift nurses' meeting.

much information it takes longer. There is no flag that gets raised, but all of a sudden it just makes sense. You have to keep learning, but once you have it, you have it.

The public doesn't realize what broad knowledge nurses need. You need to know equipment, medications, and side effects. You need to be a little bit of a social worker. You need a little bit of legal background to understand all the rules and regulations.

At the moment, we have one nurse with an elbow injury who has been out for six weeks. Another nurse has been on light duty for a couple months because of her back. A third nurse is just getting off light duty because of her back. Another nurse has just had an MRI for her back. All these injuries were caused by patients who jerked. Injuries happen no matter how great your posture or positioning is. These are the physical injuries.

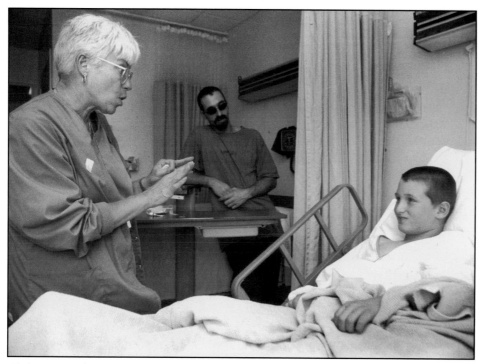

Clark sees very few children at Porter today, largely because many childhood problems, like asthma, can be treated at home with new medications.

There is also emotional and mental burnout. There aren't too many other professions that have our stress.

I can go home and talk, without breaching confidentiality, with Jim, and he has a complete understanding. He can do the same thing with me. When the kids were young we could say, "Bad day in the ER or bad day on the floor," and the kids would understand.

That's a real advantage.

At the hospital when we have had a major crisis or disaster, we have a gathering so people can talk about it. Several years ago after one of our nurses died, we had a memory gathering for ourselves. She had been in the hospital, and we had taken care of her. It wasn't closure, but we were able to bond together and it was helpful.

I've changed over the years. For one, I'm not as sweet as I used to be. I wasn't ever sickly sweet, but I always, always gave people the benefit of doubt. Now, I joke that I'm the gray-haired bitch. If I want something done, I'm more direct with patients, staff, anyone outside the hospital, because I feel the time constraint.

Patients don't want to hear, "I don't have the time. We don't have the staff." I try and be more creative and say, "I'm sorry, I need to know now."

You have to give and receive so much infor-mation in such a short time and document it. You really can't get this information in a conversational way, especially in the ER when there are people waiting.

Sometimes nurses may appear to be uncar-ing. If they look like they are not focusing on you, it is probably true. It's not because they're uncaring, but because there may be a crisis or a problem that can't be solved right away.

Another change is that I'm more physical with patients. I'll take someone's hand and hold it while trying to get information. If I have to, I will sit on the bed, especially if I know the person and they have been in Porter before. Infection-wise that may not be good and maybe it's not dignified, but it's friend-lier and sometimes comforting to a patient who is apprehensive about being hospitalized.

If I had a magic wand, I'd hire more LNAs because they can do the vital signs, glucose mon-itoring, the "fluff and buff" of a really good scrub-bing and bath. They are absolutely marvelous, hardworking, and very observant. And we don't have very many, six, to cover three shifts: a 7 a.m. to 7 p.m. day shift; a 7 p.m. to 7 a.m. night shift; and a 3 to 11 evening shift.

Some days LNAs are paired with an RN for a high-need patient. Some days the acuity may not be as high, but it may take two people to move the patient and get them out of bed.

With more LNAs we could spend more time sitting with a patient, on education, and not be so harried because somebody needs a bedpan. Some of the newer nurses probably wouldn't be as comfortable in delegating responsibilities. The Porter approach is not team nursing. You're assigned to a patient and take care of all that patient's needs. But team nursing may happen with the shortage of nurses.

Whether she is a floor, charge, or supervising nurse, Clark has to document the treatment of the floor's patients. On Clark's wish list—bedside computers and a fully computerized hospital.

Another thing that I'd do, and this may seem strange, I'd give nursing homes the respect they deserve. I'd double the salaries of LNAs and hire more nursing home staff. I'd start with nursing homes because our population is aging and people are living longer and healthier. But quite a few still need long-term care. In the past they came into the hospital, because there weren't nursing home beds.

Doing this would alleviate some of our frustrations when we have a patient who is not acute. Some of these non-acute patients take up the time that we would be giving to the really sick. This isn't the problem it used to be because more money has been funneled into home care and because we have better communication with the nursing home with our full-time RN discharge planners.

Would I become a nurse again? Absolutely.

You help people feel better. You teach people how to care for themselves or loved ones. You are constantly learning about people, good and bad, and encountering caring, loving families.

You learn to accept the death that we all face and be a resource for others, a shoulder to cry on. And yes, I cry, too.

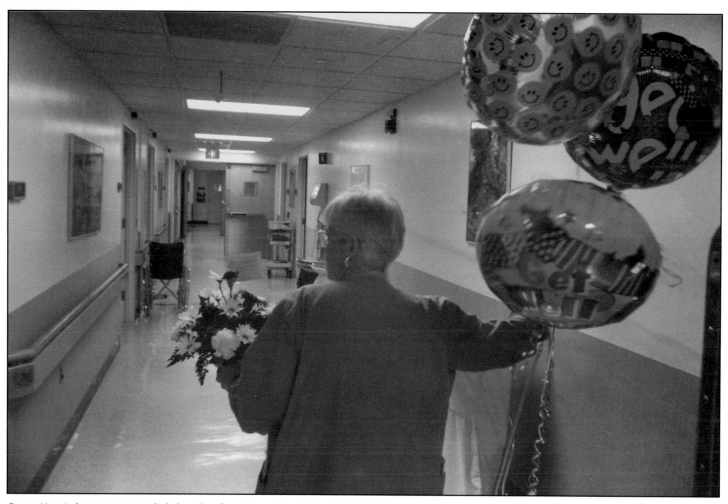

Porter Hospital stays average a little less than four days—scarcely time enough to deliver get well balloons, prepare the patient for home care, and say good-bye.

Barb O'Hehir, RN

Addison County Home Health
and Hospice

Once a Nurse,
Always a Nurse

Barb O'Hehir, like many in the 1960s, chose nursing because it provided a stable and challenging job at a time when there were far fewer career opportunities for women. She has been a home health nurse since the late 1960s, when home health began its rapid expansion following the passage of Medicare and Medicaid programs.

There is no middle ground when it comes to home health nursing. You either love it or hate it. In home health nursing, you're responsible for the patient 24 hours a day. Your conscience is looking over your shoulder, and if you're good you have to pay attention to all the details. People either like this autonomy and responsibility or they leave.

We have had some hospital nurses who worked here and missed the hospital's structure and returned to the hospital. They don't have as much paperwork and are not responsible for providing total patient care. What are the patient's social needs? What equipment do they need? If they are not happy with their doctor how do you deal with that? It's a much different relationship when you're dealing with a patient at home.

I started working at Addison County Home Health in 1979. We had five or six nurses and rented space on the third floor of Porter Hospital with the public health department.

Then Porter needed the third floor for doc-

tors' offices so we moved to the front part of Dr. Bryant's office on Court Street. We outgrew that space and went to the Marble Works and outgrew that space and moved into the old Sugar House Restaurant off Route 7.

We kept growing because hospitals were not keeping patients as long. Hospitals were being hit with DRGs (Diagnosis-Related Groups, a Medicare funding schedule that paid a fixed amount for procedures regardless of the patient's length of stay) in the 1980s and people were coming out faster and sicker. We're doing procedures now, like intravenous pushes, at home that used to be done only in the hospital.

We are not only providing more skilled care, but we are also managing patients' total care. Medicare patients can only have skilled nursing care at home as long as they have acute care needs and are "homebound." But patients may still need the help of a home health aide and long-term supervision. Nurses supervise the home health aide and the patient's overall well-being.

Although the Medicare law has never changed, people have reinterpreted the regulations. In the Reagan years, homebound meant almost exclusively confined to bed. They were so strict that it was really hard to see anybody. It was all to save money.

Then Bush came in and things loosened up again. Then we got into the prospective payment system in the 1990s. Under the prospective payment system, we are paid a certain amount of money per diagnosis and per therapy.

In the 1980s, we had our nursing data base, which was the physical assessment of the patient. You signed your problem list, planned for them, and carried on. Now we use the much longer OASIS (Outcome and Assessment Information Set)

"There is no middle ground when it comes to home health nursing. You either love it or hate it," says O'Hehir.

assessment form, which is 22 to 23 pages long.

The governing principle behind OASIS seems to be get in and out of the home very quickly. Do the teaching and then leave.

Yes, you can teach an elderly couple how to manage congestive heart failure with a better diet, how to use weights to improve their fitness, and that kind of thing. But that 85-year-old man's heart will get worse no matter how much care the wife can provide. It's still going to fail, and he needs assessment that the family can't do. This is the piece that is getting lost.

We try and work around these restrictions and

Home health nurses are like the family doctors of old. They make house calls. Addison County's 30-plus nurses made about 19,000 skilled nursing home visits in 2004.

provide the care the patient needs. A home health aide, for example, can't prepare meals because that's not a Medicare covered service. But there's no law that says you can't do something extra as long as you have provided the reimbursed service. So the aide can help a person with a shower, which is reimbursable, and fix lunch during the visit.

It's short-sighted not to do it, but Medicare won't pay for preventive services and tries to avoid paying for chronic care. But if patients don't get lunch, they don't eat. If patients don't eat they're just going to get sicker.

Take alternating air pressure mattresses. Many homebound have poor circulation from diabetes, vascular disease, and poor nutrition and develop pressure sores and open wounds from spending many hours in bed or sitting. You can prevent a bed sore by spending $35 a month on a good mattress. But Medicare won't spend $35 up front for prevention and instead ends up with bed sores and ulcers that cost billions of dollars each year to treat.

16

So we find other ways to help patients. We go to Neat Repeats (a used clothing store in Middlebury that supports area non-profit agencies) and get them to pay for the mattress.

Medicare has loosened up some on its definition of homebound. In the past if patients went to Project Independence (an adult day care center in Middlebury) they were not considered homebound. But they have changed that. They now consider that a therapeutic experience.

I always check "homebound" on the paperwork of one of my patients. But in Medicare's view, he can use a motorized wheelchair and is not homebound. But he's a paraplegic and someone has to help him out of bed with a lift or he can't go anywhere. To me that is homebound.

Medicaid is less restrictive, but if Medicare denies a service Medicaid will often follow suit.

Addison County is divided into six territories with one to three nurses per territory. Essentially you take everything that comes into your territory. I am a floater now and cover for people who are on vacation or who need a day in the office for paperwork.

As a floater, I also work with patients who require more time than a nurse with a 30- to 40-patient caseload has. And I have a particular inter-

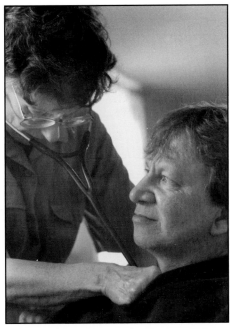

Clients are sent home "sicker" from hospitals today and may need physical, occupational, and speech therapy and personal care help.

est in bone problems and wound care so I get consulted on those patients.

I always remember that I am a guest in their house. Older people can get crotchety, but you listen and talk with them and you can get through that. Some people are angry at the system. Some

people don't want to be bothered by us. You just have to let them get that out and go from there.

A first home assessment visit can take two hours. Subsequent visits might be half an hour. It doesn't happen often, but sometimes a patient may not want me to visit. In one case, a woman who needed care didn't want me to visit. She was still upset because I had cared for her husband and he died. We honor a patient's request.

Dealing with all the rules and regulations is frustrating, but the satisfactions in working with patients haven't changed. The thing about nursing is that once you're a nurse, you're always a nurse whether you keep your license current or not.

I wouldn't have the energy at 70 to do what I'm doing today. But I think even when I retire I would still want to do some volunteering where you can do something that is nurturing.

I can remember visiting Henrietta Wilcox in the Helen Porter Nursing Home after she had a stroke. She had been a nurse for many years. She reminded me to keep washing my hands. She was 85 years old, but she was still a nurse. "You know," she said, "Your nursing skills never leave you."

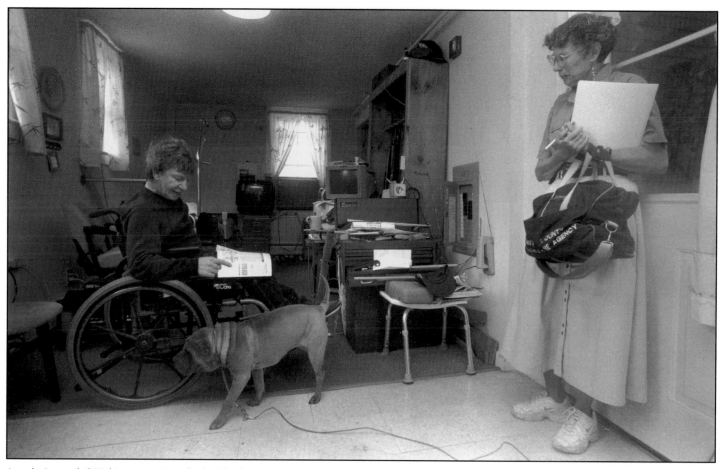

In a day's travel, O'Hehir may monitor the health of a paraplegic; check the leg wounds of a diabetic; evaluate the changing needs of a middle-aged man with multiple sclerosis; discuss family concerns with a mother caring for a quadriplegic son.

Pat Jannene, RN

Vice President, Patient Care
Services, Porter Hospital

Why Would a 17-Year-Old Kid Want to Become a Nurse?

Pat Jannene graduated from nursing school in 1977 when there was a glut of nurses and worked as a critical care nurse in Boston before coming to Porter in 1981. She is now in charge of Porter's 80 direct-care nurses (40 full-time equivalents) and faces a problem common to hospitals in Vermont and throughout the country. There is a shortage of nurses with no quick fix in sight.

Nurses' most common complaint is stress, says Jannene. Some days it is a dying patient; on others, it is unplanned admissions. Most of all, caring for patients is physically demanding and emotionally exhausting.

I was one of those people in the mid-1970s who felt that there were still few choices for women. You became a teacher or a nurse. Today, people aren't going into nursing.

If you pick up the front page of newspapers all over the United States, you read about nurses who are unionizing or are unhappy or on strike or who feel that they are underpaid.

Why would a 17-year-old kid want to become a nurse? You have to admit that nurses are required to do things that most kids consider fairly disgusting. Emptying bed pans is not very appealing when there are so many options out there.

There were about 173 RN graduates in 2000 in Vermont compared to 270 in 1995. And many graduates won't take or pass the licensing exam. Back in 1999, I didn't have any applications for work.

A graduating nurse could then make more money somewhere else. In 2000, the Porter board approved roughly 12% increases in our hourly wages for nurses so we could be more competitive in Vermont. In the *Boston Globe* they were advertising then for registered nurses for $40 an hour. If you work full-time that is $80 grand a year and benefits are on top of that. We can't compete with that.

Today (2004), we are competitive with other Vermont hospitals. Starting graduates start at $20.25 with senior nurses making $28 an hour. We have good differentials for night shift work, and being small and non-union we can individualize schedules in ways that bigger, unionized hospitals can't. And we have worked hard to build relationships with nursing schools like Castleton. Their students enjoy training here. We get to know them and hire some when they graduate.

We have relatively little turnover, perhaps 5% a year, but finding nurses is still not easy, especially for the operating room, emergency room, and intensive care where you can't hire a fresh, relatively inexperienced graduate to work there. And there are a lot more opportunities in nursing for nurses.

It used to be if you were a nurse you worked in a hospital. Now nursing homes are an option. Home health is an option. Physician practices and nursing practices are an option.

A hospital is not always the most attractive place to work when you have to work evenings, night shifts, weekends, Christmas. Those are real lifestyle issues. Your friends don't work on weekends. Your family doesn't work on weekends. We do.

The problem is going to get worse. We can pay people more to work evenings, nights, weekends and pay holiday differentials. You can make a little more working here than in a doctor's office. But the reality is that even for time and a half, all of us would rather be home with their family on Christmas.

You know the schedule comes with working here. You can minimize or overlook it, because what you do here is enjoyable and fulfilling. But again, working in a physician's practice is 8 to 5, Monday through Friday.

I have had to hire traveling nurses in the past in the specialty areas to fill in, because I can't find enough in the local area. Hiring a traveling nurse is expensive when you figure in the cost of advertising and paying the going rate of $75 an hour for a 48-hour week.

I see this shortage continuing for at least the next five to eight years, and we haven't yet seen the spike in retirements from the baby boom nurses. Our average age profile, 45 to 48, is probably similar to the state average. I worry not just about replacing theses nurses over the next 10 years but losing all their years of experience.

I hope nursing will have improved its professional image and standing enough by then so we can recruit new people into the field. In the future, I think you'll see some redefining of nursing roles. Care that doesn't require a RN won't be done by a RN. You'll see an increased use of nurses' aides, which is a real professional dilemma for nurses. Does a registered nurse simply tell someone else how to take care of the patient? Most RNs didn't become RNs to do that. They enjoy hands-on care.

And you'll see a decreasing number of patients staying in the hospital, and those that do stay will be sicker. Patients' perception that they are being discharged earlier is true. Twenty years ago you could stay almost as long as you wanted. You expected to go home pain free. If you didn't

feel good, you weren't ready to leave. Today, when you go home you may not feel good and you may not be pain free.

If your pain is manageable at home through medication and you have help from home health and family, we can't keep you the way we used to. Insurers are constantly calling us and wanting to know the status of patients and when they are going to be discharged. And we as a hospital are paid a fixed rate for many procedures whether you stay five days or ten days.

But when patients present for care, I don't care how the hospital gets paid. I care how care is provided and how well the patient does. I don't want nurses making decisions based on what insurance is going to allow or not allow. I want them making decisions on what is best for their patient.

We will deal with how it gets paid for later.

Occasionally the insurance company says the patient has to go home today. Most of the time they are reasonable, but their criteria can be very inflexible and don't take into account individual circumstances. Say someone lives at the end of a dirt road that isn't plowed, can't get home, and doesn't have money to buy pills, the insurance company doesn't care.

Occasionally, we have people who have been denied a day of hospital care because we couldn't find a long-term care nursing bed that day.

We try and argue all of them. When we succeed, that's great. When we don't, we have planned for some contractual losses.

So there is a lot of change ahead of us.

What hasn't changed much is patients' expectations. Patients expect nurses to be sensitive and caring, the person who looks out for them and provides comfort.

Sometimes nurses don't have the time to spend with patients that they'd like. Sometimes they have to ask the patient to do things the patient doesn't like. But what is nursing all about?

It's about nurturing and caring. Providing information. You're the person who softens their fears and is at their side. That has always been and will continue to be the patient's expectation.

One of the most important questions and responses in our emergency room survey is how friendly was the nurse. She or he could be totally incompetent, but if patients felt cared for and the nurse was friendly they were happy. I'm not saying it's OK to be incompetent by any means. I'm saying that nurses are judged on a scale that is not necessarily equivalent to their professionalism.

If someone doesn't know what they are doing, that's easy. You teach them how to do "that thing." It's very concrete. But the way nurses are perceived by patients is not very concrete and changes from moment to moment. If you come across as stern or uncaring that can be a problem, and it is harder to correct.

It used to be that as long as you took good care of a patient that was all that counted. Now it is important that when people leave they feel you cared about them as well as that you cared for them.

This has been a very healthy and a very difficult change. For people just out of school it is nothing new. For some people who have nursed for a number of years, it's been real hard to make that change.

This is a philosophical change that the patient has demanded, and it's really been out of the control of the nurse.

Chapter 2

Growing Up

Who Am I in This World?

Adolescence

An ounce of prevention is worth a pound of cure.

What parent hasn't wondered how that nostrum translates into raising one's two-year-old or teenager?

What community organization dealing with the problems of families and their children hasn't asked if they could have done more earlier?

If prevention, be it responsive listening or early intervention, is a good part of the answer, what are our kids telling us about the pain of growing up? Are we getting it?

What lessons from our life experience are we trying to convey to them? Are they meaningful? Are they hearing us?

What indicators should we use to profile a community's well-being and the support it provides its youth? The percentage of kids in families receiving Food Stamps; kindergartners who are fully immunized; youth reporting parental involvement in schooling; 8th graders who smoke regu-

larly; 10th graders who have binge drinked; teenagers who have sexually transmitted diseases; the number of high schoolers who volunteer in their community?

The Vermont Agency of Human Services' Community Profiles and 2003 report on "The Social Well-Being of Vermonters" use these indicators and 50 others.

The reports' bar graphs and trend lines are valuable benchmarks and are often cause for celebration: the state is first in the nation in immunization rates for children; second lowest in the rate of teen births; in the top 10 in the rate of low birthweight babies and child abuse and neglect.

These indicators bring both numerical good news and bad news. But for most they convey little sense of the drama of growing up.

In the following narratives, Sharonlee Trefry, an elementary school nurse, examines her changing role—more involvement with emotional and

social problems and fewer skinned knees. Pediatrician Jack Mayer discusses how he attempts to help parents sort their way through conflicting advice on parenting—grandparents, Dr. Spock, Oprah, the Internet.

Adrienne Cohen, the State Department of Health's prevention consultant, discusses why kids use drugs and how parents, teenagers, schools, and community organizations can respond. Sue Harding, the co-director of the Parent/Child Center in Middlebury, the first federally funded rural parent child center in the country, discusses the center's efforts to help teens discover who they are in this world. Jill Smith, a 19-year-old center participant with two young children, ends the chapter with reflections on the challenges she has faced at home, school, and in the workplace.

PRECEDING PAGE: *The Parent/Child Center's innovative Learning Together Program offers educational, employment training, and child raising programs for Addison County teenagers.*

Sharonlee Trefry, RN

Bristol Elementary School
Nurse

The Friday Afternoon Stomachache

Sharonlee Trefry has been involved in school health for the past 15-plus years—the last 10 years at Bristol Elementary School and prior to that with Handicapped Children's Services in the Department of Health and in the Department of Education's Migrant Education Program. She was president of the Vermont State School Nurses' Association from 1998 to 2000 and is now on the board of directors.

What do you remember about your school nurse?

Mrs. Jones did bandaids, took temperatures, checked your hair and height. Looked at your back. Gave you shots.

Since then a lot of family and academic structures have changed. Cultural expectations, consumerism, and affluence have affected children tremendously.

An elementary school child in the past went home after school or to an activity. Today that same child may move between two homes, have two sitters, be in an after-school program and activities. In the space of 24 to 36 hours, a child can be in five different settings.

Look at that from nothing else other than exposure to communicable diseases. And from a mental and emotional health standpoint, the fallout has been tremendous.

The nurse of the past wanted to make sure she saw every bandaid. Now I have a self-service

State standards require that there be a school nurse for every 500 students or that the system be working toward that goal. Trefry is the full-time nurse at Bristol Elementary School, with an enrollment of 340 students.

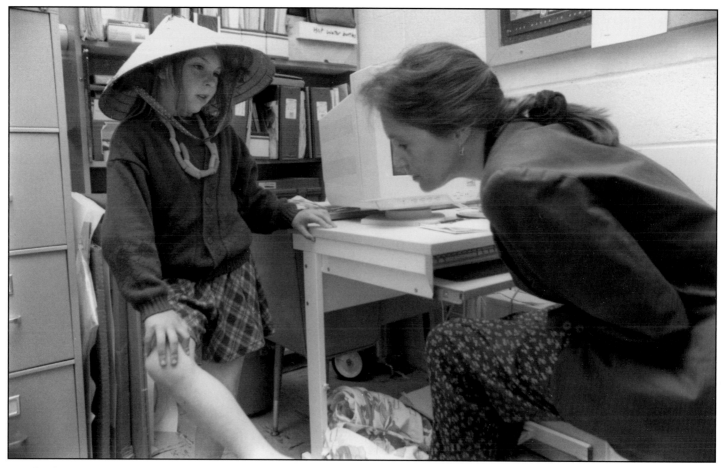

Faced with a nationwide nursing shortage, some school districts have difficulty finding licensed nurses. About 6% of the state's nurses work in schools, and the Department of Education now requires districts to submit a detailed annual report on nursing coverage and school health.

center. The kids wash their hands and take care of their own bandaids.

In a typical day, I'll see or talk with 40 to 70 students, staff, and parents. I'm spending more and more time on the phone, calling people, sending emails to parents and staff. I'm also seeing more chronically ill kids—children with asthma, diabetes, Crohn's disease. Kids are coming to school sicker and staying sicker longer.

Juvenile diabetes has increased almost 50% in 10 years. Major childhood obesity is on the increase. Children with eating disorders are increasing.

Ten years ago, you might have immediately sent a child home with conjunctivitis and sterilized the whole room. Now, conjunctivitis is treated with medication, education, and hand washing, hand washing, hand washing.

In-school medications have probably grown by 75% to 80% in 10 years. Antibiotics use has declined slightly, because the newer versions are given twice a day and some just once a day. You have more antidepressants and controlled substances, like stimulants such as Ritalin. There is now a new form of Ritalin that lasts all day and can be taken at home.

Monitoring drugs and controlled substances takes education and time. This is even harder when you have a "blended" family where drugs must go from the house of one parent to the house of the other parent to the sitter in the after-school program.

Students who don't take their morning Ritalin for attention deficit disorder or attention deficit hyperactivity disorder may be so distracted that they effectively miss a day's worth of instruction. Ideally there is always medicine at school, but if there isn't I may spend an hour on the phone tracking it down.

The biggest change since I have been in Bristol has been the increase in special medical needs. Kids may have an IV line in their arm or a port. They might have external traction where the pins in the leg are showing. They might have a pacemaker. They might have an EEG monitor.

The medical community is saving more preemies and ill babies, but the school has to cope with their learning problems and disabilities. Having these children in school is a plus in the long run, because children are exposed to the needs of others. But who pays for the one-on-one LPN that some may require? There is some federal special education money for this, but most of the cost falls on the local community.

~

About 60% to 80% of my time is spent dealing with mental and emotional health issues. Children are coming to kindergarten now who are less ready than when I started 10 years ago. These are kids who need management programs for violent behavior.

Families are under more stress and face increased expectations and demands while they have less support from the community and their extended family. There was a recent study that found children who spent the most time away from home had the most difficulty with behavioral issues in preschool and early elementary. Kids who spent the most time in poor-quality day care centers had a higher level of behavior problems. Kids who spent a lot of time in high-quality day care did very well.

What do young kids worry about? They worry their parents will lose their jobs, be fired or be promoted and have to move to California. They worry about who the boyfriend will be tonight and if they will have to protect themselves. They worry that a parent will be maltreated by a partner. They worry that they will have to go to their father's tonight and be babysat by his girl friend and have to fit in with her children.

These stressors often show up in the stomach-aches on Friday afternoon when kids are anxious about going home. First it's a stomachache. Then it's a migraine. Then the child's heart is racing. Then the shoulder hurts. As each problem is cared for, there is a new one. It is usually pretty easy to see around these "frequent flyers" with psychosomatic complaints. As a nurse, I can rule out the organic causes—no fever, no sore throat, no swollen glands, no fracture—and then offer emotional support.

The big picture is understanding that we can't fix all the problems we see. In the small picture, you have to ask what can we do to help this child to be comfortable today. It might be a nap or a time to relax or a head massage or someone to

About 60% to 80% of Trefry's time is spent on emotional and mental health issues.

talk to. It might be a regular appointment to the health office, scheduled with the classroom teacher's permission.

My ultimate belief is that parents and children are very capable of helping themselves if we give them the skills. Sometimes we talk on the phone. Sometimes it is a home visit. Sometimes I work with the guidance counselor or refer the child to the guidance counselor.

There is no such thing as a dysfunctional family, in my mind; families function to the level of their ability. My approach is to support the family and to help them problem solve. This could range from helping a family get a smoke detector to

More special medical needs and medications, more obesity, more behavior problems is a short list of the changes Trefry has seen in 15 years of school nursing.

reporting parents to SRS (Department of Social and Rehabilitation Services) if they are abusing their children.

I don't look at SRS, for example, as an agency that just takes children away from abusive parents but as an agency that has a variety of resources to help parents. SRS may say, "It's not OK to leave your children alone at 4:30 in the morning when you go to work until the bus comes at 7:30. They're too young. We'll make money available to

get someone in the house."

Our first concern has to be the child's safety. State law mandates that anyone who works with children must report suspected abuse or neglect.

I will ask students how things are at home, but you have to be careful. Some parents may misinterpret your question and think you are prying. I asked one child with frequent nosebleeds how her home was heated. I got a phone call from the parent saying, "It's none of your business how we heat

our house." I said, "I don't care how you heat your house. I was wondering if dry heat from a wood stove might be contributing to that nosebleed."

Then it was OK.

So my job is education every step of the way. Educating the child, the parent, the grandparent, the teacher, the special educator, the principal.

School nursing is a high-stress position. Yet from the outside it looks like you just help kids wash their hands and send them home.

More and more school nurses are saying they can't take it any longer and are getting into other areas of nursing. I wouldn't say burnout is higher in schools than in hospitals, because hospital working conditions and understaffing are really difficult.

But school nurses work in almost total isolation from their peers. You have to follow the law and best practices in a setting where many people have no idea what you're doing or to whom you're responsible. A teacher can ask an aide to cover chapter 2 in the history book or follow a general lesson plan.

We can't always delegate easily and are responsible for any nursing procedure and treatment at the school. I face outcomes where a student could end up in the hospital. Our medical responsibility is different from a teacher's educational responsibility and administrators and teachers may not always appreciate that.

Children will express their appreciation, but it is different from how they express their appreciation to their teachers. And it is nothing like when I worked at Handicapped Children's Services and the Migrant Education Program. You were in the families' homes. The connections were different, and there was a much closer bond.

But I like working with school-age kids and

"We educate children to graduate magna cum laude, but if they can't make healthy life choices they won't survive to graduate from high school," says Trefry.

families because I get to watch growth. I've seen some kids since they were in diapers. If I stay here, I'll see them in sixth grade and later in the community when they are in high school. That's a tremendous pleasure.

But many people who work in human services are frustrated by what they see as this huge black shadow of unhappy events in a child's life. My goal is to live in the here and now and to find small victories. Every day gives us an angel, and I need to find mine.

Today, it was a child who has been a "frequent flyer." I hadn't seen her in a month. Victory number 1 was that she had learned some coping skills. Victory number 2 was that she didn't come in with a problem. She came in just to say "Hi" and give me a hug.

Don't expect Jack Mayer to tell you how to raise your kids. That's not his role. Information, advice, collaboration, yes.

Dr. Jack Mayer

Pediatrician

Parenting Is a Moving Target

Since his medical school training in the late 1960s, Jack Mayer's goal has been to practice rural pediatrics. He was the lone pediatrician in the eastern half of Franklin County for 10 years before moving to Middlebury in 1987. Today's families have more information on parenting than ever—from grandmother to the Internet—but he finds that raising children remains as confounding as it has always been.

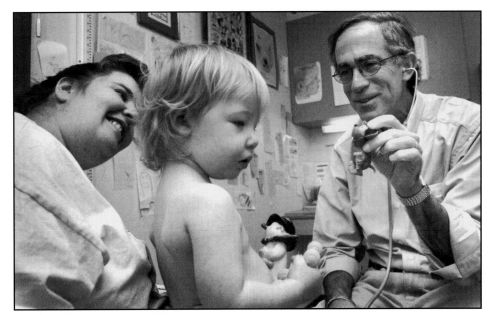

Trained to be Mr. Science in medical school, Jack Mayer has found that many traditional health beliefs are comforting to parents and work just fine.

Parenting is a moving target. Two generations ago people grew up in extended families, and the wisdom and philosophy of parenting came from the extended family. Sometimes it was good. Sometimes it was bad. Sometimes it was horrible.

In the 1960s the extended family started to break down, but parental advice still largely came from that culture. Now the extended family is either a myth or it no longer serves as a source of wisdom or control with respect to parenting.

Even if the extended family is physically present, the weight of family advice has declined. Our cultural revolution of the last 30 to 40 years requires that we create our own present instead of living out our ancestors' past. It has become not only OK to do that, but it has become a cultural imperative. All the messages that we receive are "find your own path, find your own personal integrity."

Parents like that sense of feeling competent and in control and that they are forming their own familial ethic. When things are going well parents can do a pretty good job and feel pretty good about themselves.

But when a crisis occurs they are not well-equipped and parent "from the hip," which is often disastrous. Their sources of authority—friends, television, neighbors, parents, Oprah—have become completely diffused. Parents are faced with these choices, which can be confusing and unsettling and demoralizing.

There also can be too much information. We are learning the dark side of the Internet, which can have unregulated, unedited, and sometimes flat-wrong information. And a parent who wants a good book on parenting will find a whole shelf of books that range from hard-core conservative Christian right to let-your-kids-do-anything-they-want.

When parents interview me about being their pediatrician, I say, "Don't expect me to tell you what to do. That is not my role. I can give you information. I can be your advisor. I can tell you what works for 95% of the people. You can tell me what works for your child and it may not be what works for 95% of the people. We can then work together collaboratively."

I was trained to be Mr. Science in medical school. When I came to Franklin County, I was armed with the absolute, latest, greatest information about pediatrics from Stanford. I could take care of your one-pound baby, but I couldn't take care of a diaper rash.

I quickly learned that I was not well equipped to be a primary care practitioner. There are many "old wives' tales"—I don't call them old wives' tales

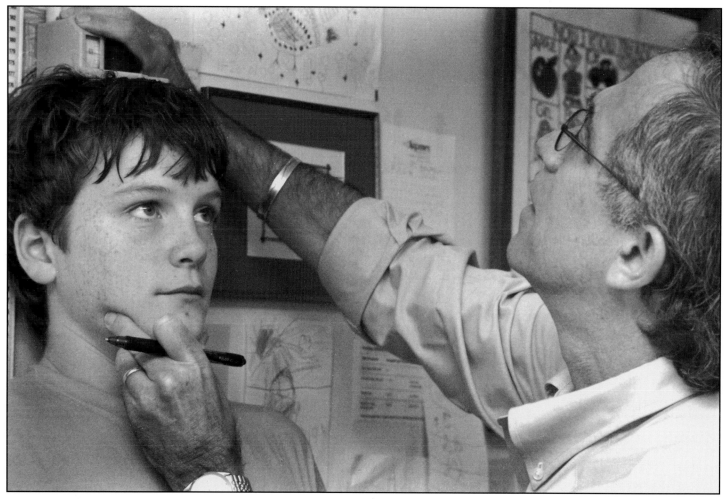

Jack Mayer still sees lots of colds and earaches, but an increasing number of consultations are concerned with school, behavior, and psychosocial problems.

but health beliefs—that I don't tamper with now, because they are not harmful and engender confidence and predictability in a crazy world.

In Franklin County, everybody used Save the Baby when they had colds. It wasn't hurting them and the name in itself was healing and a balm for the worried and tired parent.

Many times those health beliefs made it easier for me as a physician to avoid prescribing undesirable drugs. Parents would want penicillin for their child's cold, which is the wrong thing to do. But if I could say, "Do you have some Save the Baby?"

Many things we do for children's illnesses and for each other as adults are healing rituals, pantomimes, healing dances. The latest "wisdom" of gastroenterologists and science is that you don't have to change your child's diet with intestinal flu. I tried that advice, and it fell absolutely flat.

Parents want to feel like they are doing something. So I give them a recipe for homemade Pedialyte, which is an oral rehydration solution, and a diarrhea diet of rice, bananas, toast, apple sauce. Even if the outcome is no different this gives parents the sense that they are in control.

European countries are much more accepting of health beliefs and natural curing and don't use nearly as many antibiotics as we do. They practice a very different kind of pediatrics, which stresses a psychosocial model of wellness rather than our scientific germ-phobic model. One result is that we are depriving our immune system of the challenges needed to remain effective. Babies that are kept scrupulously free of germs become immune cripples.

I see both sides. I don't see either-or. I have some families who want to hear Mr. Science. They don't want to hear about the spiritual values of medicine. They don't want to hear about healing. They want curing.

At the other extreme, I have the hard core back-to-the-earth folks who will have nothing to do with immunizations and don't want any medications.

As the years have gone by, the extremes have dropped off, which pleases me because it is really difficult to deal with either extreme. At first Mr. Science and health beliefs felt like a conflicted set of philosophical underpinnings, but with maturity and wisdom I have learned that they are not conflicting at all. They are complementary. What looks at first like a divide is really a porous membrane.

When I started practicing, parents normally came with physical problems, like the child's earache, and I would then uncover school and social problems. Today a large proportion of my visits are specifically about school, behavior, and psychosocial problems.

Social psychologists and epidemiologists disagree over whether there are more psychosocial and learning problems today. Some say there are more. Others say it is a diagnostic bias. We are picking problems up and calling them something.

My sense is that we are realizing that behavioral problems are the final common pathway of social problems, emotional problems, learning disabilities, ADHD, physical problems, neurological problems.

We are now trying to untangle these causes and do something about them. Rather than put kids in the bad apple bin, we're saying let's figure out why this kid is behaving this way. Let's tease out these issues, some of which are very amenable to treatment or alternative strategies at home or in school.

My job is to find out if these kids have a medical problem or a psychosocial issue that is causing school problems. It can be something as simple as anemia or bad vision or poor hearing. Or students may have a genetic problem that predisposes them to having school problems or an underlying neurological dysfunction that is causing attention problems and hyperactivity.

This team approach of the last 10 to 15 years has been challenging and something new for pediatricians. I'm a member of the school health advisory council in the district, and we're still trying to figure out how to make this team approach work. It is not easy. We all come out of our separate traditions and don't have established pathways between us.

The other question that often comes up is how do we develop prospective programs for parents. We have so many good ideas, but traditional approaches—send information home, have a meeting, have a lecture in the evening—don't reach the parents who need it most.

I have a captive population. Kids come here for their shots and for physicals if they want to play sports. And I recommend to parents that I see teenagers once every year and that we establish a limited confidentiality agreement that does not cover harm or abuse. I do that so that we can have some conversation about sex, drugs, and rock and roll. Yes, rock and roll is in there.

If teenagers say all they like is dark, rave, hard-core Goth music that is a yellow flag for me. I'm reassured when kids say they like rock, jazz, country, heavy metal.... No one says they like Frank Sinatra.

Kids who are antagonistic and distrustful and have already put walls up are not going to be forthcoming. I don't have any illusions about that. But I tell them that my door is always open if they have questions about drugs, sex, relationships, about anything that bothers them. So they have another option to go to.

Unfortunately, these conversations don't happen that often, and it's hard to know how to tune that up. Part of it is the normal development of adolescence. Kids are not open to authority figures.

Drugs, smoking, drinking will always be front burner issues partially because of the way our culture deals with adolescence. We have a very antagonistic and moralistic approach. The "just say no" approach to adolescent problems doesn't work.

I don't know what does work, but there are a lot of good minds thinking about it. We each have a little piece but to really put it together is hard.

School officials may believe that smoking, alcohol, and drug abuse are increasing, but Department surveys say they aren't. Kids in distress are being identified better and getting help, Cohen believes.

Adrienne Cohen

Prevention Consultant,
Vermont Department of Health

What Works Is Hearing It from Their Peers

Adrienne Cohen views her job as the Department of Health's drug and alcohol prevention consultant broadly—she is a resource for the county's schools, parents, community organizations, and law enforcement. Everyone from preschooler to senior citizen, she believes, needs information and support in making healthy decisions. In the following section, Cohen discusses the use of drugs and alcohol during one of life's difficult transitions, adolescence.

Conventional wisdom is that kids use drugs to rebel. I don't think that is the reason. They use because popular culture tells them they are supposed to. If you brag about how you got drunk on Saturday and your friends think that is a big funny deal that becomes a norm.

I spoke at the high school in Middlebury and played the norm game with them. Many students remembered taking the Department of Health's risk behavior survey. Did they get the results? No. So I asked them what percentage of 10th grade students smoked marijuana in the last 30 days.

All their guesses were way high. In Addison County, 12% of 8th graders and 31% of 10th graders used marijuana in the last 30 days (2001 figures).

Thirty percent may sound high, but that means 70% are not using. That's the way I would rather look at it. So when students think everyone is doing it, everybody isn't.

Since that survey we have seen improvements in Addison County and throughout the state. But we are also seeing a very small segment of youth get involved in heroin. This drug wasn't even on the radar screen in 2001. In general, these youth are out of school and our contact with them is through the courts and treatment system. It's a scary development.

We see higher use rates of alcohol among athletes than any other segment of the population. They cluster. They get together. If drinking is the team's normative behavior then kids want to be part of that team.

After the last game of the season many sports teams have a big party with a lot of alcohol. In talking with a coach, I said, "You have an opportunity to give a message to these kids on the day of the last game."

The coach said, "I do. I tell them to be careful, to be responsible and that we don't want a bad reputation."

I said, "What I heard is go and do it but don't get caught." The message should be, "Don't do it. It's dangerous. It's illegal. It's unhealthy."

If you ask a young person why they use drugs, they will often say they are bored and there is nothing else to do.

Wait a minute. Where is your personal responsibility for your own behavior? As a parent I often say to my kids, I am not the cruise director of your life. That is not my responsibility. You have to come up with your own ways.

I always say to young people, "Don't tell me about peer pressure, because that says you are not responsible for your own choices. You are the ultimate decision maker in your life."

Kids have to feel empowered to make choices. It doesn't mean that they are always going to make good ones. But as soon as they start believing that parents must keep them from doing something bad or that other kids made them do it, then they have lost all kinds of personal power.

Both my children tried to use the other-kids-made-me-do-it argument only once. If kids don't have a parent who holds them to account, then hopefully they have a role model in school, a neighbor, a friend, or someone in the community.

In the 1960s, we believed in scare tactics. Drugs will kill you. The problem with scare tactics was that anyone who had used marijuana knew that you don't start shooting up heroin two days after smoking pot.

My favorite prevention program that didn't work was the Reagan Administration's "Just Say No" campaign. "Just Say No" works for third, fourth, and fifth graders who have very black and white thinking. Tell them drugs are bad, and they won't use them.

But somewhere around 6th or 7th grade kids start to perceive the world as gray. Nobody taught them why they should say no. That campaign did more to set back substance abuse prevention than any other campaign.

We need to teach our kids how to say no, spelled k-n-o-w.

The Reagan Administration also cut substance abuse prevention dollars, and we started dealing only with kids "at risk." But you can't always identify kids by the way they act. A lot of girls don't act out. They act in. They are very well behaved, but on the inside they are drowning.

"At risk," what a nasty label to put on a kid. Your father is an alcoholic, and we know that you have been fighting in class. It's almost setting a kid up to have a problem when you identify them as being "at risk."

If you have limited resources, you should focus on effective prevention strategies. Focusing just on "at risk" kids misses other kids who are not labeled.

The most recent trend has been to look at risk factors and protective factors. But we don't have research that shows that by doing x, y, and z we will enhance kids' assets and self-esteem and that they will be less likely to do drugs. Nothing at all.

A kid can have really great self-esteem but for the wrong reasons. I can chug five beers. I am so cool. Many kids have high self-esteem and still use drugs. Using drugs is not just a self-esteem issue.

On the national level, there has been a movement to research-based prevention programs in the last five years. Prevention has become a science, and we can prove what works and what doesn't. But evaluation doesn't happen overnight. It can take 15 years.

We know scare tactics don't work. Getting a recovering alcoholic up in front of a room doesn't work. One-shot deals don't work. That doesn't mean a health day shouldn't be part of a comprehensive program, but one-shot deals don't work.

Presenting studies and my making pronouncements don't work. We are looking at denial. Yes, it happened to them, but it won't happen to me. This is normal adolescent development.

Adolescents will look at immediate and more minimal consequences. If you want to help a young person stop smoking you don't say, "Some day you may have emphysema." You say, "Your teeth are going to get all yellow and yucky. Your hair will smell nasty. You won't do as well in sports."

The same with alcohol. "You will make some bad choices. You'll throw up all over your mom's car and you'll have to clean it up."

You look at the less dramatic and the more likely to occur so that kids will know someone who has had that experience. What works is hearing it from their peers.

I have been amazed at how often school officials say things are getting worse. According to our surveys we are getting better. What is happening is that more kids are being identified and schools are hearing the noise. We are identifying and getting them the help they need.

Since 1970 when the drinking age was increased from 18 to 21, alcohol related car fatalities have plummeted. Teenage alcohol use rates among high school students also plummeted when they no longer had easy access to alcohol.

The benefits of saved lives and money outweigh the personal rights of 18- to 20-year-olds who have proven they are not able to drink responsibly in our culture. The later people start drinking the less likely they are to develop a problem with alcohol. So I strongly believe that 21 is the right drinking age for our country and our culture.

What works is comprehensive, community-based, family-based, school-based programs. We need to teach kids life skills. That works a lot better than teaching them that drugs are bad.

A lot of people are working very, very hard. Schools are incorporating a research-based curriculum in what they are doing. A lot of communities are striving to do prevention. But there is a lot of work we still need to do. We need to see more in elementary and high schools to equal the work in middle schools.

We have to do a lot more to make kids feel that they are being valued by us as resources and members of the community. We need to give them more opportunities to mentor, to do community education, to do volunteer work and community service.

In the survey, we asked kids how many hours they volunteered. Many kids were volunteering a lot of hours, but they didn't feel valued by the community. A lot of media coverage of our youth is negative. Kids are doing amazing things and are not getting recognized.

I would also like to see a comprehensive support network for parents that begins with pregnancy and continues through high school. We have a lot of parent education and support, but it is not consistent and coordinated. Ideally one organization would coordinate education and support programs that would explain what is happening developmentally with your child.

Many parents feel that they are alone and isolated. It is easy for kids to tell their parents that they are the only parents on the planet who don't let their kids drink and make them be home by 11 o'clock.

If I had a magic wand, I would want people who are struggling to have a place to go, both formal and informal. Maybe you need professional therapy. But we also need to acknowledge that the informal support structures in our community are just as valid if not more valid than the formal structures. Being able to talk to your best friend or the hairdresser can be just as helpful.

And I would wish that people could be more content with their lives. People look to drugs when they want to change the way they feel. If people could be more content with who and where they are, they wouldn't be looking outside themselves to change the way they feel inside.

I would want everyone to be content and happy. But that would take magic.

Sue Harding

Co-director, Addison County
Parent/Child Center

Who Am I in This World?

*The Addison County Parent/Child Center opened
in the basement of the Congregational Church in
Middlebury in 1980 in response to the concerns of
a community task force that young parents and
children under age 3 needed to get off to the "right
start." Funded initially by one of four demonstration grants from the federal Office of Adolescent
Pregnancy Programs, the Center's comprehensive
in-house and outreach education, employment
training, and child-rearing programs have since
become state and national models. Housed now in a
colonial-style home in a residential area, the
Center's staff of 25-plus works with about 1,500
county residents annually.*

*Sue Harding has been co-director of the Center
since its founding.*

The early childhood world has dramatically changed in one generation. Now doctors, educators, and
caregivers are much more assertive with kids with disabilities and realize that mental health and
behavioral issues must be dealt with early on, says Sue Harding.

Many people aren't aware of the incredible stresses that some kids are under. They aren't eating regularly. They are sleeping on a friend's sofa. Their parents are badmouthing them and making them feel dumb.

Single parents go to work before their kids get up in the morning. Kids make their own breakfast. They come home in the afternoon, and their parents are asleep. They make their own dinner.

Children as young as elementary school age are left alone, because child care is hard to come by and expensive. These are not always dysfunctional homes, but poor families where parents have to work two jobs. Even if parents wanted to help, they don't have the capacity.

We see teens who are thoroughly disenfranchised. Teachers don't have high expectations of them. Their peers don't like them. They have become popular by being willing to smoke dope. By junior high they are alienated from formal educational and social service providers and are gone.

These kids are right when they think we don't value them. The places where they hung out are gone. The bowling alley is gone. Calvi's (an ice cream shop) is gone. The coffee shop down the hill is gone. They are not allowed to hang out at the College's Crest Room anymore.

There is no teen center. The idea of a skateboard park went down the tubes. The town used to run dances. That went down the tubes. Everything little by little disappeared. The hockey rink was built because there were sports fanatics who were getting up at 4 in the morning to get their kids to hockey. But the bulk of kids don't play hockey.

How welcoming are we to them?

Change has to come from parents. One or two people can't do it. It has to be a community thing, "Hey, we have to take care of the kids."

Our Learning Together Program is about reparenting teens who weren't parented well the first time. Expecting these troubled teens to be good parents is like expecting them to speak Greek

35

Center participants are "in-house experts" and meet weekly with Donna Bailey, center co-director, and Harding to discuss programs and staffing.

without ever having heard it spoken.

The only criterion for the program is that the applicant wants to be here. It drives me nuts that social services have these elaborate assessments of who should or shouldn't be in a program. People know whether a program will work for them if you just say, "Here's what we have to offer. If you feel that this would help, you are welcome."

Most people who come here are under 19 or 20. Almost all are pregnant or have very young children, under 3. Many will have a history of sexual and physical abuse and have been in the foster care system.

Very few will have their high school degree. Very rarely will an applicant not know other people here. Besides word of mouth, schools and guidance counselors refer kids to us.

We also started serving at-risk kids in the early 1990s, because we found in our home visits that there'd be a couple kids lying on the sofa who weren't parents. What could be better than an apartment with a full fridge and no grown-ups? These apartments have become de facto homeless shelters for teens who aren't making it at home.

We didn't want to give the message that the key to getting support from us was to get pregnant or get someone pregnant. So we routinely began offering services to whatever kids we came across.

For many of the 30 teens in the program the chance to get a high school degree is a major reason for coming. Kids universally want their diploma, but many have social and emotional issues that make it impossible for them to be successful in traditional school settings.

Many people in social services don't understand this desire. Their attitude is that if kids want a degree bad enough they will get it in a regular school. I'm amazed when I go to welfare reform meetings and hear people say that we have to kick these kids in the butt.

Do you think for a minute that people want to be on welfare? What could be more humiliating? Go in to the welfare department and see what it feels like to sit in the waiting room. See how you're treated. People hate to be on welfare.

Kids know they need more skills and training. So since the mid-1980s, participants have helped run the center—child care, food service, administration—and are paid a stipend of up to $25 a week. We tell them if they complete the program and do it well that they will come out of here with a job reference. We can tell an employer that the applicant is reliable, dependable, can work with co-workers, and takes supervision well.

So the educational and work component is a big draw.

The other big draw is the infant/toddler child care program, which is a learning lab for young moms and pregnant teens. Developmentalists call adolescence the second toddlerhood. Adolescents are facing the same development issues that toddlers are going through: Who am I in this world? What are my boundaries? How independent can I be? Having those two populations together in toddler care figuring out the same stuff is fascinating.

Being a good parent means providing for your children emotionally, physically, and financially. At 14 and 15, even at 16 and 17, you are too young for these responsibilities. If kids have graduated from high school, are in a stable relationship, and want to have kids then that is not bad at all. But 16 or 17 with no job skills and no steady relationship? No.

We do teen panels in schools and our participants will say, "We love our kids, but if we could do it over we'd never become parents this young."

~

Once a week, Donna (Donna Bailey, co-director and education coordinator) and I formally meet with the participants during "home room" to discuss the program and, most importantly, work out any interpersonal or group dynamic problems. It's easy to assume that these kids are so young and messed up that we have to tell them what they need. With teenagers you learn the hard way to pay attention and listen to them.

I consider them our in-house experts on programs and staff. They told us they wanted a GED program. For many years, we were the only parent child center in the state that had an in-house education program. Now other centers are trying to start similar programs. They told us they wanted a driver's education program, so we started one.

We don't hire staff without their approval. I totally trust their judgment here. If their instinct is that they don't like the person, we won't hire the person.

Home room is also the place where kids gain skills in working together when things aren't going well. Employers are looking more and more for these soft skills.

Most of these kids are hands-on learners, but there are essential life skills that we try to teach in weekly workshops. About a third of the time, we discuss grown-up topics, like sexually transmitted

Vermont has one of the lowest teenage pregnancy rates in the country. Addison County, in part because of the center's efforts, has the lowest rate in the state.

diseases or substance abuse or how to write a resume or balance a checkbook. Again, they tell us what they want to discuss. About a third of the time we discuss kid-related stuff, such as how to read to your kids. And about a third of the time, we have simply fun stuff.

Society presumes that when you become a parent you are an adult and will function as an adult. We have found that adolescence is really about mastering a group of tasks before moving to adulthood. Kids who are developing normally have lots of time to get through these tasks.

Our teen parents have no time to figure out who they are and how they will relate to the opposite sex. But if they are not allowed to continue to be kids as teens, they never complete those tasks.

These issues will come up again when their own kids are adolescents. Then you get teens whose parents are still teens developmentally. That's not a pretty picture.

In 2001, we received a $675,000 grant from the Office of Adolescent Pregnancy Programs to help other centers in the state replicate our in-house education and work programs over the next five years. Everyone thought there was something magical about Addison County and that our programs couldn't be replicated. I had some doubts, too, that you could get this magic mix of people elsewhere. But it is working everywhere exactly the same way.

Part of the reason is that an intensive program for teens like ours is very rewarding for staff and participants. In six months, you see someone parenting their kids differently, relating differently to their peers, and taking supervision where in the past they got fired from job after job. There is not very much in education or social work or health care where you get to see results before your eye. That is pretty intoxicating.

As new programs for families with children from birth to three have emerged, Addison County has smartly said let's keep them all at the Parent/Child Center. Parents can get what they need in one place. That's not true in other communities.

The most recent example is CUPS, (Children's Upstream Program Services) which supports mental health assessments and services for parents and young children. We are the only parent child center in the state doing CUPS. Everywhere else, the area counseling service runs the program. We don't want families who have a concern about mental health or behavior to have to go the counseling service.

Other parent child center directors say they would love to be able to do what we do. What it takes is innovative partnerships to get around state and federal regulations.

Medicaid regulations do not permit parent child centers to bill for mental health services. So our staff provides the services, but we bill through the counseling service. It's not a drain on their staff, and we work hard to make sure that they get their fair share.

We have the same arrangement with home health. We are the only parent child center in the state to have a nurse on staff, because we want to offer pregnant teenagers wraparound services. Medicaid doesn't permit parent child centers to

bill for those services either so we bill through the home health agency.

Most parent child centers probably bill Medicaid from two or three streams. We are supported by Medicaid from 10 different streams, because of the diversity of our programs and the partnerships we have developed.

We have been on a roll. Once you start developing a reputation of being innovative and fun to work for then you can hire and keep people who are creative and interesting. Unlike many social service agencies, we don't have a lot of turnover. On our staff of 37 (29 full-time equivalents), 16 people have been here 15 years and 10 of those have been here since our founding.

Part of our success stems from our programs, but we have also done some interesting things as a business. We have no middle management. If you go to the counseling service or home health, there are divisions. When we started we were part of the counseling service and had divisions. There was director of child care and a director of outreach. We eliminated all that in the first couple years.

People now get paid basically the same with a differential based on years of experience and educational level. Every job is considered equally important. I write grants and deal with state partners. This is no less or more important than the person who picks up kids in the van or works in the kitchen or in the infant care room. And we all wear many hats, pitching in wherever help is needed.

Our salary range runs from roughly $40,000 for people who have been here a long time with master's degrees to $20,000 for a new employee with a child development certificate. When we give raises, we split the pot of money equally so the people at the bottom get a bigger

percentage raise.

And we manage by consensus. Before we change or start programs, participants, staff, and board discuss how they think it would work. If all three groups say, "Yes, this is a good idea," it probably is.

National statistics say that 50% of the children of teen parents will become teen parents themselves. We now have about 225 to 250 kids of child-bearing age whose parents went through our program. We could rightfully expect to see 125 or so of these kids be teen parents. We have seen fewer than 20. Even those few who have become pregnant are older than their parents and in each case are doing a better job of parenting.

We are proud of these statistics and that we have broken the cycle of teen parenting. But the state has this new obsession for outcomes research and wants us to do pre- and post-tests on how participants' parenting has changed. With any individual, you are never going to know what changed them. Are they simply six months older? Did they switch boyfriends? Was it the home visits? Was it the Learning Together Program?

We are constantly asking each other and the kids about what is working and how to make the program better. What works with kids hasn't changed much since I started. Be nice, listen to them, and trust that they know themselves. If you really listen, they will give you the clues.

This is not a pre- and post-test. This is listening constantly.

"Teen parents have no time to figure out who they are and how they will relate to the opposite sex. If they are not allowed to continue to be kids as teens, they never complete those tasks. These issues will come up again when their own kids are adolescents. Then you get teens whose parents are still teens developmentally. That's not a pretty picture," says Harding.

Jill Smith
Teen Parent

Now that I Have Children
I Have Different Views

Each year about 4% of Vermont and Addison County high school students drop out of school. About 2% of Vermont's teenagers, age 15 to 17, annually become pregnant.

About 8% of all first births in Vermont are to unmarried women under 20 with less than 12 years of education. According to national statistics, families with all three "risk" factors—unmarried status, teenage, little education—are 10 times more likely to live in poverty than those with none of the three factors.

Jill Smith was part of that risk factor group when she first became pregnant as a high school sophomore. Navigating school, parent, and family relationships since then has been a challenge that has aged her beyond her years. The first part of the interview was conducted in June 2002, the second part in January 2005.

I was 16 when I became pregnant.

There wasn't any support at the high school, because the administration, teachers, and guidance look down on people who are pregnant. My guidance counselor told me I should drop out, because I probably wasn't going to finish school anyway. If you are pregnant they think that you are a bad influence on the rest of the kids.

I would have stayed, but I was in alternative ed already. If I had been in high school I would have stayed and told them to shove it. I would have been fine in high school, but the assistant

"I wish I would have waited to have kids. I could have gone to college and not had to worry about baby-sitters and day care. But I wouldn't take it back. When I look at my kids it's satisfying to know that I'm making them who they are today," says Smith.

principal didn't like me. I got good grades, but I was kind of a troublemaker.

It wasn't that bad; I only pushed around like two people when I was a freshman. The problem was that I was dating Kevin, and he was a troublemaker when he was in high school and she didn't like him.

She thought I was bullying people and skipping because of Kevin, but I got in trouble before I started dating him. It took her about half a year to get me out of the high school. She thought I was a bad influence because of my freshman year, but my sophomore year I was doing fine.

But she just said, "You're gone." That was December-January of my sophomore year.

I didn't want to be in alternative ed, because

of what I had heard about yucky people over there. My mom wasn't happy with my going to alt ed. She wanted me to stay in high school.

Kevin had a cousin who went there because she was having a hard time passing her classes. That's how I found out about it.

I was in alt ed for about a year and three-quarters. And looking back, I'm glad that I went, because I was able to finish early. If I had been in high school when I was pregnant, I don't think I would have gone back, because the high school isn't as flexible as alt ed.

There are only 25 to 27 students with three teachers. A lot of people think it is for like troubled people and people who can't make it in high school. But it's not. It's for people who want one-on-one teaching and who want to work each week at their own pace.

Once I got there I liked it, because it was more lenient.

They had TV and couches where you could sit and do your work. You couldn't watch TV unless it was news for history or Discovery Channel for geography. If you didn't have cable or a satellite dish at home they could record the program there and you could see it the next day.

They had a gym class in the municipal building to play basketball or in nice weather you could go to the rec park and play all different kinds of sports. One of the teachers used to be a dance instructor, and you would work on dances.

At the end of each semester, everyone got together and said what they had gotten for credits. You would perform your dance and read what you thought was your best piece for the quarter.

Alt ed is more lenient, but it's also stricter than high school. You have a contract each week that says what you have to get done by 3 o'clock

"I didn't really want to come at first, but it was better than sitting home and doing nothing. Poppy (a counselor) said center programs would pay you to be there with your child, which is what I would have been doing at home. And she said I could further my education toward college," says Smith.

on Friday. If you were behind one week, you got a write-up. If you're late to class you can get a write-up. You are only allowed four write-ups a quarter and then you get kicked out.

But if you have all your work done by 11:30 on Friday then you could leave. That was a special privilege.

If you were three weeks behind, you got kicked out. They wouldn't put up with people not doing the work.

~

My friends didn't say anything when I got pregnant.

"Whatever. It's your life."

I was OK with being pregnant. I wasn't worried about myself or Kevin. I was thinking about what my mom was going to say. I thought she was going to kill me and didn't tell her at first.

I told my sister Kim, who is 18. She was really happy. I have five siblings, three sisters and two brothers, by my mom. I told Kim, because she was still living with my mom, me, and my stepdad.

It was Thanksgiving when I was two months

pregnant that my mom found out.

My mom was fine. We all knew she wouldn't kick me out. Because my oldest sister Kelly got pregnant at 19 when she was still in high school and was eight months pregnant when she graduated.

My mom said, "I love you, but if you're going to have a baby you need to grow up," and that I needed to get an apartment.

That was fine with me. I didn't want to live at home with my stepdad, because we don't get along.

I didn't really move out. My stepdad was working construction then and was away for the

41

Some people here don't have supportive parents. All kinds of things come up like how do you stop your child from being mean? Or if your child isn't sleeping at night, what can you do? The parenting class is helpful because you get to hear different views, says Smith.

whole week and only home on the weekends. I would stay at home during the week with Kevin. On the weekend, I would go to Kevin's parents' house. I moved some of my stuff there.

Kevin's parents were a little upset. He was 20 and I was 16 and they were afraid that my parents might press charges, but my mom isn't like that. She knew we had been together for two years.

One of my alt ed teachers said I should talk with Poppy Cunningham, an outreach worker for the Parent/Child Center, about any concerns I had about being pregnant.

I really didn't know what the center did. I thought it was a day care center where you sat there. But I started meeting with her once a week and then every other week.

I wasn't worried about parenting. I was more worried about how we were going to pay for everything. We didn't want to stay with Kevin's parents with a baby so we started looking for a place and saving money.

Our first apartment was on Exchange Street in Middlebury. We moved in when I was 8½ months pregnant. That was $550 a month for two bedrooms with heat. We thought it was high at the time, but we pay $650 now (2002) for a trailer in Ferrisburg, which doesn't include anything except snow plowing and lawn care, and we don't have a lawn. And $650 is cheap for a trailer.

Poppy helped us fill out the applications for apartments and in coming up with a deposit. I was underage, under 18, and Poppy told me to go to

welfare. They wouldn't count Kevin's income until after the baby was born. He was working at Speedi Lube then and was probably making $7 an hour.

So I went there and got like 300 some odd dollars a month in ANFC (Aid for Needy Families with Children), then I got like $130 for food stamps because I was pregnant and in school.

I wanted to pay half the bills so they gave me more money and more food stamps. For two months that helped us out a lot. I got like $500 and our rent was $550.

Poppy also helped when we didn't have a car. I didn't yet have my license, and Kevin had lost his license. When he first got his license he had speeding tickets and lost his license because he had so many points. When we got our 1999 tax refund, he paid off all the fines, which was like $1,800.

If I or Kevin had a doctor's appointment and needed a ride, Poppy would pick us up. Some times she would bring Kevin to work at Speedi Lube, which was a long walk, about two miles. Some days he would ride a bike to work.

She went a little beyond what she should of but that was cool.

When you are at the Parent/Child Center you set goals and when you reach the goal you get money. I said I wanted to get my permit, my license, and my diploma. They gave me $100 for every grade I completed. So I got $200 for that. When I graduated I got $150.

Then when I got my permit, I got $50. When I got my license I got $75.

The money was funneled through the center so you don't have to go to the welfare office.

And after we got a car and it broke, Poppy helped us out getting it fixed. The center has a family assistance fund, where you can get up to $150 a year. We used that to help fix the car.

I started coming to the center in the fall of 1999 when Orianna was three or four months old. I had completed all my high school credits that fall but wouldn't get my degree until June.

There are like five of us here out of 30 who have our diploma. Most everyone else is working on their high school diploma or GED. There are classes at the center and child care, which makes it easier to get your degree.

I didn't really want to come, but it was better than sitting home and doing nothing. Poppy said the center had programs that would pay you to be there with your child, which is what I would have been doing at home. And she said I could further my education toward college, even though I wasn't thinking about college then.

At first, I just wanted to be with Orianna all the time. I had to leave the infants' room for lunch, and I didn't like that. It was my first baby, and I was really scared about leaving her with anyone.

But Linda (a staff member) was in the infants' room, and she was OK. Her daughter graduated with my sister Lynn, and they were college roommates. So I've known Linda for a long time and felt comfortable leaving Orianna with her.

I knew a couple people at the center, but I didn't like them from high school. And some didn't get along with my sister so I just didn't talk to anybody.

My attitude was, "Don't talk to me or my baby."

~

The Learning Together Program at the center has some requirements, like attending home room, which I thought was weird at first. Why do I have to go? Home room is for high school.

We'd talk about stuff that I really didn't care about. But this year I'm paying more attention. The staff is really good about listening to what we like and if we don't like it, about how to change it.

I'm not quiet in home room now. Like I wanted to make sure that I was on the committee for hiring new staff. I don't want someone in my daughter's room who I don't care for or trust.

The majority wins, but we have a lot of say because if we don't trust the staff then we won't leave our children.

Another part of the program is the parenting class. I was really comfortable about parenting and if I had questions I had my mom or my sister Kelly, who is 12 years older and has three children and one stepson.

But some people here don't have supportive parents. All kinds of things come up like how do you stop your child from being mean? Or if your child isn't sleeping at night, what can you do?

No one is going to say, "I'm a horrible parent." A lot of people will say, "I think I'm good," but no one will say, "I'm the best parent there ever was."

I like it, because you get to hear different views on how people handle discipline. Like some people spank. Some don't.

The staff tries not to judge your parenting skills and won't say you're doing something wrong unless you will really hurt the child.

This past year, I have gotten involved in the women's group where you discuss problems in your family or life and get advice from other people in the group and from a staff member or from a counselor from the counseling service.

The center is supposed to be a non-violent, safe place. If you don't get along with someone you just can't go bash them. You have to talk it out.

I've never had to do it, but you can bring in Donna (Donna Bailey, center co-director) or a staff member that you're comfortable with. They will help you reassess the situation.

There is another rule here. Don't gossip. What is said here is supposed to stay in here. When we are in home room and someone says something personal it is confidential. But nine out of ten times it does get out, because there are so many people here.

The job part of the program has been most valuable for me. I worked at the Co-op as a secretary for two months this spring. I got the job partly because I had experience and references from working in the office here.

There are different jobs, like working in the kitchen, in the child care rooms, in the office. Many come here for an education so they are in the classroom and that's considered a job. You get a stipend for your job, up to $25 a week, which works out to about $1 an hour.

The center puts together teen parent panels that go into high schools to talk to health classes about what it is like to be a teen parent. I went to Mt. Abe (Mt. Abraham Union High School in Bristol) once and brought Orianna with me.

You try and scare them and tell them how hard it is. Like if you want to go out and party, you can't do that. You have children for 18 years and can't get rid of them. You don't want to leave your kids with just anybody, because you're responsible if something happens.

When Kevin and I got our first apartment, my friends thought it was cool and would come and visit. But I don't like smoking and when Orianna was born I said there was no smoking in the house. So my friends stopped coming.

I never had anyone come and talk to me in high school. No, that's not right. We had like three people, but it went in one ear and out the other.

I don't think teen panels would have impressed me. I've always liked kids and used to baby-sit my niece and nephews.

It didn't bother me when I got pregnant. I wasn't very careful and felt if it happens, it happens.

But Kevin didn't want kids. Kevin was afraid that I wouldn't finish school and didn't want to see me working at McDonald's.

His mom got pregnant when she was 16, had 12 kids, and never finished high school.

That was like 30 years ago. All the kids said she should go back and get her diploma. She was worried about two of the boys and said that if they graduated than she would go back. That was an incentive for them.

So she went back to night school when she was in her 40s. She graduated when I was a freshman.

I've just turned 20 and was 18 when I got pregnant a second time. It was a real role switch. Kevin was happy. It was unplanned, and I was really upset.

I was afraid that I would have to share my love, and I wanted to keep it all to Orianna.

And two kids get expensive. They have to wear Pampers, which are the most expensive, because they break out in a rash if it is anything else.

We get Medicaid for all of us. I pay $2 every time I go to the doctor, but I don't pay anything for Orianna and Olivia or for their prescriptions. Kevin and I pay up to $4 for our prescriptions.

I feel that I can call my doctor any time, and I'm paranoid about my kids so I call all the time.

But we don't get any other help, except for WIC (Women, Infants, and Children program of the Department of Health). I nursed Orianna until she was 15 months and stopped when I got pregnant. I was getting 3.5 gallons of milk a week, cheese, apple and orange juice, and cereal from WIC. Later I got formula, but not enough, and formula is expensive.

We don't really budget. Kevin works for a tent company and gets $10 an hour for a 40-hour week; more if he works overtime. That's too much income for welfare but not enough for us.

So far he has been working 40 hours, but this week has been horrible and he has had three days without work.

When the bill comes, we pay it and hope we have money when night comes. Kevin gets paid four times a month and we take $150 to $200 out of each check for rent, which is $650. Garbage and recycling, $40, comes out of the first check. We take $25 out of each check for electricity. The phone bill is like $100 so we take $25 out for that. Food is when we need we go buy it. That's probably $300.

We go out to dinner at least three times a month and to the drive-in at Malletts Bay once a month. At the end of the month we are broke.

The center owns a two-unit apartment building now and rents out the apartments. The building was donated to the center and a lot of center staff and participants helped fix it up. You can only live there for a year, and then staff sets you up with references and a good budget plan and helps you find a new apartment.

Kevin and I would have loved to have done that, because we would learn to manage our money a lot better. We do good now but if we had more experience that would help.

I wouldn't change anything at the center, but if the center had another four or five units to rent that would be good.

I've been trying to find a job. I'd like something secretarial, but I'll take anything because we need extra money. I have put in resumes and have had a couple interviews.

There were a couple secretarials in the paper, like a two-week job at Vergennes in a law

firm. But I don't want just two weeks.

If I get a job, Olivia will come to the center for day care, and Orianna will be at the Play Lab, which the center runs at the vocational school. That would be four days a week: Monday, 9 to 11:30, and Tuesday to Thursday, 9 to 2:30. Child care here is free.

When Orianna is 3 she'll go to Mary Johnson (Mary Johnson Child Center). The center charges $125 a week. I couldn't afford that, but the state child care subsidy will pay for her.

I don't know where I want to be in a year or two. I don't want to look that far ahead.

I have talked with VSAC (Vermont Student Assistance Corporation) about what help I could get for college. I'm thinking about nursing or social work. I'm still just looking and haven't applied. I visited Castleton and liked their nursing program. I'd like to complete English and math before I decide what I want to do. That would be a while because I'd go part-time and try to take courses on-line until the kids are a little older.

I wish I would have waited to have kids. I could have gone to college and not had to worry about baby-sitters and day care.

But I wouldn't take it back. When I look at them it's satisfying to know that I'm making them who they are today. Orianna has an attitude, but she's the sweetest kid. Olivia is becoming like a little person and is getting her own attitude.

Of course it is frustrating when they're not listening and there is nothing you can do. Like it's a full moon and nothing works. All you can do is just walk away for five minutes.

Sometimes I think that if I didn't have Orianna I might not have graduated. I got good grades, but I just didn't like being there.

Now that I have children I have different

The center puts together teen parent panels that visit high school health classes. "You try and scare them and tell them how hard it is. If you want to go out and party, you can't do that," says Smith.

views. I didn't want to be like my Mom who dropped out when she was in the 11th grade when she got married.

We used to ask her for help with homework, and she couldn't help half the time. I wanted to make sure that I had at least a high school diploma so if my kids had algebra questions I could help them.

Kevin and I are supposed to get married. But it depends. He has a settlement pending from a car accident two years ago. There is a 97% chance that he will have some disability for life. The doctor has said muscles in his back and neck are permanently pulled.

It is hard for him to work, because he can't stand or sit for a long period. But he has to work, because he has a family to support. If he gets a settlement this year, it would pay for the wedding.

If he doesn't get it this year then we will do it the following year.

What I'd really like is to have a college degree and a good job. The job would pay a lot but wouldn't take up too much time so I could still be a full-time mother and work full-time.

That would be nice.

45

Center programs can help teenagers learn to parent differently, relate better with their peers, acquire workplace skills, accept supervision, earn a stipend for work, gain a high school diploma. Spring graduation recognizes these achievements.

January 2005

I began subbing at the Otter Creek Child Center in October of 2002. I had enjoyed volunteering at the Parent/Child Center and saw an ad in the newspaper that Otter Creek needed a sub.

I looked at the nursing program at Castleton but decided that nursing wasn't for me. This August I was hired as a full-time teacher, and I'm now working with 10 two- and three-year olds. I'm working on a teaching certificate, which involves 120 hours of workshops, which are given after work at the Mary Johnson Child Center. If I didn't have family responsibilities I could probably finish in a year but we have three kids now—Kevin, Jr. was born November 12, 2003—and it will probably take a year and a half or two.

Kevin got a small settlement for his back injury, about $5,000, which we used to buy a car.

We got married May 15, 2004. For the past two years we have lived in a three-bedroom apartment in Bristol. It's in a great location and has a great yard. The rent is $870 a month, which includes heat, plowing, garbage collection, and lawn maintenance. We pay about $70 a month for electricity. For what we have, it really is a good price.

Right now we're trying to pay off health and credit card bills, about $4,000, so our credit will be good. Our lease runs out next summer, and we want to try and buy a house.

Since I began working full time, we have lost our health insurance. I make about $20,000 a year. Kevin is looking for full-time work and makes about $15,000 a year from his seasonal work. That's $35,000 a year, which is not a lot for a family of five. The kids are covered by Dr. Dynasaur, but we make too much for Medicaid. We do qualify for the Vermont Health Assistance Plan, but that would cost $140 a month and we don't have that.

We also lost our child care susbsidy when I started full time so a lot of our money goes to child care. Kevin, Jr. comes with me to Otter Creek and that is $190 a week. Otter Creek gives me a discount, because I work there and I get $2,000 in flex funds so that pretty much takes care of that. It costs about $125 a week for Olivia at Mary Johnson, and Orianna is in an after school program at Bristol Elementary School, which is about $27 a week.

The only way we can afford child care is because we get federal Section 8 assistance with our rent. We only pay $315 for rent. Without that help, we couldn't afford child care and I'd probably have to stay home with the kids because it would hardly pay to work.

We probably spend $500 a month on groceries. We lost food stamps when I began working full-time. We could use the help, but what I really miss is health insurance.

I haven't really been sick since August, except for the flu at Christmas. If I were really sick I could go to the regular doctor I used to see. I'd have to make payments. A friend at work just told me about the free Open Door Clinic, which has office hours Thursday nights in Bristol. I may look into that.

Chapter 3

The Uninsured

I'm Not One to Run to the Doctor

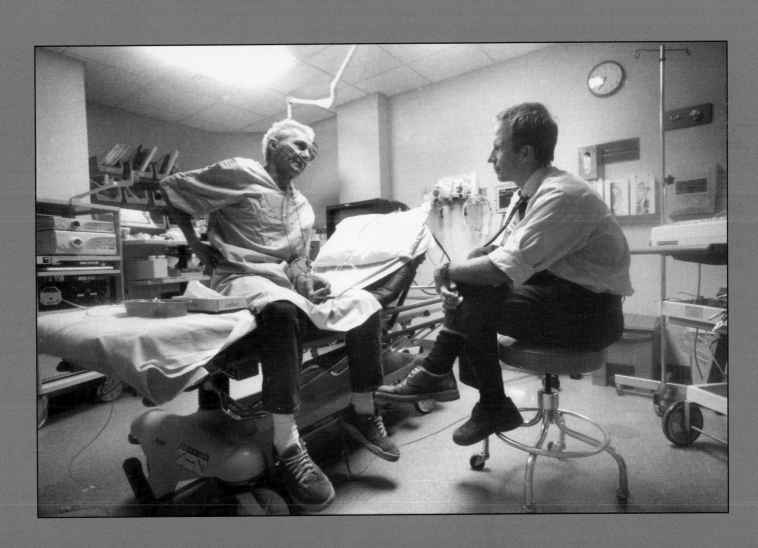

Uninsured Vermonters

In the fall of 2001, after a year-long study by the Lewin Group, a health care consultant, the Vermont Agency of Human Services issued a report on expanding health insurance coverage to uninsured Vermonters.

The good news was that about 96% of children (0–17) and 90% of adults were covered. The bad news was that about 51,000 Vermonters, about 8.4% of the state's population, did not have health insurance during 2000. And about 69% of these Vermonters had been without health insurance for over a year.

Who were they? About 51% of the uninsured had incomes below 200% of the federal poverty level (for a family of four about $36,000). Another 22% had incomes between 200% and 299% of the poverty level, while 26% had incomes over 300% of the federal poverty level.

About two-thirds of the uninsured adults had full-time jobs and another 10% had part-time jobs. Only 27% of firms with five or fewer employees provided health insurance; over 90% of firms with 50 or more employees did.

According to state surveys, most of the uninsured once had insurance but lost it when they changed employers. Many acknowledged that they were "gambling with their health" and would enroll in a plan if they received a significant raise.

The main barrier to coverage? The multi-thousand-dollar cost of many health insurance plans.

The chances of expanding coverage? Not great.

Given the "bleak short-term economic forecast," the state should focus on maintaining existing levels of state program coverage for the low income. As the state's financial capacity improved, the state could expand income eligibility requirements and increase coverage by several percentage points, the report concluded.

In short, the report held out no immediate prospect of universal health care coverage, short of a single-payer system funded primarily by an employer payroll tax. This approach, the study said, did not appear politically feasible.

By 2005, when the state legislature considered legislation leading to universal health care, the numbers had worsened. Businesses and individuals were dropping or reducing coverage because of annual double-digit cost increases. An estimated 63,000 Vermonters were now without health insurance and another 100,000 were underinsured, i.e., they had high-deductible insurance coverage and out-of-pocket expenses exceeded 10% of their incomes.

Few if any of these developments would have surprised Addison County health care providers. Over the past 10 years, the state's Dr. Dynasaur health care program has expanded to cover nearly all children of low-income families. Medicare covers the 65 and over population—less than 2% of this age group does not have insurance.

Low-income and low-asset adults without children are eligible for the Vermont Health Access Plan coverage, if their incomes are below 150% of the poverty level, or about $18,000 for a couple, and 185% if they have children.

That largely leaves the "working poor" who live paycheck to paycheck. This group makes too much for state and federal low-income programs but too little to afford the multi-thousand dollar premiums of many private insurance plans.

Addison County has pockets of "good" jobs that provide health insurance and a growing number of low-wage, no-benefit "bad" jobs. Middlebury College sociologist Margaret Nelson discusses this trend and its implications for family life.

County health care, like care throughout the country, is marked by good care for those with health insurance and spotty or limited care for those without insurance. Community activists started the free Open Door Clinic to serve the uninsured. Sonja Olson chronicles the creation and the struggles of the clinic, an admitted stop-gap solution.

The DeGraafs, a farm family, are typical of the "working poor"; they raised four children largely without health insurance.

Dr. Fred Kniffin, director of emergency services at Porter Hospital, sees the uninsured, who often postpone seeing a doctor, and the insured, who depend on the department's 24-hour availability. Residents come to the ER, he argues, because they have no other place to go.

Finally, Tom Plumb, past director of the county's low-income advocacy agency, examines the quality of life in the "Dairyland of Vermont" and how the working poor struggle to make do.

PRECEDING PAGE: *Porter Hospital's emergency department sees about 13,000 patients a year. According to Dr. Fred Kniffin, director of emergency services, about 15% have no health insurance.*

Margaret Nelson

Professor of Sociology and
Anthropology, Middlebury College

We Are Doing It Wrong

*Prof. Nelson has taught at Middlebury College since
1977, focusing much of her research on the needs of
low- and middle-income working families and single
mothers. In her most recent book,* Working Hard
and Making Do—Surviving in Small Town
America, *Nelson examines the impact of the replace-
ment of many "good" jobs in the contemporary labor
market with jobs that don't provide a livable wage,
permanent work, and secure benefits, especially
health care insurance. These "bad" jobs have created
a "fundamental disconnect," she believes, between the
aspirations and real-life possibilities of many working families.*

*Nelson is a long-time board member of Commu-
nity Health Services of Addison County (Open Door
Clinic).*

Lifetime employment, one-wage-earner families, and secure health and retirement benefits are now
the exception. Families must be assured health care coverage if they are to regain that lost quality of
life, says Nelson.

Since researching *Surviving in Small Town
America* in the early and mid-1990s, small
firms in Addison County that pay relatively low
wages and don't offer benefits have continued to
grow. It's not surprising that those firms don't offer
benefits. They are operating on a small margin.
But it is precisely the issue of benefits that makes
the difference between a "good" and "bad" job.

There was a time in our history when blue
collar men could get a job, have long-term security, and see a long-term obligation from their
employer. Most of the employment in the county
today doesn't have that kind of social contract.
People are much more on their own.

This is the way it is around the country.
Addison County is not unique in this. I haven't seen
the 2000 statistics to compare with 1990 statistics,
but those secure blue collar jobs are going.

The loss of "good" jobs is largely the result of
the movement of large capital out of the state. You
can read about it every day. IBM has laid off people. Standard Register has laid off people.

The trend is delayed in Vermont mainly because large-scale capital came here later and is
moving out later. It used to be that people with a
high school education or less could work at
Simmonds (Simmonds Precision, a major manufacturer of aviation systems) and have a very good

life for their family. When we were writing the book,
Simmonds' employment was cut in half. People at
Simmonds (now B. F. Goodrich Aerospace) still
worry about their jobs.

The largest employers are probably the
College and Porter Hospital. But they are not as
steady as they used to be. The hospital doesn't necessarily hire people in "good" jobs; they have a lot of
part-time shift work. The College still offers a kind of
social contract, but it doesn't always hire people in
"good" jobs either. Faculty, yes, but staff, no.

Vermont like every place else depends on
what the national economy does. If it goes up, we
will go up afterwards. If it goes down, we will go

down afterwards. But I don't see any developments that are unique to Vermont. When what used to be Simmonds downsizes, small businesses aren't able to provide health insurance to fill the gap.

I don't see any major shifts comparable to what I saw over the last quarter century in Addison County when the economy moved from agriculture to manufacturing and then to services. The big turmoil in the loss of good employment was in the early 1990s. There is not that much left to lose.

Vermont's quality of life brings in people who want good jobs, but it doesn't bring good employment for working class people. I don't see something like IBM coming into Vermont anymore. That investment will go overseas. Capitalization at that level is over.

Small companies, like Otter Creek Brewery, will grow and may start to provide better jobs. But I see mostly small-scale employment, some of which will grow to be good stable employment. But you're not going to have IBM coming in again.

That's history.

I look at people's lives and say, "People cannot take care of themselves unless they have steady employment and basic benefits." A livable wage is something like $38,000 for a family of four, and many people don't earn that kind of money.

Unless families have a livable wage there is always going to be a demand for supplemental services from the state. Many working class people pride themselves on being able to live without government assistance. So government programs can't come with stigma attached or be viewed as charity.

I'm not an economist. I'm not a planner. I have no idea how to do those things. But I have a very good sense of what people need to lead a good and dignified life. People need health care. They need good jobs. They need a livable wage. They need an education.

We have fine public education, but we don't provide health care and that has serious consequences for how people lead their lives. Health care is central, partly because it costs so much and because it shapes people's employment opportunities in bizarre ways. People stay at low-level jobs so they can continue to qualify for VHAP (Vermont Health Access Plan, a state health care program for low-income adults) or take a low-wage job because it has health insurance.

Vermont has relatively low rates of people without health insurance, but that's because of programs like Dr. Dynasaur and VHAP, not because of the quality of the employment. Something like the county's Open Door Clinic is a stopgap. This is what we do, because this community doesn't have anything else.

We need single-payer universal health insurance. Barring that, everyone has to be in a position where they can purchase the health care they need, but I think that is the wrong way to go. If people were freed from that burden of paying for their own health care they could put together their lives in more meaningful and positive ways.

I'm not interested in thinking about society in terms of words like "compassionate." Those words have been corrupted. I would much rather think in terms of what rights people should have.

People have always wanted health care to be a right in this country. Its lack has not been a matter of public opinion or support. It used to be the American Medical Association. It's now opposition from insurance and drug companies.

If the government offered comprehensive health care for everyone, people would not see the government as an obstacle but as an ally. But we have politicians who say that government programs are a barrier to your independence.

People accept VHAP. It's a very welcome state program. Dr. Dynasaur is certainly a welcome program. People use those things.

Several years ago, I co-wrote a comparative piece about maternity services in the United States and Sweden. In the United States, maternity service outcomes varied with race, class, education, income, and almost every indicator we used. Almost none of them did in Sweden. They are doing it right. We are doing it wrong.

Any society, like Sweden, that makes the same health care available to everybody is doing a better job than we do.

Robert and Joan DeGraaf
Dairy Farmers

I'm Not One to Run to the Doctor

Robert DeGraaf was born in the Netherlands where his father had an eight-acre farm. In 1958, the family moved to Vermont and in 1960 his father bought a 250-acre farm with 28 cows in Panton for $32,000. Robert and his younger brother Harold now farm about 350 acres with 300 head.

Joan DeGraaf's grandparents immigrated from the Netherlands. She grew up in southern Massachusetts and met Robert in the mid-1960s when she moved to Vermont to work. The interview was conducted March 2001. A December 2004 postscript follows.

Dairy farmers Robert and Joan DeGraaf, like 1 in 12 adult Vermonters, do not have health insurance. About three-quarters of Vermont's uninsured are employed; two-thirds have full-time jobs that don't provide health care benefits.

Joan: We have four grown kids, Diane, Christine, Robert, and Marcia. None work on the farm.

I had health insurance for Diane because I was working at the Weeks School in Vergennes. I saw a private doctor in Middlebury for her.

The last three we didn't have health insurance. For those I went to the medical school's clinic up in the old DeGoesbriand Hospital in Burlington. I saw different groups of medical students as they rotated through, but I thought I had good care. Your chart is your chart, and they study it.

The clinic was free, but we had to pay for the hospital and the delivery doctor. The hospital said, "Don't make paying hard on yourself." So we paid $50 a month. It took 13 years by the time we got the second, third, and fourth paid up.

We went to the Department of Health's well child clinics in Middlebury when the kids were growing up for sight and hearing tests. We would also see doctors in Vergennes.

We were pretty fortunate, because we didn't have anything real major when our kids were growing up. One of our sons had a hip displacement and a limp and that required surgery.

We had a health insurance policy for self-employed people from a company (Fortis) in Texas for that surgery. This was our first insurance since I worked at the Weeks School (1968-73). The operation cost $3,750 and insurance paid what they said was the reasonable and customary fee of $1,200. We were stuck with the rest.

We didn't expect the surgeon to lower his fee, because the surgery took hours. Robert is 22 now so that would have been eight years ago.

We were paying around $2,000 a year for major medical coverage with a $1,000 deductible. We talked to them over the phone, but they said, "No, that's all we're paying."

It took us two years to pay off the $2,500 we owed the hospital for the surgery.

The Texas plan wasn't too bad. We were worried about the major stuff and had that covered. We picked up the small stuff on our own.

ROBERT: We set aside $500 a quarter and the farm paid it as part of my wage package. Then

51

they went to $740 a quarter. Once you have it, you say you'll keep it. So we kept it. That plan covered the family.

Then about three or four years ago Fortis gave us notice that they were leaving the state. They said they were losing money and couldn't survive the state's regulations.

They gave us some options and we looked at them. Boy! The option would be to increase premiums to $2,900 for just the two of us, with a $2,500 deductible for each of us. That sure is a lot of money when you're making $2,500 a month from the farm.

We looked at getting insurance from Blue Cross and Blue Shield at one time, but it was a dream. They're good, but they were one of the highest.

How much can we afford to pay a month for health insurance? That's a hard question. The cost of everything just keeps going up. I looked at the HMOs after the Fortis company left, and I thought they were pretty reasonable, but they keep going up.

What can we eliminate? It's that simple.

We don't spend money on things that aren't necessary. We've never bought a new car. Our only vacations are to visit the children. We have taken the family to the Netherlands once and that was a gift from a grandparent.

Do we get rid of our house and move back to the old farmhouse? We have rented that out now and it is used as a home business. When Joan's mother and father died, they left her a little money so we put it into this house. You can blow it on a car or a trip, but we started a house.

We did a lot of the inside work and moved in without a kitchen, sink, or stove. We couldn't afford to have anyone finish it, so we just moved in.

We've been it in four years and still have things to do.

I'm not real happy about not having health insurance, but I'm not one to run to the doctor. If I were a sickly person, I'd probably look at it differently. But if you can't afford it, you just don't have it. I'm guessing that it would cost us $500 a month now to get insurance.

I'm lucky I've never had back problems like most farmers. Except one time I was milking and a heifer came and hit me on the side and whew that hurts. That time I saw a local chiropractor for three months, but I didn't gain much.

JOAN: So he's careful the whole fall and then the next spring I get this phone call, "Come get me." He's lying on the barn floor with the sweat pouring off his face, and he couldn't move.

He was carrying calf pails, and he twisted. So some friends took him to a chiropractor in Rutland because I couldn't move him. He saw a chiropractor three times and that fixed it.

I had a kidney stone last fall (2000) and ended up in the emergency room at Porter Hospital. I didn't stay overnight. That came to $770, which we paid ourselves.

ROBERT: We couldn't handle $1,000 in a month, but we had room on our credit card and put it on that. It costs money to keep it on your credit card, but I don't want due statements coming from the hospital. I didn't ask the hospital if we could stretch out payment. It said due immediately, and I didn't pay until we got the second one.

JOAN: Last year, we took out long-term care insurance in case he needs more care after 65 than I can give him here.

We just got the bill, which is $2,000 a year. The company has just been bought up, and we're told the premiums are going to increase. We have the plan which will pay up to $219,000 over a five-year period. If he is home, I would certainly care

for him, but if he needed specialty people to come here or if he had to be in a nursing home for rehab then we had to have coverage for that.

It really scared me when he got hurt. After the chiropractor he was OK. And then he hurt his arm and that took three years to get better.

We've been using the free clinics (Open Door Clinic) in Middlebury for ourselves and for our kids for some time. When we had kids going to summer camp, we'd take our kids to the free clinics for camp physicals. The camp cost us $100 for three kids, and it would have cost us $120 each for the physicals from our doctor in Vergennes. We couldn't afford that, and the kids wouldn't have gone to camp.

It was $5 at the clinic for a camp physical.

ROBERT: Our kids didn't qualify for the Dr. Dynasaur program. According to their forms, we make too much money, because they consider the partnership's "profit" part of our income. But we never see any money from the "profit," it's all in the farm. It's not like at the end of the year we have $50,000 that gets added to my income. It's not there.

JOAN: Going to the clinic for us is like having a pre-check before you get into something worse. You can find out if it's worth going further, and it doesn't cost you $125.

We don't mind paying a reasonable amount for care, and we feel like other people end up paying for us. That bothers me. We've told the clinic we'd be happy to pay a minimum fee, and sometimes we give them more than $5. They give us vouchers for blood work at Porter Hospital; we would pay for that.

It doesn't bother us that we don't always see the same doctor and that the clinic is only open on Thursday nights. I like the multiple points of view. When you see someone new, they'll ask, "Have you done this? Have you looked into that?"

We don't qualify for free drugs because of our income, but the clinic has given us free samples of the drugs that we need.

ROBERT: Some people run to a doctor very quickly. Others don't. I went to the clinic about three years ago, because Joan was going for a problem she had. The upper part of my back was sore, and it wouldn't go away. I wasn't having trouble breathing, but I was sweating very quickly.

It turns out I had pneumonia. I got a shot and took some pills for two weeks and that fixed me up.

The clinic picked up my high blood sugar then, and I have changed my diet. I've always been a sandwich man, and the nutritionist gave me an education on how this turns to starch and this turns to sugar.

They wanted to send me to an eye doctor to get an eye exam because of my diabetes. But at this point it would just be a waste of money. I'd go if I thought I had an eye problem, but I see fine.

If I could get a good major medical policy at a reasonable price that would carry me to retirement age, I would still want to use the Open Door Clinic for a check-up. We get good check-ups, and they'll tell us if we need to see a specialist.

JOAN: We don't believe in not paying our bills, so we don't ask for anything more than we think we can handle. When you go to a doctor's office, you don't discuss what it's going to cost with the doctor. You discuss it with people in the office.

After our son had his hip surgery, we brought him in for a check-up in Burlington. They moved his leg, put it up over his head. He wasn't in the room more than five minutes, and the bill was $70. So we decided we wouldn't come back and canceled the last visit.

I have used the emergency room three times,

The weekly Open Door Clinic in Bristol and Middlebury provides free services and helps qualifying area residents enroll in state Medicaid programs. Clinic volunteer Polly Birdsall, a Porter Hospital dietician, advises Robert DeGraaf on diet modification to control his diabetes.

and I absolutely want to know what something is going to cost before they do it. One time my Vergennes doctor sent me to the ER, because he was concerned that my chest pain might be a heart attack.

The ER doctor came over and said, "I understand you don't want to be admitted into the Emergency Room." I said, "My Vergennes doctor wants me to be checked with a blood test. If it clears, I'm fine."

Well, he wanted to admit me for about 24 hours. And I said, "Well, on what do you base this? You know I don't have the money to be waiting here with you running tests all night long."

I had a blood test and went home.

JOAN: Our daughter Christine moved to South Carolina last year and had been at her new job for seven weeks when she had appendicitis. Her job had insurance, but she wasn't covered until she had worked for 90 days.

Her surgery was simple enough, but then she developed a bad infection and the doctors didn't catch it. Her heart quit. Her lungs quit. Her kidneys quit. She ended up spending nine days in the intensive care unit and almost died. She spent another five weeks in the hospital and then recuperated at home for another two months.

When she finally went home, the hospital bill

was $140,000. There's no way she could pay that, but a group of businesses in the community have some kind of coverage and paid the hospital bill for her.

But she still has the surgeons' and doctors' bills and they come to $25,000, which she doesn't have. Some people told her to declare bankruptcy.

ROBERT: She doesn't want to, because someone said it would take her 12 years to clear her credit record if she declared bankruptcy. So she wants to pay if off and that will take a long time.

She has talked with the surgeon about possibly cutting his fee in half.

I know if we had a $100,000 bill today, we'd probably lose everything we have.

December 2004

JOAN: Bob had a mild stroke on June 18, 2003. He was lightheaded, nauseous, and felt funny, and thought he should go to the hospital. He had been in the barn that morning, and I told him he'd better get cleaned up because he stank. We laugh now that he could have died while he was getting cleaned up to go to the hospital.

They did all these tests at Porter and sent him up to Fletcher Allen. He was only in Porter for a couple hours and then in intensive care and rehab at Fletcher Allen for over a week. He is back to normal now, but he was totally exhausted then and didn't go back to milking until the middle of August.

Bob's 61 and had expected to farm until he was 66. This was a real eye opener for him. It made him realize that life is short and he's not as young as he used to be.

He stopped milking this last May and is now selling his share of the farm to his brother, who is a lot younger. It was easier for him to stop milking because he had something to do—run our store (B&J's Farm Supply) that I had been running for 15 years. He always loved the store and had had his hand in it and this was good for him.

He hasn't missed milking at all. This past Thanksgiving we had some friends in Florida who said why don't you visit. So we visited over the break and one of our daughters watched the store.

So we literally lucked out. The mini-stroke wasn't that bad and got him to thinking. And we had been able to find health insurance with a $3,500 deductible. So all we had to pay was the deductible.

That company has since left the state and we've been without health insurance for the past several months. So we're still using the Open Door Clinic.

Our daughter won a lawsuit against the surgeon. He's no longer allowed to practice in the state because of all the operating mistakes he made over the years.

We had to sue because the hospital wouldn't give us any information. I don't know the size of the settlement, because I never asked. I know she didn't get wealthy. The lawyer took 40%. She paid doctor's bills and other bills. With what was left she bought a small house, which gives her some security. She feels good now, but she went through a lot.

ROBERT: I was very fortunate. The stroke—first they called it a mini-stroke then they said it was a little bigger—was in a good spot and I haven't had any side effects.

As far as insurance we had gotten hooked up with Mutual of Omaha. About $400 per quarter per person, which wasn't too bad. There was a $3,500 deductible for each of us and an 80/20 split after that with a maximum out of pocket of $5,000.

I don't know what the hospital bills were. Intensive care was very good to us at Fletcher Allen. I think they negotiated with the insurance company so all I had to pay was $3,500.

Mutual of Omaha has since gone out of the health insurance business all across the country and since June 15 we haven't had any coverage. I checked out one company and they wanted $1,152 a month. No way! I have sold my share of the cows to my brother, and I'm not getting a monthly milk check anymore. For years we didn't take any money out of the store. The store is now paid off, and we're just starting to take some income from that.

It looks like our income is way up this year, because we sold some property that we owned for 30 years. But we reinvested all of it so we will have a little more for our retirement. Joan is on social security now but doesn't get very much. I'm trying to hold off until I'm 66 so we will have a little more for retirement.

As far as getting health insurance, I feel pretty healthy right now. I'm watching what I eat and checking my blood sugar. I've been reading a good book on diabetes. I bought two copies and am going to leave one at the Open Door Clinic. The book says if you watch your diet and get proper exercise you can get off pills.

Before I was discharged, Fletcher Allen said I should have a local doctor for follow-ups. I saw the doctor once. He did some tests and was going to see how things turned out. He didn't contact me so I've been going to the Open Door Clinic. They keep tabs on me.

Sonja Olson

First Director, Open Door Clinic
of Addison County
Coordinator, Vermont Coalition
of Clinics for the Uninsured

I'd Expand Access So We Could Go Out of Business

Addison County is known around the state for its innovative approaches to meeting community needs, an abundance of civic-minded volunteers, and a cooperative spirit among its health care and social service providers. Where does this culture come from? Observers cite long-standing relationships among agency leaders, staffs, and their boards; a pragmatic problem-solving approach to community issues; and activists' flexibility and resourcefulness in starting programs on a shoestring. Sonja Olson, a long-time health care activist, recounts here the history of the County's efforts to offer free clinics, an admitted stopgap solution, to meet the health care needs of residents who are underinsured or who have no health insurance.

Patient visits to free clinics in Addison County in 2003 grew by 25%, an indication that many area residents are losing their health insurance. Vermont's eight other free clinics experienced similar increases, says Olson.

I'd give Jack Mayer (a Middlebury pediatrician) and a group of community social workers, who were concerned that many low-income people did not have access to health care, credit for starting the Open Door Clinic. This was in the early 1990s when the whole country was galloping toward universal access to health care.

I was working then at the Parent/Child Center, and we were seeing children who weren't visiting a doctor regularly. I was a member of the planning committee and after meeting for about a year we developed a proposal for funding a mobile health

bus and submitted it to the Jessie B. Cox Charitable Trust. Our idea was to go into communities and help people understand the importance of preventive health care, immunizations, diet, and exercise, and prepare people for universal care that was coming. We would offer initial, fairly modest physical exams and refer patients when possible to a family physician.

The Cox Trust awarded our new group, Community Health Services of Addison County (CHSAC), $127,000 over three years. I then became the director of CHSAC. Our plan was to go into a community one day a week and park the bus next to a school or church or public building.

This would be less frightening than visiting a doctor's office for people who have been pretty intimidated by the health care system.

We bought a school bus that had been used in a pediatric clinic in Maine for $20,000 and started going out into the communities in 1994. The van was baby blue with a fully outfitted exam room, a little lab, and an intake room. We put out flyers, had public service radio announcements, and ran our schedule in the paper each week. A Vergennes minister, the Bristol town clerk, and social workers were also wonderful in getting out the word.

We had several institutional barriers in going after a population that hadn't used health care very

The Open Door Clinic began serving county residents in the mid-1990s with a converted school bus staffed by a nurse practitioner or physician's assistant. One problem was that low-income residents were too proud to seek medical help.

often or regularly. Porter Hospital is fairly traditional, and they questioned how we could give good care. A health bus seemed a little 60ish, "hippy-ish."

Some physicians were also uncomfortable with the project. It was hard for them to understand the need for the project because they believed they were already providing free or reduced fee service. They also did not want competition for patients who had the ability to pay—through insurance and Medicaid.

They also could see the limitations of a mobile unit. The bus certainly could not bring comprehensive health care into a community. And they felt that people with the ability to pay would be better served by having a medical home—a physician's office where they receive routine medical care. And finally our planned use of a mid-level provider was new to Addison County, and many physicians were uncomfortable with a nurse practitioner or physician's assistant serving as the health care provider.

One worry that people who could afford to pay would take advantage of free health care never happened. Instead, the problem we faced then and now is that people who should come are often too proud to do so.

In 1995 the directors of the four free clinics in Vermont and I began meeting to collaborate on data collection and program development. Although the health bus was not a traditional free clinic, our mission was similar. The State's progress toward universal health care had became bogged down, and we realized that access to health care would be an unsolved issue for some time.

In light of this and because the Cox funding was ending, the CHSAC board began planning for a transition from the mobile clinic to an evening free clinic that would be staffed by volunteers. We saw this as a way to bring less expensive and more comprehensive primary care to people without health insurance.

Peggy Nelson, president of the board, and I began interviewing area physicians to assess their willingness to support the free clinic. While younger physicians seemed more supportive than the older physicians, almost all the primary care physicians agreed to help. And some specialists also agreed to accept referrals. Porter Hospital and the radiologists agreed to continue to donate lab tests and the readings of X-rays as they had for the bus.

We started the Open Door Clinic, in January 1996, with enough volunteer physicians to offer a free clinic one night a week in Jack Mayer's Middlebury office.

In March, the five Vermont free clinics formed the Vermont Coalition of Clinics for the Uninsured and applied for a Rural Outreach grant from the federal Health Resources and Services Administration. We were awarded $660,000 over three years, with about $40,000 a year coming to Addison County for the Open Door Clinic. I was then hired to be the grant administrator and part-time director of the coalition.

This federal funding gave credibility to the free clinics and also required a comprehensive annual review of the program. All the clinics—there are nine now—agreed to collect data on their patients and services. This data have painted a picture of the otherwise hidden uninsured and helped us explain our work to the Vermont legislators. In 1999, the year the federal grant ended, the legislature awarded the coalition $300,000 a year to be safety net providers. The funding has been re-awarded annually at the same level since then.

Our annual surveys show that about two-thirds of the people who come to the clinic are employed. About 80% have incomes of less than $30,000 for a family of four. They may have two part-time jobs or one full-time and one part-time job. But the jobs of most of the working poor simply don't come with benefits.

About 80% have no insurance, and the other 20% have insurance with huge deductibles. We see people, for example, who are paying $400 to $500 a month for catastrophic insurance coverage. They come to us because they have a $5,000 deductible and are, for all practical purposes, uninsured for routine health care.

Most of our patients are between 18 and 65 and have incomes below 200% of the federal poverty level, approximately $36,800 for a family of four in 2005. People over 65 are covered by Medicare. Youth under 18 are covered by Medicaid or the state's Dr. Dynasaur program, which covers children in families with incomes up to 300% of the federal poverty level.

About 60% of our clientele say they have delayed seeking care because of an inability to pay. People do take their debt very seriously, and it's often very hard for a person with a $10,000 bill to feel comfortable in returning for needed care.

Many of these people are unaware of state programs, such as the Vermont Health Access Plan which began in 1997 for low-income adults without children, or affordable care programs of hospitals. Screening people for eligibility and helping them enroll are time consuming and many physicians' offices don't have the staff for this.

Most physicians don't like to or don't have the time to discuss payment. They want the front desk to take care of it, and the front desk can seem like a formidable gatekeeper to patients. The result is that it is often not easy to broach the subject of payment in a doctor's office. So the Open Door staff works hard to help patients enroll in these programs.

We are able to enroll many of our clients in VHAP, but even if they do qualify there can be a year's waiting period if they have dropped their private insurance or have just moved to Vermont. But once they are enrolled in VHAP they don't need us anymore, because community physicians accept VHAP patients.

We offer free care for adults with incomes up to 200% of poverty level at the clinic (about $18,600 for an individual, $25,000 for two). But some people who are over the income guidelines still can't afford health insurance. We consider extenuating circumstances and do not turn away people above the income limits. However, some free services are not available to them. Those who can, donate $5 for a visit.

About 50% of the people who come in say they do have a regular physician. But a "regular physician" can mean very different things. In many cases, they may have seen the doctor once.

I called a doctor's office recently about a patient who we had diagnosed with diabetes. They said, "Well, actually he's never been to us. He did call once with a question."

We send reports to let the physician know that patients felt unable to return for whatever reason and so that their chart is complete.

About 60% of our patients are women and many have not received medical care for years. We expected and found that most people had been denying themselves dental care and checks like Pap smears, mammograms, blood pressure screenings.

When we first started, some physicians said it was like being in the Third World. They were seeing problems that were difficult to diagnose, because they had been neglected for so long.

I can remember a 19-year-old with a terrible skin condition on his feet who came to the clinic in the middle of the winter. Doctors treated him over a period of weeks and finally figured out that he had trench foot, which was something that doctors saw in World War I.

Visits to our Middlebury clinic and our Bristol clinic, which we opened in 1998, have remained steady for the past several years, about 700 to 800 between the two clinics. We have attempted to keep costs down in the past by having two part-time nurses run the clinics and by relying on over 60 volunteers: physicians, nurses, nurse practitioners, several physical therapists, mental health counselors, nutritionists, and community members. And we use physicians' offices one night a week in Middlebury and Bristol and two Saturday mornings a month in Middlebury at no charge.

Free clinics are not a perfect solution. We are staffed by a rotating slate of doctors, which can be a problem for patients with chronic illnesses. These patients will probably be treated by a different physician each time they visit. Because of this lack of continuity some area physicians will see these patients at no charge in their offices as part of their

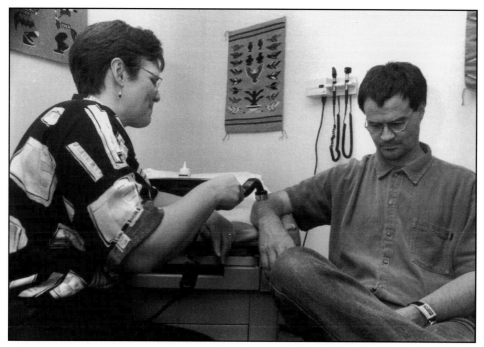

The Open Door Clinic, with a full-time case manager and part-time executive director, relies heavily on a volunteer staff of 60-plus doctors, nurses, therapists, and community members.

regular practice. This is a wonderful service for people with illnesses like diabetes or hypertension that require regular monitoring.

Even with $100,000 a year in volunteered services, the clinic has direct costs of about $90,000 a year. The cost per patient is high, $100-plus per visit, and we can't provide the medical home found in a regular doctor's office.

But if there were no Open Door clinic, many of our clients would end up in the emergency room, which is even more expensive.

Two issues continually arise at the open door clinics: the need to expand dental care and the high cost of prescription drugs.

According to a past Department of Health survey only 50% of the children who are insured by Dr. Dynasaur are seeing dentists now. Dr. Dynasaur has generous income limits so almost no child in Vermont should be unable to see a dentist because of inability to pay. But many kids don't see dentists.

Why? Parents who are working at low-wage jobs have a hard time taking time off from work so they are reluctant to make dental appointments. There is also a fear of dentists and a lack of understanding of the need for routine dental care. There is almost the cultural acceptance of having extraction and dentures rather than prevention and ongoing care.

Dentists are resistant, too, for some good reasons, in taking Dr. Dynasaur kids. There is a fairly high no-show rate. If a pediatrician has a no show, it's not a problem because they are so double, triple, quadruple booked. But dentists don't double book, and if there is a no-show they lose that income.

And the reimbursement rates are much better from private insurance so dentists limit their percentage of Medicaid patients. A year or two ago, pediatricians were desperately looking for dentists to see Dr. Dynasaur children who were in a lot of pain and distress. That's still the case.

We talked to area dentists several years ago and proposed bringing another dentist to Addison County. They said they would support our bringing a dentist to the community to serve the Medicaid population and people who can't afford a sliding scale fee. But they wouldn't support a dentist if that person went after patients who are insured or have the ability to pay.

At that point the dentists did not want any more competition. I believe they assumed that we would subsidize the dentist. We did support a dentist briefly back in 1997 when she couldn't find local employment, but she left the community.

Dentists definitely would like to see free clinics take over the Dr. Dynasaur and Medicaid population and that is happening in several parts of the state. There is a school-based clinic in Bennington, for example, run by a retired dentist.

The free clinic coalition is looking for federal funding for more dental clinics, but it is very difficult to get funding without support from the dental community. The Dr. Pete Society here in Addison County has received some funding to explore expanding dental coverage. There is a good chance that they may be able to pull together more community support and that we could get another dentist or better coverage in this community.

Addison County is probably no worse than other parts of the state, but we are facing a real problem. Many low-income people have not grown up with preventive care and are now in very bad shape.

Paying for prescription drugs for people with chronic illness is another big problem. The Open Door Clinic can provide a two-week dose from free samples, but getting reduced price or free drugs from pharmaceutical companies for patients with chronic problems takes a lot of work. Each drug company has a different application process and requirements to get reduced price drugs.

We have developed software that helps us here. In the first six months (2001), four clinics obtained free prescription drugs from the drug companies' indigent patient program. The drugs were worth well over $100,000, but that is just the tip of the iceberg as far as need. In 2003, the Addison County clinic helped patients get $55,000 in free drugs through pharmaceutical programs.

The coalition supports the effort to create a drug buying pool of Northeastern states and strongly supports the prescription drug benefit of the Vermont Health Access Plan.

We have urged the legislature to maintain what we have now and not cut back on drug coverage, which would only cost us more in the long run. Given the state's budget problems that may be all we can expect.

If I had a magic wand, I'd expand health insurance and access for the low income so free clinics could go out of business. I'd have Porter Hospital expand its free care guidelines, take over the clinic, and be the provider for everyone in the community.

Free clinics are not the answer to our health care crisis. We refer patients on a case-by-case basis to specialists and for inpatient and outpatient hospital care and can arrange for free prescription drugs and some testing. At best, people then have access to care in their community, but if they travel to another area they are again without access to care.

Even in areas where the hospitals, such as Fletcher Allen, Gifford, Mt. Ascutney, and Dartmouth Hitchcock, have expanded their free care guidelines to cover any free clinic patient, this is not the answer. In that expanded system, there are still understandable limits on the free care that the hospital can provide and that care is not portable.

Governor Dean broadened the eligibility for Medicaid programs, but the state, facing multi-million dollar Medicaid deficits, can't afford further expansion now without more help from the federal government. But I'd still like the state to expand VHAP coverage to adults without minor children from 150% to 200% of the poverty level. This would be another step toward universal access to health care.

But along with expanding access, we need to address physician and hospital reimbursement rates, particularly Medicaid but Medicare also. Both are lower than private insurance. Many worry that as the Medicaid population increases

physicians won't accept new Medicaid patients because Medicaid reimbursement is so low. At one point, 5% of a physician's practice might have been insured by Medicaid. Today it can be 25% because of all the new Medicaid programs.

At some point, the problem of health care access and costs is going to blow up statewide if not nationally. I had thought that concern over the cost of prescription drugs might lead to systemic change, but that hasn't happened.

We're still not willing to say everybody deserves health care and a livable wage. Perhaps that is because many of us have good health insurance and are divorced from the cost of health care.

We put a lot of money into designer drugs, end-of-life care, female care, and transplants, and it will be very hard to discuss legitimate, honest rationing of medical care. We have avoided that discussion and have rationed access and care by income and lack of insurance instead.

Many of our problems— the cost of prescription drugs, the growing number of uninsured people, the lack of access to dental care—are getting worse. I just don't understand why we are still not ready to talk about where we put our health care dollars, because everybody is complaining.

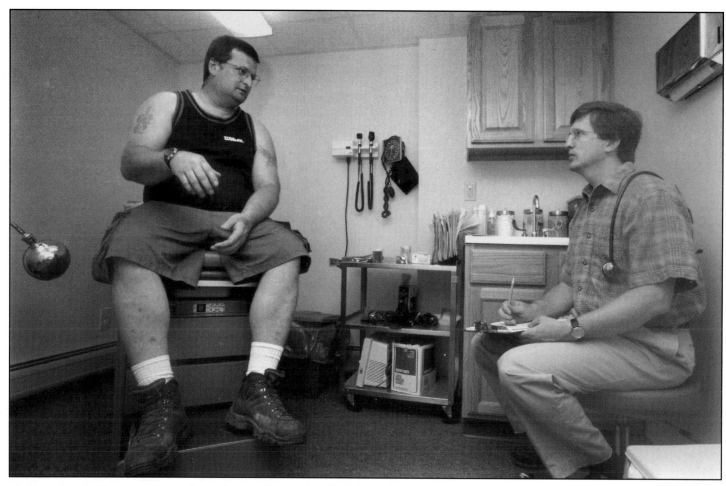

The Open Door Clinic screens patients for Medicaid and VHAP eligibility, helps patients obtain free drugs, and provides patients with vouchers for lab work and X-rays at Porter Hospital. Vermont Coalition of Clinics for the Uninsured programs provided over $500,000 worth of prescription medications to their clients in 2004.

Dr. Fred Kniffin

Director of Emergency Services,
Porter Hospital

We Shouldn't Slam
The Door

Emergency room care consumes 1% to 2% of the American health care dollar, but its use and alleged abuse is at the heart of any discussion about health care reform. It's expensive and inefficient and used by too many people with sore throats who don't need emergency care. It's an essential community hospital service—about 35 patients a day use the Porter ER—and a last resort for people without a family doctor and health insurance. Dr. Kniffin has heard all the criticism but believes that until there are better options the ER is a bargain.

As head of the ER, I'm the complaint guy. About a quarter of the complaints are about quality—my diagnosis was this and it was that. It's much more likely to be the doctor didn't care. I didn't get the sense he listened to me. He was hurried or distracted.

Their sore throat is number one on their agenda. To suggest that they should have seen the problems of the critically ill patient next door, just doesn't cut it.

You certainly don't learn how to deal with these transitions in medical school. People who can make these transitions survive in an emergency room. The people who can't, don't.

What also drives people out of ER is the total lack of control over what comes in, the fact that you have to see everyone, and that patients can all show up at once.

"Some politicians and regulators think it is the hospital's job to reduce usage. Yet the law says the ER has to treat everyone," says Kniffin.

One of the nice things about the ER is that you work 12-hour shifts and go home and you never wear a beeper. The flip side is that you work nights and weekends. But people who go into it just for the schedule just don't make it. You can't do something you don't like for simple scheduling reasons. You'd go bonkers.

My basic approach is still the same, but over 10 years I have developed the need to get better at what I do. When I started here in 1990, I didn't have a ton of ER experience; that was the standard at Porter then. It was nerve wracking coming to work and not knowing what was going to come through

the door and not feeling completely prepared.

I have more experience now and have taken ER boards. That took a fair bit of preparation and really helped.

Nothing keeps me up anymore. I worry from time to time, but I worry a lot less. But I still worry about difficult airways and people that I just can't intubate.

What I love is the level of commitment. When a patient is in the ER, I'm totally committed to that patient. I'll do whatever it takes to get them what we think is right. When they're gone or I'm gone there is no commitment. I think people understand that at the end of the shift Dr. Kniffin goes home, and they are on their own.

In an office setting it's not so clear. You're supposed to be totally committed to patients when they're in front of you, but then there's also a level of commitment when they're not in front of you.

Some people do it well, but many doctors give so much commitment when the patient is there that the patient goes home with an unreasonable expectation about what the physician can provide at all hours.

I just like the clear boundaries.

But the fact is that patients' expectations are very high. Turn on the Discovery Channel and doctors are sewing hands back on. People see this and need their expectations adjusted. Many times you just can't figure it out.

We see tons of chest pain in the ER and many people suspect they have heart disease but don't. It takes a long time to explain that there is no test in any ER that will tell us with 100% certainty that you don't have heart disease.

People assume that if you do the right tests that it will be obvious. It's not. I'm not uncomfortable telling people that they're going to be OK

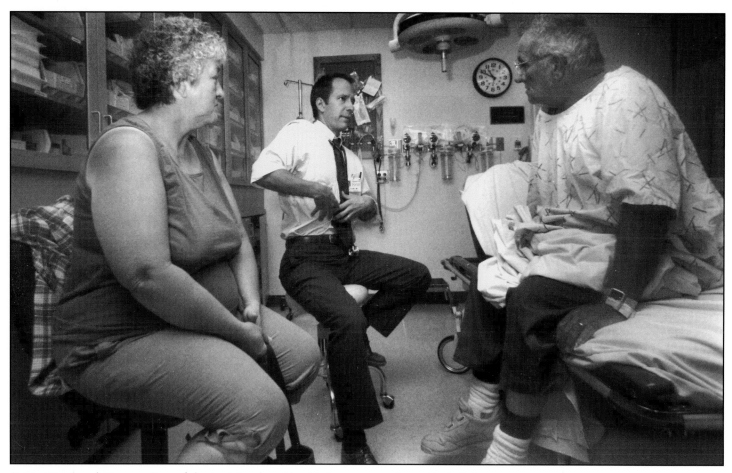

Emergency room doctors see "tons of chest pain" and must be able to reassure anxious patients that their pain is not life threatening even when they do not know the cause, says Kniffin.

even if I don't have all the answers. Most people will understand that.

Ten years ago when you picked up *Newsweek* or *Time* you'd read that doctors are ordering tests or doing procedures because they directly benefit from fees for these services. For the last couple years, the stories have been that your doctor and hospital are withholding services that you really need.

By and large I love working in Vermont, because patients are very trusting. People generally take me at face value. But I still think attitudes are changing and people are thinking, "Are they doing this to save money?"

I don't think a patient's insurance coverage or lack of it affects decisions in the ER. You're not supposed to ask patients anything about their ability to pay before they get their medical screening exam.

If a hospital accepts Medicare and Medicaid payment you have to see everyone and treat them appropriately. I will occasionally have a discussion with people who have private insurance or Medicare or Medicaid, but generally I say about 10 words and I'll hear, "We're here. Let's X-ray it," which is fine with me.

If I see someone who I think is self pay and they're having a heart attack and need x, y, and z, we don't talk about it. We just do it.

But many people who don't have insurance appreciate a discussion of options. If you have rolled your ankle, there are pretty good criteria for determining who has a sprain and a break. If the person meets the criteria, I'll order an X-ray.

Most of the time it is probably a bad sprain. Even if there is a broken bone, we won't lose anything by letting it sit for a few days. Ice it, evaluate it, and keep weight off it and see your doctor in three or four days. We can do that and save the expense of an X-ray.

Insurance also comes up in prescribing medications. Suppose you come in with a cough, fever, and are bringing up some green phlegm.

I can prescribe erythromycin, which costs about $15 at the most, maybe $12 for 10 days, to treat your chest infection, but it has a higher incidence of diarrhea, vomiting, and stomach cramps. If you're that one in ten you're in for some misery. Or I can prescribe Biaxin, which has no higher efficacy but will have a much lower incidence of GI side effects. That would cost $80.

If you have Medicare or Medicaid or a medication plan, it's a no-brainer. But if you're uninsured, paying out of pocket, you may say I'll take the $12 prescription. If my stomach gets upset, I'll tell my doctor and switch to something else. Nine out of ten times the cheaper medicine will do it.

"Overuse" of the emergency room is a hot topic, and my view is pretty contrarian. ER usage just topped 100 million visits a year in the United States. Back in the late 1980s and early 1990s when managed care was coming around, people

Treating sore throats is expensive while life-saving interventions are relatively cheap. High-volume "little stuff" subsidizes costly complicated procedures in this skewed fee schedule, says Kniffin.

were saying ERs are going to go out of business. Places that actually managed care kept people out of the ER. I think that was a matter of rationing by inconvenience, but maybe they were doing the preventative care. But use has taken off again.

Some ERs are opening up observation units where they are keeping people 8 to 10 up to 24 hours and are almost providing inpatient care. There has been (federal insurance) money, so they have gone after this money.

We are legally obligated to provide what is called a medical screening exam for everyone, and we are also legally obliged to provide necessary services within the capability of our facility, which means doing an operation or a CAT scan, but we are not obliged to order a CAT scan for

every patient who walks through the door.

You come in and are feeling fine but are worrying about your sore knee. You want an MRI, and you want it now. We don't have to do that. We have to see you, evaluate you, and hopefully take care of you, but we don't have to necessarily do the MRI.

Most patients understand that. I'm certainly service oriented and I want the customer to go home satisfied. I'll try and do something unless it's really absurd. Maybe we can come to some kind of compromise. It's 2 in the morning and we just can't do a CAT scan. Wait until the morning and we will do it then.

There was a landmark study done several years ago by some ER physicians from Michigan. They looked at the marginal cost of seeing non-emer-

63

gency patients in the ER, given that society wants an emergency room that's open 24 hours a day, seven days a week with staffing to deal with a crisis.

So what is it going to cost to run a bunch of sore throats through there? They came up numbers that were really minuscule.

Our staffing and equipment costs are fixed. Our revenue comes from the little stuff, because that is where the volume is. If we figured out how to remove the little stuff than we'd be in trouble.

Look at the charges. A level 2 charge is a pretty uncomplicated sore throat, about $80. A level 3 would be a bad ankle sprain, about $120. A level 4 would be a complicated case, something like appendicitis, that's about $250. If you come in absolutely dying, and I intervene in some way and literally save your life, what do you think my charge is for that?

$400!

So we are charging $120 for an ankle sprain that arguably a nurse practitioner could take care of and $400 to really save someone's life. Maybe what we should do is cut our ankle sprain charge and increase our life-saving interventions to what? $5,000, $10,000?

But if we could increase our charges to where the math worked out, no one would pay them. So we're stuck with this dysfunctional system where we're charging ridiculous amounts for ankle sprains. That $120 charge is just my fee. When you add the hospital charges for X-rays you're going to end up with a $300 bill.

The ER is a very expensive place. We all feel some guilt over that. But in the big scheme of the health care system the numbers don't support the charge that the ER is where the financial hemorrhaging is.

I dare you to go to the ER and say "You really don't belong here." People are here for a reason. It

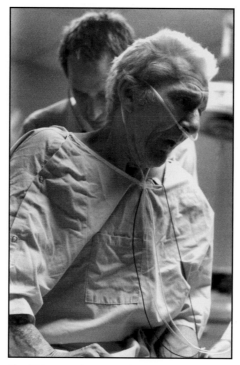

The ER's cost, about 1% of our health care budget, is a bargain, says Kniffin.

may not be an emergency in the sense that they're going to die, but there are reasons.

Some people don't have phones so they can't pick up the phone and call their doctor for an appointment.

Some people don't have the wherewithal to make an appointment and the transportation to get there.

Some people don't have a doctor.

Some people don't have the skills to know what's an emergency and what's not.

Theoretically, the higher you go up the socioeconomic ladder the better someone is able to know what's an emergency. But we see college

professors, board members, the cream of the crop in the ER at 10 o'clock at night because they think it's an emergency and it's not.

And then there are the financial barriers. You don't have to pay before you leave here. A lot of doctors' offices require some kind of payment upon service rendered. For all these reasons people show up in the ER without emergencies. Not because they want to be here, but because it's their only option.

From my position, the ER is a great deal. One percent of our health care budget covers the cost of all the 5,000 ERs in the United States.

In the average ER about 5% of the people are critically ill. Another 15% are really, really sick and ought to be there. Another 30% could probably be managed somewhere else.

You're left with the 50% who are not emergencies. They belong in a 24-hour walk-in clinic. But that would probably cost another $750,000 a year in Middlebury.

We're seeing about 13,000 people a year in the ER. And the volume is going up no matter what people want to say or do about it. People don't sit at home and say, "Let's go to the ER." People come here for a reason. If they had a better option, they'd go.

I'm not opposed to exploring better places, such as a walk-in clinic. I'd love for the average sore throat not to have to wait for three hours in the ER because we're so busy with other people. I would love to have them going to a place where there is continuity of care.

We should continue as a society to look for better options. In the meantime, we shouldn't slam the door and say "Stay home."

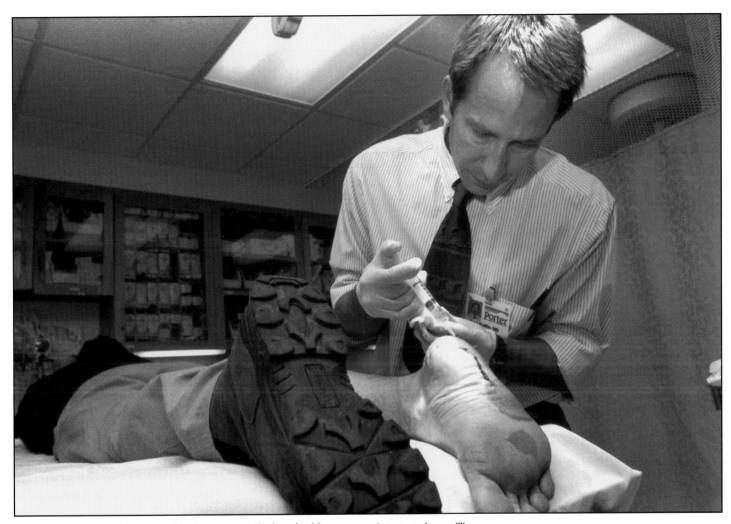

"Ultimately it's society's job to decide that we want the best health care, want it now, and are willing to pay handsomely for it. Or we will have pretty good health care with a little bit of wait. I would either change the expectations of the American public and sober them up or create a bucket of money that is so big that we can have everything," says Kniffin.

Tom Plumb

Executive Director, 1981–2000, Addison County Community Action Group

The Working Poor Fall Through the Cracks

Tom Plumb was executive director of the Addison County Community Action Group, a non-profit, community-based, anti-poverty agency, from 1981 until December of 2000. Plumb is now a full-time volunteer working on Rotary International community development programs in Honduras for half the year and raising money for the projects in Vermont the other half. The first interview was conducted in August of 2000 while Plumb was still executive director. In the epilogue, he discusses his experiences over the past two and half years following his retirement in finding and paying for health care coverage for himself and his wife.

Rising health care costs, the lack of a living wage, and shrinking social programs are squeezing the working poor. Faith-based initiatives and charity cannot meet the needs of people who fall through the cracks, says Plumb.

We are an agricultural county, which means that our farm workers generally aren't covered by most medical programs unless they have kids. We also have our fair share of low-paying jobs, service-sector jobs that may or may not include medical coverage.

Although we are the "Dairyland of Vermont," I'd imagine conditions are pretty much similar throughout Vermont. Except we do have the benefit of being a retirement community. The College attracts a lot of retirees and well-to-do types, professors and the like, and with Porter Hospital here we have that medical community.

This is a double-edged sword. These people increase property values, which is a strain on those who are already here and can't afford a home or drives up their rents. The hospital was started by the College back in the 1920s. If you're going to attract students, one of the concerns for parents is medical care in the area. The College has been very supportive of the hospital and probably would kick and scream if there was any thought of closing it down.

Then again, I think community care is the best care. It would be a shame if smaller hospitals closed down for larger complexes. I don't know if I would go to Porter for brain surgery, but I would go there if I had pneumonia.

Overall the College is a positive. Their students don't put the same kind of housing strain on the community that students at UVM do. And the College helps with things like the fire department and with child care. If it somehow benefits the College, they are more than willing to help financially.

And the College attracts a group of people who are giving of themselves. A lot of college professors' spouses come here, are looking for something to do, and become very active in the community. I started at the community action group in 1972, directing the summer camp, when I was still a Middlebury College student.

The county has a justified reputation statewide as being the most integrated, cooperative county. That's often why many new programs start or are piloted here.

One reason is that many directors of the agencies that started in the late 1960s and 1970s stayed for many years. They knew each other so well that cooperation was easy. That's not the case so much today, but the historical cooperation has continued.

We, as the community action agency, serve the gamut of folks receiving federal assistance, from welfare to the working poor. People can't survive on a monthly welfare check of $500 or $600. That does not pay the rent or much beyond the rent, so we have emergency services, food, clothing, utility assistance, dental assistance to get people over the hump. And we have job training.

The working poor fall through the cracks, and we serve them. Elders getting a $500 or $600 check from Social Security can't cut it either. Living on welfare is not a piece of cake, but it helps enough so people don't revolt. Most working people we serve are one paycheck away from being in poverty and homeless.

When I came the health of people we served was terrible, especially dental care. During the 1970s, ACCAG ran a dental clinic using a National Health Service Corps dentist. One of the first things I had to do as director was close it, because federal funding ended.

But health care has improved. A lot of that is because of Medicaid and Dr. Dynasaur. Dr. Dynasaur has had a dramatic impact with children.

Those who do fall through the cracks are pretty much the 18- through 50-somethings who don't have kids, who don't have health insurance at their jobs, who don't make enough to afford private insurance, and who don't qualify for Medicaid (an income below $18,000 for two adults without children).

There's always been the fear that if you left welfare and made too much money you'd lose your Medicaid. That's still the case, but your children can stay in Dr. Dynasaur, so the risk is just covering yourself. And here Vermont's liberal legislature has been very good in creating a window, as long as two years, for low-income Vermonters to retain Medicaid coverage when they return to work.

When I began in the 1970s our social service programs weren't as extensive as they are today. There is some Republican in me, and some people became more demanding and less self-reliant. So I supported welfare-to-work legislation, which was opposed by many other social services people, as long as there was a support system to make it work—child care, transportation, continued health care benefits. If you eliminate all these barriers then everyone has something to give and should work.

You can have a workfare mindset that is punitive or compassionate. I never believed that allowing someone to sit home, eat Ring Dings, and watch television was being compassionate. Even if people just volunteered in the ACCAG clothing room it gave them some self-respect.

I support national health insurance. A healthy life is the one thing the country should provide its population.

It's ironic that the very poor and the very rich have the best coverage. Those in the middle are left out. If we were to throw out all the various systems and create a single coverage some people would object, saying it's socialized medicine. But we already have a national Medicaid and Medicare system that's like socialized medicine.

During World War II, many recruits were rejected because they were malnourished. The subsidized hot lunch program was created so that the military would not have a malnourished force again. What are we defending with our defense budget if our population's unhealthy today? Medical coverage, especially preventive medical care, strikes me as being a right.

This is too big for Addison County. But the state and the federal government have this budget surplus (August 2000) that they could decide to invest in health care. I don't think they will, but because the economy has been so good, companies might offer sweeteners like health insurance.

It would be nice if the Feds provided coverage for everybody, and I would like to see prescription care coverage for the elderly. Short of that it would be nice if all employers provided health care coverage and a living wage. The best way is to pay a living wage so that people don't have to come to a place like us. Put us out of business.

Our problem at ACCAG is that if we paid a living wage of say $14 an hour to all our staff, we'd have to cut our staff in half. We pay $6.25 to $7.50 for people who have worked here a long time. What keeps them is the health care benefit. Once people come here, they don't want to lose their health insurance.

One of my greatest fears has been that when I leave this job I won't have health insurance. I don't worry about eating beans and rice in Honduras, but I'm nervous about not having health coverage.

September 2003

When I left ACCAG I could have continued my ACCAG plan with Blue Cross for 18 months, which would cost $600 a month or $7,200 a year for my wife Carol and me, or found other coverage.

I couldn't afford to take our chances without health insurance, because a catastrophic illness could wipe us out. At the time I didn't think we would consume $7,200 of health insurance a year, and I ended up with a Mutual of Omaha policy that had a $3,500 deductible for each of us. I was also interested in their worldwide coverage, because we would be living in Honduras for half the year.

Their policy cost $2,600 the first year, increased to $3,000 the second year, and to $3,600 and change this year. That's just for basic coverage. They have limited accident coverage which costs us another $365. Dental is another $720.

We're now spending $4,600 for health care plus long-term care coverage. Both of us have parents who have needed extensive care. I've told Carol to push me off a cliff if I end up like my father in a wheelchair with Alzheimer's. But I'm afraid when it comes to that point she might have second thoughts.

My hope is that if I needed long-term care I could stay at home, which this plan allows. I pay $108 for Carol and $113 a month for me. If we ever break the coverage, which is $165 a day, we would start over at a new premium rate.

So we're spending about $7,000 on health and long-term care insurance. We haven't claimed a dime from our policy, and we have had thousands in out-of-pocket expenses because we have never reached our deductible.

Did I think we would end up spending $13,000 last year between insurance and out-of-pocket expenses? No I didn't.

There aren't many "retired" 50-year-olds like me. I chose to retire early, because I wanted to be done with a 9 to 5 job and to volunteer. My father died in January of 2000 and since the end of 2001 I have received a monthly annuity payment from a small inheritance, which I use for health care expenses.

I'm fortunate I can pay for our health insurance, but most people can't.

I become quite cynical when I come back from Honduras and see how far $500 goes there—it can build a water system or start a medical clinic. Honduras is the second poorest country in the hemisphere with a per capita income of $560; it essentially has no social programs. The homes of the folks that I work with are tin, mud, sticks, cardboard. If you're sick you pretty much just live with it or die with it.

We don't want Honduras's health system. We are a wealthy country and could pay for universal health care if we chose to and could save money if we covered everyone.

But now with our multi-billion-dollar federal budget deficits, we will be defending what there is. George Bush has pretty much tied the hands of anyone coming up with new programs, because there won't be any money to pay for them.

The surplus we once had is going to tax cuts and wars and not to social services. Republicans view support of national defense and security as government's only role. If you create huge deficits then you have to shrink or eliminate social programs. That leaves social programs to faith-based initiatives and charity.

But how much can charity do? Look at the United Way, which is one of the best charitable ways of raising money. Their goal is $615,000 to help support nearly all the social service and health care agencies in Addison County. You're not going to save the world or Addison County with $615,000.

Some of my fellow Rotarians understand my views that health care should be a right. But most are businessmen and would say our system is what the market dictates. But they also understand that health care costs are getting out of hand and are struggling to cover their own employees.

They know that people need health insurance and as insurance becomes more burdensome for them there will be more of an uproar to have some kind of national program.

So far there hasn't been a big backlash about cuts, because poor people don't vote. But if the President cuts Medicare then he will be facing the elders' wrath.

Chapter 4

Home Health

There Are No Low Points about Being Home

HOME HEALTH'S ROLE

In 2003, Addison County Home Health and Hospice staff served 1,436 residents in 21 communities. The bulk of the staff's 72,042 home visits fell into four categories: about a quarter, 18,767 staff visits, were a Medicaid program that funds services that enable residents, primarily the elderly eligible for nursing home placement, to remain in their homes; another quarter, 18,054, were nursing visits—nurses are the liaison with the supervising physician and provide skilled medical care; slightly less than a fifth, 15,087, were home health aide visits—aides, working under the supervision of a nurse or therapist, provide personal care, such as helping with bathing and therapy exercises; and the last major category consisted of 5,836 physical therapy visits.

The average cost for a home care visit for Vermont's 12 private, non-profit home health agencies in 2002 was $76, a bargain compared to the national average of $102 per visit. The bill for Vermonters' home health services? About $81.5 million, with Medicare, the federal program for the elderly, paying about 50% of that amount, and Medicaid, the state-federal program for people with low incomes and disabilities, paying about 31%. Private insurance paid about 6% of the bill.

What do these numbers tell us?

First, Vermont has cost-efficient home health care—in the mid-1990s the state's home health agencies were the lowest-cost providers in the country and are among the lowest today. At the same time, Vermont is the only state in the country whose home health agencies guarantee access to medically necessary services regardless of a patient's ability to pay. Addison County home health, for example, provides about $100,000 of free service annually in its nearly $7 million budget. This deficit is offset by contributions from area towns and the United Way.

These efficiencies and the guarantee of care result, in large part, from the state's system of non-profit, non-competing agencies. Unlike other states that have a combination of for-profit and non-profit home health agencies, Vermont legislators and regulators have historically strongly supported non-profit community-based organizations and discouraged care by for-profit organizations and national chains. This policy is now being challenged by a private, for-profit nursing business that would like to be eligible for Medicare and Medicaid reimbursement.

Vermont's home health agencies, which served 21,449 Vermonters in 2002, have historically worked well together and avoided the turf battles found in other states, supporters of the current policy contend. In other states, the for-profits often "cherry pick" the better paying and least-costly-to-serve patients and leave the poorer and resource-needy populations to the non-profits.

Second, home health is a bargain compared to the costs of nursing or hospital care. According to the federal Centers for Medicare and Medicaid Services, a year's home care service in Vermont cost $2,395 in 2001. (The national average was $2,960.) A year in a Vermont nursing home can cost $50,000-plus at Medicaid's daily reimbursement rate of about $150 and up (2005). Labor- and resource-intensive hospital care is a quantum cost leap. A semi-private hospital room, before medical tests and services, runs $800 a day and up. The bill for a typical-length Vermont hospital stay, four days, averages $8,000.

Given these relative costs, today's health care mantra is, not surprisingly, keep people out of nursing homes, shorten hospital stays, and return people to their homes as quickly as possible. For home health staff this translates into sicker patients and patients with increasingly debilitating chronic problems who require a constantly changing mix of medical, therapy, and homemaking services.

At the same time that home health agencies are being asked to provide more service per patient they are facing the same Medicaid and Medicare underpayments and staffing shortages that are found throughout the health care system. Despite this challenging set of hurdles, the state's home health agencies have usually been able to stitch together a web of services for even the most resource-needy patients.

What these trends and numbers don't convey

is the nearly universal desire of the recovering, the sick, and the elderly to remain or recover in their homes. Keeping people at home is thus both good economics and popular health care policy.

The following narratives examine how Addison County Home Health and Hospice has responded to the desire of Gary Huntley, a quadriplegic, and his family that he be cared for at home. Huntley was paralyzed in an April 1999 motorcycle accident and is one of the most demanding around-the-clock challenges that the agency—and a home health family—has ever faced.

Lucille Huntley and Sue Nagy, Gary's mother and sister, discuss Gary's hospitalization, his treatment in an out-of-state rehabilitation center, and his desire to return home. Diane Cushman discusses the home health agency's efforts to arrange care, the limits on the care that it can provide, and the ongoing questions facing the agency and family. Beth Thibault, a long-time family friend, describes the day-to-day care of Gary while Gary reflects on the quality of his life at home.

Sharon Thompson, clinical director of the agency, concludes the section with an assessment of the present and future challenges in providing a seamless web of home and health care services for the county.

Families need advocates to guide them through the health care system. Home health nurse Barb O'Hehir, left, has known Lucille Huntley for more than a decade, first working with her after her husband suffered a stroke and now consulting as case manager with her son Gary.

Lucille Huntley, left, quadriplegic Gary Huntley's mother, and Sue Nagy, his sister, have never doubted that removing Gary from an out-of-state rehabilitation center and caring for him at home was the right course.

Lucille Huntley and Sue Nagy

On March 30
He Came Home

What if you or a family member were struck by a car or had a paralyzing stroke or had a degenerative disease like Alzheimer's and faced a lifetime of care and enormous medical bills? How would you manage? Who could help you grapple with life-and-death questions?

The Huntley family faced those heart-stopping questions, like most families, with no forewarning.

Gary Huntley, then 49, became an instant quadriplegic in the spring of 1999 when a drunk driver struck him while he was riding his motorcycle. Lucille Huntley, his mother, and Sue Nagy, an older sister, recount here the family's ongoing efforts to find the most appropriate care for Gary, leading to his return to his mother's home in Leicester.

August 2000

SUE: Gary had his accident a year ago in April of 1999. He was riding his motorcycle and had slowed down and put his direction light on to turn into my brother's driveway. This young girl was going 55 miles an hour and hit him.

Gary went up the height of the telephone pole and landed on my brother's lawn.

First, he went to Rutland Hospital. He had a brain stem injury, and his spine shifted, but it didn't completely break in two.

LUCILLE: The next day a doctor in intensive care told us that we should let him go, because he would be a vegetable. We were quite disturbed. If he had been in a coma for a month that would have been different. There was another younger doctor and we told him what had happened and that we didn't want to see this doctor again.

Two days later Gary came out of his coma.

SUE: After a month, he was moved to Dartmouth Hitchcock for rehabilitation. They put two rods in his back to give it strength and took his spleen out, which was damaged.

He was in Dartmouth for a month and then he went to Burlington to the old DeGoesbriand Hospital, which has a rehabilitation unit for paralyzed patients like Gary who is a quadriplegic with no control of his arms or legs.

He was afraid of trying to learn how to talk, because he depended on a breathing tube. You have to cover the tube so air goes over your vocal cords and not out the tube. He can breathe now some on his own, but he was scared then to try and they didn't do much speech training.

Fletcher Allen didn't think there was a lot of hope that he would be able to do anything. But as time progressed, they found that he could blink his eye. His mind is not damaged at all. His comprehension is fine. Oh my Lord, yes.

LUCILLE: And they worked with him on using his computer. He could blink his good eye and select letters. In 10 to 15 minutes, he could write 10 lines.

SUE: In September he moved to Willowood, a nursing home and rehabilitation center in Williamstown, Massachusetts, because Fletcher Allen couldn't keep him any longer. Medicare only covers 100 days of hospitalization and Addison County Home Health had already gotten a waiver to allow him to stay longer in the hospital.

Willowood is a wonderful facility, and it's supposed to be one of the top places to send someone like Gary. The only other place was in Ascutney, but it was full and too understaffed for Gary, who needs high-tech, 24-hour care.

When we got to Willowood, we saw that we were just spinning our wheels and that nothing was going to happen. They said that they had to stop therapy, because there was no progress. I don't know if the policy is driven by Medicare and Medicaid, but they said they couldn't justify bringing a therapist in when they could be with somebody else.

After two months, around Christmas, we started working on bringing him home to stay with mother.

LUCILLE: They said they checked on him all the time. But they came to the door and never made eye contact or spoke to him. He thought he was sitting there alone for 4 to 5 hours, and he was scared because you have to suction off his mucous or he can't breathe.

SUE: Doctors in Burlington kept telling us don't let people tell you that progress is impossible. One of the doctors, who was the head of rehabilitation for Gary's type, said he did see progress in some people. But all the facilities were always saying don't give Gary any false hopes.

I won't give Gary false hopes, but I don't think it's true that he has no hope of ever moving anything again. He's moving his head up and down which he couldn't do before.

Caring for Gary Huntley requires a team approach: an endocrinologist for his diabetes; an ear, nose, and throat specialist for his tracheotomy; surgeons for his skin problems; nurses, physical and occupational therapists, and aides from home health; and family members. Family physician William Barrett, center, made a house call before the Huntleys had their customized van to transport Gary.

You hold his hand, and he will push against it. He couldn't do that before. I know it's going to be a long time, and we have told him that.

We're hoping that there will be a light at the end of the tunnel, but we have to work at it. If he wants it bad enough then he has to work with us, because we can't do it for him. That's the type of attitude we have had with him.

This wasn't supported down there. They said, "We have seen more people like him, and it's never happened so why would you give him a false hope."

When we said we wanted to care for Gary at home, Willowood said, "No problem."

First, we met with Gary Boyce, the state official in charge of Gary's Medicaid coverage. We were told that Gary's needs were the greatest that the state had ever tried to meet in a home.

They never sugarcoated anything. They said, "You realize if you do this, you have to be available to provide care."

In order for him to be home he had to have a full-time caregiver at home. Mother is that caregiver. My other brother and sister and I said we would be available for anything that wasn't nurses-only type of care. I live half an hour away in Rutland. My sister, Margie, lives by Lake Dunmore, 10 minutes away. My brother, Obie, lives in Forestdale. He's 10 minutes away, too.

We knew as a family that we just couldn't leave him down there. We just couldn't do that.

Gary Boyce was supportive, because they really don't want the money to go out of state. They really do try and get people in the home, because it is better mentally to be there.

We were on the phone with each other, with Gary Boyce, and with the visiting nurses. We kept talking. Here's where we are. It will be so long before we have our house ready. We have done this and this and this.

Home health had to learn how to deal with Gary. Diane Cushman, the high-tech nurse at home health, and Mary Scarborough, who's the Medicaid advocate for patients, went to see Gary. Gary Boyce also went down to Willowood.

We needed to get training. Diane Cushman set up appointments for mother, me, and my sister to have training at Willowood. We learned how to do trach care, suctioning, feed him with his feeding tube, move him back and forth. We got a list from Willowood of his whole program.

Mother is Gary's guardian. She had to sign lots of paperwork at the beginning so he could get help. The nurses have done all the paperwork since, so I don't know what his care costs.

I had drawn out how we could add on to mom's small old trailer so Gary could stay here. But I thought Gary would never be able to move about, because the doorways and everything were so small.

Then we looked at new trailers and saw the layout of this home, which is twice as wide as mom's trailer, which is perfect. Gary can come up the ramp and go right into his room, which has a 14-foot-long closet that is 6 feet wide and big enough for all his supplies and clothing.

It was designed with 36-inch doorways, which are wide enough for his wheelchair and carrying sling. It was a modular home, so they could change some things that they can't in a trailer. We put in a special bathroom and shower with no doorway so all the lifts can go back and forth.

Gary had liability insurance on his bike which helped pay for this, and my mother traded in her trailer. Otherwise there was no way we could have afforded it.

We ordered it and mother stayed with us for six weeks while the dealer took her trailer, and the new one came from Pennsylvania. It was winter, but they were very good at getting it together because we were working on deadlines.

Addison County Home Health told Willowood that they wouldn't have the staff to take care of Gary until the first of February. Then it was the first of March.

Home health contracted with "The Bus," which is a special bus in Rutland that can pick up handicapped people, to bring Gary home. It's cheaper than an ambulance. Diane Cushman and the LNA went down with oxygen and everything that Gary was going to need with him on the trip back.

I drove down and brought back his television, stereo, computer and all the stuff out of his room.

Gary gave the staff at Willowood a big cake thanking them for all their help. I think they understood. They weren't angry and were very helpful. They knew that being shortstaffed they couldn't do any more. They knew that it was better for Gary to be home.

On March 30, he came home.

LUCILLE: We never doubted that we were doing the right thing.

December 2001

LUCILLE: Marge and Sue and Obie will come and help if it's an emergency, but it's not a regular thing. Sue has arthritis and has hurt her back and can't sleep. The others work during the daytime.

I'm with Gary every day by myself from 3 to 10. Tuesday and Friday mornings I can leave anytime after 8, but I have to be back by 3. It takes two to get Gary out of bed and into his chair and Barb (Barb O'Hehir, case manager from Addison County Home Health) comes those mornings.

It's been pretty spotty on weekends getting help at night. We can't get just anyone to come in. LNAs have to be able to suction and do things like that and some haven't had the training. Last month, a LNA started coming every other weekend from 10 to 6.

That helps because I can sleep through the night and not worry about Gary. It's been tiring for me, but I'm not much for going out and visiting people.

We have had the van for pretty close to a year. The last of Gary's motorcycle insurance paid for it. Gary can go out whenever he wants. We have used it to go for rides, to the hospital, to shop, and for two weddings, Sue's daughter and a nephew.

At first, Sue or Beth (Thibault) would drive it and Barb would stay with him in the back. Someone has to stay with him, because the roads are bumpy and his head has to be supported. At first, they didn't ask me to drive so I didn't offer. But now I drive.

Gary has his motorized chair now. He drives it when we go places and around the house, but it weighs like 500 pounds and it's hard on the rugs. We're still trying to support his head better.

Most of the time he stays in his room. He's more comfortable there than in the living room.

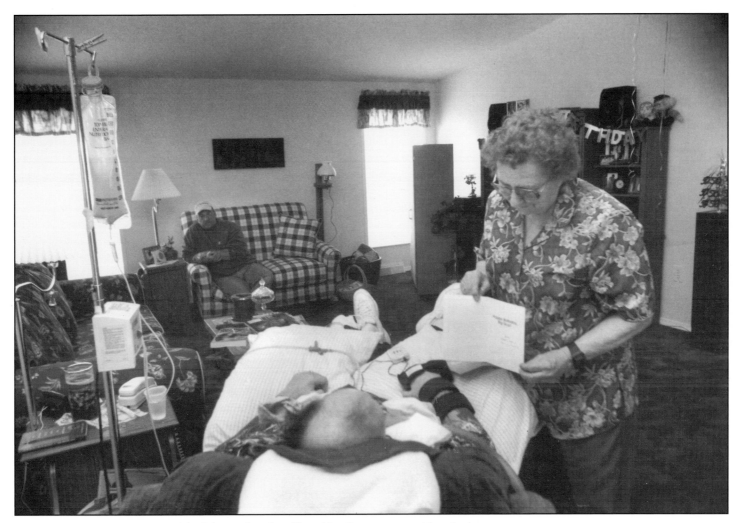

Lucille Huntley, showing Gary a 50th birthday card, replaced her old trailer, too cramped for wheel-chair movement, with a modular home with an extra-wide bathroom, closet, and doorways.

He has surround sound and a big TV. He can put 200 CDs in his changer and they play one after another. He probably has 500 CDs, but what else does he have? That's the way we look at it.

The Dynavox came this summer. The computer people and Beth have been working on setting it up and programming in phrases and words.

Gary's attitude has changed for the better since he's been home. He's more comfortable here. But he's kind of quiet and will say things to Beth that he won't to me or Sue or Obie.

Beth tends right to him and knows what's bothering him.

Diane Cushman, RN

Director of High-Technology Services,
Addison County Home Health and Hospice

We Do the Best We Can

A responsive health care system requires a seamless web of services that meets a patient's changing needs in a hospital, community care facility, or private home. As its part of the web, Addison County home health nurses, therapists, and aides make 70,000 home visits annually, enabling hundreds of area residents to remain in their homes. Meeting the multiple needs of Gary Huntley has raised fundamental questions for the agency: How should cost affect the services that the agency provides? Can home care, when it is more expensive than institutional care, be justified? How much care should families be required to provide?

Medicaid started the high-tech program in 1990 to support people with disabilities at home rather than placing them in a residential care facility in Vermont or out of state. The program, which I oversee, pays for high-tech equipment and for private-duty nurses.

Three years ago Gary Boyce, a Medicaid supervisor, called and said there was a fellow in a nursing home in Massachusetts who was a quadriplegic and wanted to come home. We have served quadriplegics in the community before, but they haven't required as much complicated care. They could eat and talk. They could help a little bit with their mobility.

This person, Gary Huntley, was different. He has equipment that needs constant attention—a gastric feeding tube and a tracheostomy that needs to be suctioned. When he came home he was on oxygen and an oxygen monitor. Except for some facial movement, he has no control of his body.

He weighs over 215 pounds, and one person can't move him. Communication is another big piece. His tongue is partially paralyzed. He can communicate through sounds but can't form words. Unlike my three other high-tech clients he is 100% dependent on caregivers and that moves him to a different level.

I met with the family first and got their perspective, because I knew that we weren't going to be able to provide all the care he needed. They wanted him home at all costs. Lucille, his mother, was driving down to Williamstown, Mass., several times a week, and they knew he would be happier at home.

After we figured out how much care was involved, we met with the entire family: Lucille, Gary's brother, his two sisters, and Beth, a LNA (licensed nursing assistant) who is a family friend. We told them that we were willing to bring Gary home, but that we couldn't provide all his care. There would be occasions, like a snowstorm, where we might not be able to be there. Were they willing to accept 24-hour responsibility for him in an emergency?

From the beginning we made clear our limitations. We never promise 24-hour coverage. For the first week or two, we can provide up to 22 hours a day. Then it drops to 16 to 18 hours.

Many families can take this on. But most 75-year-old women like Lucille would not take on the responsibility of learning the care and being the primary caregiver for the family.

Gary gets 16 hours of coverage from us and eight hours from Lucille. But Lucille has been doing even more, especially on weekends. Gary has been understaffed for two years, because we can't find high-tech, private-duty nurses.

It has been a real challenge. First, we didn't have a registry of nurses to do private-duty care because we had never needed that. So I had to find and train nurses and set up a scheduling, supervision, and payment program to have private-duty nurses on our payroll.

These people are home health employees, but they are a unique category. They are per diem high-tech nurses. They work as needed.

As years went on we created two full-time benefited positions. Beth (Beth Thibault, Gary's primary caregiver) is now a full-time employee and receives benefits. I have one other nurse who is in that category.

All the rest are truly per diem. If their client goes in the hospital, we are not obligated to give them any work. Many are fine with that. They are piecing together work and are happy to not be obligated to work.

When I call them and say, "I need someone to cover next Saturday, Sunday, and Monday nights," they can say, "No."

So staffing is a constant that gnaws at me. I have to call up his mother and say, "Nobody is coming tonight. You're going to have to do it yourself."

That phone call is difficult, but I have made a million of them so I'm getting hardened to it. Mrs. Huntley doesn't complain, but I feel guilty.

We thought it would be a helpful transition if Gary could spend two weeks in the nursing home in Middlebury so the family could learn to care for him. But Helen Porter wouldn't take him, because his level of care is so high.

So they ended up going to Williamstown, spending a day here and there learning his care. Gary came home in very good shape. But Willowood is an institution, and there isn't the personal one-on-one care that families want.

Gary's home care probably costs Medicaid more than Willowood, because we customize and provide more personalized care. Some therapies were stopped because Willowood believed that he was not making any progress. That might be true. I don't know what the limitations were.

The family complained that he never got speech therapy. In a home setting we believe that there are achievable goals inch by inch by inch even if he never learns to talk. We can justify those services and do get reimbursed for them. I know in rehab centers they make decisions based on whether they can get reimbursed or not.

With equipment, we have a particular bed and lift that we want and will make the extra phone calls to get them. We got a top-of-the-line bed, because it protects his skin better. He has had massive skin problems, which will continue because of his weight and immobility.

Carla Tighe, the physical therapist, helped them customize a van to accommodate him in his chair. Vans cost about $20,000 with four-wheel drive. Customizing is another $10,000 to $15,000. The Huntleys paid for that and the new modular home.

We believed that we could justify getting a Dynavox computer communication system, and Medicaid agreed to pay for it. All these are subjective quality of care and life issues. Are we going to say to this young man who is cognitively intact that we don't care that you can't talk and can only communicate by laboriously blinking your eye at

For the past 10 years, Diane Cushman has supervised the Medicaid funded high-technology program that enables high-need patients, many of them children, to be cared for at home.

an alphabet board?

The Dynavox was probably $25,000 to $30,000. His motorized wheelchair with laser control is probably $30,000. A normal wheelchair is $5,000.

Private duty care is expensive. Gary is the first time I have used LNAs with a high-tech patient. I only did it because I couldn't find registered nurses. Beth (Thibault) and Ursula (Lajeunesse) are highly skilled LNAs who have taken on more responsibilities than the average.

My preference would be to staff it entirely

with RNs. That would be twice as expensive. LNAs are probably starting at $9.75. A registered nurse would start at $18 to $19 (2002). Then we bill at a higher rate to cover our expenses.

A ball park figure would be 80 hours a week of LNA time at $10 an hour, or roughly $3,200 a month. Then we have a RN who is working 20 hours a week on a night shift rate of roughly $22 an hour. That's $440 a week. So we're paying out close to $5,000 a month before our overhead.

That doesn't cover the twice-a-week visits of Barb (Barb O'Hehir, the agency's case manager), who is paid by Medicare. Medicare will cover her because Gary has been disabled for more than two years. Medicaid covers his medications, and occupational and physical therapy are picked up by Medicare.

I only visit once a month now since the program is up and running, but it has taken two years to get there.

We grapple with the questions of cost, but we always come back to our mission to provide service to clients in Addison County. We wouldn't deny people services because they don't have a payment source. However, we have never been asked to provide megabucks of free service. Would we provide services to Gary Huntley if he didn't qualify for the high-tech Medicaid program?

We have never been asked to do that, but there would come a time when we would have to say no. We have to look at those ethical dilemmas every day, and we don't have answers. We just try and do the best we can every day.

Is it good for a family to know what care is costing? Are we being paternalistic by not discussing it? Or is it mean to tell a family who wants their son, father, child to come home that it would cost the state thousands of dollars a month? Do you as a family feel any compunction about that?

That's a real dilemma.

I'd be interested in how people would respond. I think people would do the best they could in their own fashion. That might mean sacrifices like one person staying home. That's a Vermont ethic. You see it in different generations, but especially in older generations.

I'm sure Mrs. Huntley didn't see her future as an elderly person caring for her son. That was not a choice that she would have made, but she doesn't complain.

Home health in general does intermittent care. We may visit twice a day, but it's for only half an hour. The high-tech program is the only program where we spend hours and hours in someone's house, and families often reach a saturation point. I have had families take on the care; they say, "We love all your nurses, but it's really wearing to have someone in your house every night."

I'm sure Mrs. Huntley would prefer not to have strangers in her house all the time. Even though they are no longer strangers, they are still not family people. She has given up any privacy she has. The nurse stays in the living room. They use her kitchen. They use her bathroom. They have the run of a person's house at night.

And if you live in another person's house you get to know them at a whole other level, which is both good and bad. You learn more about their families than you do about your best friends. There are private things that you don't want to know about, and that's always discomforting.

We need to prepare families for these issues, because once they take on home care there is no easy way out. And if it is too much, are you prepared to say to your son, father, brother that you have to go back to a residential care facility?

Gary is unique in that he is an adult and is cognitively intact. It's hard enough with grandma who doesn't have her mind anymore. I'm dreading that day when it comes for Gary, because he desperately wants to be home.

Gary is quite fragile and has a lot of medical issues. He is diabetic. He has cardiac disease and had a coronary bypass when he was 45 before his accident. He spent a week and a half over Christmas (2001) in the hospital with pneumonia, which was the first time he had pneumonia since he came home. We have said from day one that pneumonia could easily kill him. The family knows that.

After he came home Beth and I talked about asking Gary again if he wants to be put on a ventilator if his lungs fail. From the time of his accident through the nursing home placement, he clearly stated that he did not want to be resuscitated if he stopped breathing. When he came home, we had to ask that question again, and he changed his mind. He now wants full resuscitation, because he is so happy to be home and pleased with the quality of his life.

If he stops breathing at home we will do CPR and manually bag him all the way to the emergency room. But if you are totally dependent on a ventilator you require 24-hour care, and we could not provide that unless staffing resources change enormously.

I don't know if Beth has had this discussion with him yet, but the pneumonia was a reminder that we need to.

The other shoe that is going to drop is Lucille. What happens if she falls and breaks her hip or dies? Some family member would have to be the primary caregiver. Beth will stay for 48 hours at a time, but Gary needs someone who is going to live with him. That is the basis of the whole high-tech program. We don't bring people out independent of their families.

Beth Thibault, Hi-Tech LNA
Addison County Home Health and Hospice

He Wanted to Be Able to Eat

Finding long-term caregivers for multiply handicapped patients is one of a family's and the home health agency's greatest challenges. Beth Thibault, who had known Gary Huntley for years, has been a constant in his care. When Thibault first started working with Gary, she had to split her time, much to her frustration, between his early morning care and that of patients at the Rutland County home health agency, where she had worked for 11 years. For the past five-plus years, she has worked full-time for the Addison agency as Gary's primary daytime caregiver.

Letter-by-letter communication with an alphabet board is slow going, but Beth Thibault, who has known Gary Huntley since high school, can almost read Gary's mind after caring for him for the past five years.

When Gary left Willowood he had several goals.

He wanted to be able to eat, which he knows now can't happen. He's had three swallow tests at Burlington and Rutland. Whatever he swallows goes into his lungs. Watching him when he found out that he would not be able to eat was my lowest point.

He also wanted to smoke his pipe. He can do that, not often, but it's the idea that he can. I hold the pipe or he can hold it if I get it just right in his mouth.

And he wanted to be able to talk. I block off the trach and he can talk to me. But unless you hear him on a regular basis you're not going to understand him. His vocal cords are completely immersed in saliva, with some paralysis, so his speech is limited.

Most of the time we use the alphabet board or the Dynavox, which has a computer voice. On the Dynavox we have a file for everything. We have programmed names of family and friends so he can pull up a name and say, "Will you do such and such for me?"

We have another file that says, "I don't feel well," and we list all the body parts. There is another file that says, "I'm sad." "I'm happy." "I'm glad." and all the reasons why. "I have a headache today." "It's somebody's birthday."

Then we have some phrases that are just him, like the word "Oklahoma." Rather than cussing when something frustrates him, he says, "Oklahoma."

He raises his eyebrow, which controls a laser beam, and the word or whole phrase comes up on a line at the top of the screen. When he has the words he wants he winks on the line and the computer voice will say it.

The Dynavox is on a stand now, but we will set it up so he can use it on his bed and take it with him in his motorized chair.

There are times, like when we first got the van, that I thought, "I can't do this. I don't think it's possible."

We're not talking about just driving down the road. You have to get him safely in the van and you need everything with you—portable suction and oxygen—in case something life threatening happens. And before we got the power chair, which is really heavy, we had to figure out how to keep him from rocking in the van. The standard chair is a lot lighter and it bounces so you have to support his head carefully.

When you think of all this stuff you go, "Whoa!"

Then you break it down a step at a time and it all comes together. It's not just one head. Gary knows how to run all the equipment and will say don't do that, do this. He has the uncanny ability to make you the best you can be.

You try something and keep going. That frustration, believe it or not, is half the fun. We build on the things that are possible and that keeps his attitude up.

The day Gary went to Rutland to pick out his own CDs was a high point for me. He went in his own van, his own chair, and drove the chair up and down the aisles.

But not everything works, like the wheelchair-accessible shower. There's a limit to what you put somebody through. It takes about 40 minutes to pack him in a shower chair and another 30 to get him out and back to bed. By the time we supported him in the shower chair with Velcro and pillows, I had about two feet of human flesh to wash.

So we sponge him off. I made a call that it was a waste of his day. It already takes me about three hours just to get him up. That's feeding with his gastric tube, catheter, colostomy, total bed bath, eye care, regular trach care. Plus there is physical therapy, which is about 35 minutes, where I move his arms and legs and bend all his joints.

Professionally, I have learned more in the past two years taking care of Gary than I ever thought possible. As a hi-tech LNA, I can do pretty much what a RN does after I have been trained and demonstrated that I can do new procedures.

It's extremely interesting learning how to monitor someone's blood sugars, to know that his oxygen is a little low when he has a certain look in his eye, to know what to look for in sweats and wounds. I worry most about suctioning. He can cough up phlegm to his trach, but he can't cough it up into his mouth and spit it out.

I don't worry that I can't relieve him from choking. He has a bell and I check him constantly, but I worry because it scares him when he's alone.

Then there's the satisfaction of having him home. The accident itself was unfortunate enough, but to have to live in Massachusetts, too. I used to go to Willowood and work a 3 to 11 shift one day a week as a volunteer after I got through my regular job.

One day he said to me, "The only time I truly close my eyes is when you and Ma are here." If that doesn't say it right there.

Plus my job is fun. Yes, you have frustrating days, and there are days when he's down. Sometimes he's crabby like you, like me, like anybody. I go about my business and before the day is over we work it out.

It's hard to put in words. I have always enjoyed doing this. It's just who I am and what I do.

Gary Huntley

There Are No Low Points About Being Home

Gary Huntley wrote this commentary with the help of Beth Thibault using an alphabet board.

In institutions, they don't care if you live or die. At home, I have loving care all the time.

I had three goals coming home: to be able to move my arms; to be able to eat; and to smoke my pipe. The first two things I cannot do, but I have smoked my pipe and cigar.

However, I have done other things that we did not think were possible. I go on short trips in the van: the video store, a couple of weddings, the doctors' appointments. I have a power chair that I can use myself, and a new computer (Dynavox) that I use my eye to operate.

The one fear that I had in the institutions was not being able to call someone if I needed help. No one checks on you very often. It was very frightening and lonely at times.

At home, I have a wireless door bell attached to a plastic plate that slides under my head. I can press it with my head and call if I need anything.

At home, I have people all around me and also privacy when I want it. With my bell, I can have peace of mind. With family and friends, I am safe.

There are no low points about being home. Sometimes insurance doesn't always cover what

The Dynavox, a computerized voice system with a grid and files of words, phrases, and sentences, will vastly expand Gary Huntley's ability to express himself, but customizing the system has taken months of experimentation. Huntley operates the system with an eyebrow-controlled laser beam.

you need and/or it takes a lot of time to get the things that you need. You have to be patient and stay ahead of the important things.

I want to work hard at getting the movement back in my arms. I want to get my Dynavox working to its potential so I can communicate better and be even more independent.

My advice in coming home is make sure that you love your family. They will help you a lot. You

need a lot of support. You need dependable people, a good network among home care agencies, doctors, supply companies, and your family.

And for me, I have a mother who watches over me in every way. Without her, I would not be able to be here. She is forever constant and never tires of all the things she does for me every single day.

Sharon Thompson, RN

Director of Clinical Services,
Addison County Home Health
and Hospice

Who Is Thinking about the Whole Person?

American health care is frequently criticized for its overspecialization and its failure to treat the whole patient. No other country, the argument goes, can rival our high-tech resources, our cutting-edge drugs, and our array of specialists. But many developed countries have better "systems" that produce equal or better health care outcomes while costing half as much or less.

The family doctor has traditionally been the patient's advocate and guide through the maze of our health care services. But what happens when the family doctor, Sharon Thompson worries, has less and less time for this role? Who will take over that responsibility of providing a "seamless web of services," the key to good community health?

A seamless web of services among health care providers requires formal arrangements and short-hand communication that develops among experienced staffs, says Sharon Thompson.

The chance for Addison County to have a "seamless web of services" is incredibly high. Those are bureaucratic words, but if you acknowledge that, you can make it happen.

Ideally, patients move in a relatively seamless way through, among, around, into, and out of different facilities and programs. They don't have to reintroduce themselves every time they move. People are connecting, coordinating, sharing information so that by the time we meet you, we already know a fair amount about you and our role.

The cruelest thing in health care is to have to keep starting back at the beginning, "When did you start having whatever?"

In a rural setting where you have highly skilled, bright people and where everyone is on roughly the same page in planning and organizing care you have the chance to make this seamless web come true.

And I believe we are making it come true. Talk to some poor soul about experiences they're having in a health care system somewhere else with people not knowing their history. In the time it takes to ask those questions you could be dead on the floor.

There is a fair amount of communication, but what makes the county work is our informal communication system, which is a result of having professional staff that has worked together and has a history of short-hand communication.

It sounds like no big deal. It's just a bunch of people talking. But that's where it fails in so many other places.

Addison County has a history of being thought of as an area where turf issues aren't as hot. I suppose that stems from the same people doing business together for a long time, people who are focused on and interested in the well-being of "our" service population. I wouldn't try and paint a rainbow, but we do have that history.

If you went to Newport you would hear a lot of the same kind of answers, because Vermont generally has a similar story to tell. But in the more populated areas, like Burlington, you'll hear a slightly different story. It isn't seamless, and they know it. It's real frustrating for them, and there's a lot of pain.

Someone can get admitted to hospitals in other communities and have a long stay for something that would be a three-day stay here. Everyone

Our aging population is reflected in the patient age mix of Vermont's 12 certified home health agencies. In 2002, 14% of patients were 85 and older; 25% were 75 to 84; and 15% were 65 to 74. Home health serves roughly twice as many females, 64% of the case mix, as males, 36%.

is on the same page here and is truly, honestly and sincerely trying to conserve resources, to do the very best for the patient and get them out of the hospital.

I don't want to sound like we know every living soul in Addison County, but we almost do. We can mobilize things quickly and can really get people out quickly. So it's not like what might happen other places where you've got this poor old girl in the hospital. She's weak, but you'd really love to get her home because she doesn't have high clinical needs any longer. But you just can't get it together to make the connections

Making those connections involves a massive amount of technical knowledge, clinical knowledge, resource knowledge. We can make it happen here awful fast. The hospital knows that. We know that.

Would other communities accept that diagnosis?

I think they would. Maybe they wouldn't love it that we said that. But it's not a judgment issue. It's not putting them down. They have people in the hospital trying to make those connections happen. It just doesn't work as fast.

The biggest federal concern now is how to cut health care spending. Cutting spending is like a mantra to them.

HCFA (Health Care Financing Administration, the federal agency that oversaw Medicare and Medicaid in the 1990s) gathers more information about you than you can possibly imagine. A lot of the information comes from us because we're mandated to give it to them.

They'd like you to believe that their motive is to have a wellness history for the country, but it really provides them with information to decide whether you deserve this health care dollar or that.

If all the trends stay in place, the picture is scary on how we will make decisions about who gets big-time care. Do you get to have a heart transplant or not, a liver transplant or not? Do we put you to sleep now?

Those things are out there and will be hanging over our heads. Decisions on paying for late and expensive end-of-life procedures will be the beginning.

I hope this will click in a real cataclysmic response with people saying, "No way. Stop it. This isn't going to happen. Back it off." We're going to have to take some control and make some decisions about health care, and you're not going to decide when I live or die or if we do this or that.

We haven't done that. There isn't that much unrest. We're too comfortable.

We spend a fair amount of time at Home Health rabble rousing. Get scared. Get yourself excited about this. Your future life and that of your children depends on decisions that are getting made now.

Patients expect less today than they used to. They don't expect you to bother to get to know or care about them. They are so pleasantly surprised that we still do.

There was this golden moment in health care when it was recognized that it's not smart to parcel people out into fragments and look at the "liver." We needed to look at the whole person and to figure out what the liver's problems had to do with the rest of your body.

Primary health care and the concept of family practice was born from that kind of thinking. One of the truly scary things in health care today is that with the pressure to see more people quickly we are seeing the death of the concept of holistic health care and a refragmentation of the human.

There are so many times now where we are the only people on the face of the earth who actually know a person's whole story. Take some poor old soul. Her cardiologist knows a piece. Her orthopedic surgeon knows a piece. Up until five years ago at least the family practice physician and home health knew the whole story. It's very much coming down to just us now.

Would the family docs agree? Absolutely. That's the very first thing the good ones will tell you. The whole idea of intelligent contemplation about the problems of another human being is the core of health care. Anyone can do a procedure. But who is thinking about the whole person?

Why do people go to a doctor? Because something is going on. You tell me that you have these three disparate symptoms. I can probably figure out what is going on with you, but it requires thought and pretty intense historical knowledge.

A family doctor has 10 minutes to figure that out. So even somebody who is really smart will probably have to glibly toss off, "try this drug," even when he doesn't want to.

There is an upside to all these changes. The massive explosion in the science of health care—new drugs and technology—in the last 20 years is incredible and, in a way, balances out the downside. So we have managed to maintain some kind of equilibrium.

One of the cool things about adversity is that over the last 20 years we have been knocked off our pedestals so many times that it has totally torn away that piece of us that would say, "Oh, that would never work." It has made us be really open to any ideas and to try and make things work.

Chapter 5

Mental Health

**Shouldn't We Be Able to Take Care of
Folks Who Are in Pain and Suffering?**

Finding Hope: A History of Mental Health Services

Mrs. S. G. Parkhill   Dec. 29, 1891
Cornwall, Vt.

Dear Madam:

Yours of the 28th received. Mr. Parkhill...is little inclined to talk & evidently thinks he is the victim of somebody's persecution. He wants to know who is keeping him here.... He eats and sleeps regularly & goes out for regular exercise in the open air. Requires thus far no medical treatment. He...is not in an excited state in any respect. Still his mind seems all wrong in respect to his illness. I can hardly expect he will ever fully regain his mind, tho time will probably gradually modify it.

He is not at present in need of any clothing but whenever he is I will send you a list of his wants with the measures or sizes.

Yours truly,
J. Draper

Dear Madam: August 25, 1894

In reply to your inquiry, I would state that your husband's mind is in such a confused state that he never makes inquiries for friends at home nor does he converse on any subject with those about him. I told him I had received a letter from you, and that you sent your love to him. He replied she is a good woman, but made no inquiries. He is located on our invalid ward, and is under the care of our best nurse, who gives him every comfort and attention. I will keep you advised in the event of any change.

Very truly yours,
S. Lawton

Dear Madam: July 12, 1895

Replying to your inquiry I have to say that Mr. Parkhill was completely demented for a period of several months prior to his death, and that he had no realization of his condition; was entirely free from suffering as he had no physical disease attended with pain. I doubt if he spoke a single word during the last six months of his life.

Very truly yours,
S. Lawton

~

What are we to make of this century-old, often poignant correspondence from the superintendents of the Vermont Asylum for the Insane in Brattleboro with a concerned and distant wife? We know very little about the Parkhills other than the dates of their deaths from Cornwall town records. The eight-year-long correspondence suggests but does not specifically describe Mr. Parkhill's problems—delusions, perhaps from a "clouded mind," and later paralyzing strokes.

But reading between the lines, there is a concern and knowledge of the patient not commonly thought to be part of institutional care and the "warehousing" of the feeble-minded and demented. The asylum, in fact, throughout its history has embodied both the promise—in its forward thinking—and the problems—overcrowding, staffing shortages, and budget problems—of institutional care.

Founders of the asylum—it opened in 1835, supported by a $10,000 gift from a wealthy land-owning widow of an area doctor and appropria-

tions from the state legislature—believed that psychological stresses contributed to madness and that each patient possessed an innate core of goodness which could be restored to health if surrounded by the proper environment and care. At that time, there were only 10 asylums/psychiatric hospitals in the country, with just four of them following this Quaker-based "moral treatment" that had its roots in England.

"Patients were to be treated with warmth and respect in a family-like setting which included purposeful work in line with the patient's background and capabilities; clean, beautiful surroundings; cultural activities, good food and daily outdoor exercise," the history of the asylum records.

This approach contrasted sharply with traditional thinking that recommended purges and bloodletting and the "bath of surprise," immersion in cold water "until he is nearly killed." If that shock didn't work, doctors could administer large does of opium or laudanum in hopes that a temporary suspension of senses would restore sanity.

Asylum founders, in requesting state support, estimated that housing would be needed for 300 residents, or about 1% of the state's population. In its 50th anniversary report in 1886, the trustees reported the asylum was treating 450 patients at an average weekly cost of $3.03. Since its opening, 6,076 people, mainly Vermonters, had been admitted and 2,398 had been released as cured.

Despite its accomplishments, the privately run asylum and its independent board of trustees had an uneasy relationship with the state. From the

PRECEDING PAGE: *Jean Shappee, manager of a group home for women, Counseling Service of Addison County* outset, there would be differences over cost, quality, and access to care.

State law required communities to support the insane locally, such as in town poorhouses or with families, or by sending them to Brattleboro. Communities generally only sent residents who were considered incurable or who couldn't work to help support themselves in town poorhouses to the more expensive care in Brattleboro.

In return for state support, the asylum was to give preferential admission to the state's indigent insane over wealthy, out-of-state private-pay patients. But the state's fee schedule did not cover the asylum's patient costs, which threatened the hospital's mission—treat patients, not warehouse them—the hospital's trustees complained.

The legislature's passage of a pauper law in 1886, which transferred responsibility for support of the indigent from the towns to the state, changed the financial landscape and precipitated the creation of a state facility. With the state now paying for care of the indigent, communities sent more and more residents to Brattleboro, a new major expense for the state budget.

In 1888, the legislature created a study commission and soon approved a $100,000 appropriation for the construction of an asylum in Waterbury to house 175 residents. But the state would be no more successful than Brattleboro in its attempts to provide quality care while controlling costs. In fact, many would argue that it did far worse, with chronic underfunding and overcrowding plaguing the state hospital for decades.

The 1898 biennial report highlights the tensions and at times conflicting philosophies of the trustees and the administration of the new Vermont State Hospital for the Insane.

"The towns and cities have found how easy it is under the statute to have their defective wards committed to State care. Furthermore, the decrease of infantile mortality of recent years tends to the survival of the unfit, and consequently the number of defective individuals will probably increase, rather than diminish. The strain and stress of modern civilization undoubtedly does and will continue to contribute to our nerve hospitals," the trustees wrote in noting that the census was now over 700.

Nonetheless, the state had an obligation to this "class of feeble-minded persons above the condition of the recognized idiot in the community ...since without special guidance they are apt to drift into immorality and crime."

Society, in essence, needed to be protected from these people. Superintendent Page saw the hospital's role differently, "Notwithstanding the general belief in the incurability of insanity, facts incontestably prove that the majority of insane do recover if proper treatment is early instituted. In a properly constituted hospital, 'care' is not the only end sought, but also cure."

Finding the balance between the demand for services, their availability and cost, and the role of public and private providers was not easy, then as today. In the space of five years, Brattleboro's census dropped nearly 300 residents, from overcrowding to empty beds, leading to even direr financial straits. In 1893, the institution changed its name to the Brattleboro Retreat to eliminate the confusion among the public with the Waterbury hospital. And it began appeals to the wealthier private-pay population, citing its wooded parks and shaded walks in its 1,400-acre grounds, its attractive and homelike rooms, and individual attention. Weekly rates for single rooms, board, medical treatment, and nursing would be $4 to $10, a level well above previous state payments.

For decades to come Brattleboro and Waterbury would have an uneasy relationship. Brattleboro served a private-pay population and absorbed some of the overcrowding from Waterbury. The state hospital would predominantly house the indigent and criminally insane.

One can only guess that Mrs. Parkhill felt these financial tensions between the state, local community, and the asylum. The asylum did not distinguish between state and private-pay patients in its care, Supt. Lawton assured Mrs. Parkhill in a letter following his death: "[had] Mr. Parkhill been paying twice as much as the State allowed he would not have received better care. He was in our hospital ward and was under the care of our oldest and most experienced nurse. The amount paid for his board and treatment by the State was $3.75 per week or $195 per year."

The mental health landscape for the Parkhills of today is vastly different. With the development of effective antipsychotic and antidepressant drugs, the creation and expansion of community-based facilities starting in the 1960s, and the mainstreaming of students with special educational needs in public schools, nearly all individuals with mental illness and developmental disabilities can now be served in the community.

But the troubled existence of the state hospital in Waterbury, which once had over 1,000 residents and now has a daily census of around 50, continues. Governor James Douglas has proposed closing the aging and understaffed hospital, which has twice been decertified by the federal Centers for Medicare and Medicaid Services because of safety concerns. This decertification has led to the loss of millions of dollars in federal reimbursement. A new state system could involve construction of a new hospital and expanded community-based services.

The Vermont State School for Feebleminded Children, better known as the Brandon Training School, opened in 1915 as a "wholesome alternative" to the local poorhouses and poor farms. During its peak enrollment in the 1960s, over 600 men, women, and children, a small village by state standards, lived in Brandon. At its closing in 1993, no Vermonters lived in any institution because of developmental disabilities—their residents having been gradually moved to community facilities, such as group homes and supervised apartments, over the previous 25 years.

Brattleboro today offers a variety of inpatient and outpatient services, ranging from alcohol and drug abuse programs to psychiatric counseling.

One can view the institutionalization policies of the past as good intentions and misguided social engineering or as harsh and often punitive segregation of "misfits." However one assesses the past, Vermont has generally been a leader in its enlightened treatment of the mentally ill.

Today, state funding and programs stress prevention and community care rather than hospitalization—Vermont has ranked fifth in per capita spending on mental health, emphasizing community-based mental health services, and 40th in per capita spending on psychiatric hospitalization in recent years. The state's mental health parity law, passed in 1997, continues to be among the most

far-reaching legislation in the country and prohibits health insurers from discriminating in their benefits against people with mental illnesses.

Vermont's actions also reflect pragmatic responses to increasing costs, class action suits, and court decisions that required the state to offer families community-based care. Family wishes, new approaches to treatment, and legal pressure aside, community care in nearly all cases is much less expensive than institutional care. By the late 1980s, the cost of services at Brandon Training School was rising twice as fast as community-based care.

Despite the gains of the past century, there is still much unfinished business. In 1999, the U.S. Surgeon General, in issuing the Department's first report on mental health, presented the country with a comprehensive progress report. The good news was that our understanding about the brain, human behavior, and effective treatments had grown enormously in the past three decades. The bad news was that mental health was "often an afterthought and illnesses of the mind remain shrouded in fear and misunderstanding." Despite the efficacy of treatments, nearly half of all Americans with a severe mental illness do not seek treatment, the report estimated.

"Even more than other areas of health and medicine, mental health is plagued by disparities in the availability and access to its services.... formidable financial barriers block off needed mental health care from too many people regardless of whether one has health insurance with inadequate mental health benefits, or is one of the 44 million Americans who lack any insurance. We have allowed stigma and a now unwarranted sense of hopelessness about the opportunities for recovery from mental illness to erect these barriers. It is time to take them down,"

Surgeon General Dr. David Satcher wrote.

In the following commentaries, Addison County providers discuss how their organizations have attempted to deal with these barriers and respond to community concerns.

Since its founding in the early 1960s, the Counseling Service of Addison County, one of 10 county-based, non-profit mental health organizations in the state, has provided the safety net for many of the area's most vulnerable residents. At its own financial peril, the agency has often identified needs, helped start or provided services, and then looked for ways to fund them.

In the late 1970s, the agency, responding to the state's long-term goal to close Brandon Training School, started a group home for six women. Jean Shappee, the home's first and only manager, reflects on the challenges in creating and sustaining a rich life for these women.

The Counseling Service's emergency crisis team receives over 3,000 calls a year from residents in distress. Marian Greenberg, director of the crisis team, discusses how team members respond to these community calls for help.

WomenSafe, another non-profit agency created by a grassroots group of concerned community members, coordinates and provides services for abused women and their children. Naomi Smith discusses how changing attitudes toward domestic violence will require a coordinated community response.

Wendy Lynch, a Counseling Service board member, and Bob Thorn, its executive director, end the chapter with a discussion of an ongoing dilemma—the community's need for services exceeds the agency's resources.

Jean Shappee

Manager, Group Home,
Counseling Service of
Addison County

I Felt a Group Home Could Be a Home and Not a Facility

In the mid-1970s the state, moving away from the institutional model of care for people with developmental disabilities, asked mental health agencies if they would open group homes. Brandon Training School residents often lived far away from their communities, families, and support system, and families wanted other options.

In 1978, the Counseling Service of Addison County started a group home on Elm Street in Middlebury for six women. Jean Shappee was hired to manage the home and has been the home's manager for the past 20-plus years.

Jean Shappee's goal for the past 20-plus years has been to manage a home with a loving and respectful family atmosphere, not a facility with a long list of do's and don'ts.

We had this institutional model for so long that we thought that people with developmental disabilities had different needs. I felt that a group home could be a home and not a facility. We wouldn't have a sign out front, because no one labels their home. We wouldn't have lots of instructions on the walls. We would have nice pictures on the walls.

And we wanted to have the women be part of the community But we really didn't know how to create this atmosphere in a group home. Getting away from the institutional model was the first step.

Sometimes family and guardians think that living here is going to be idyllic, because the staff and women seem so nice. But there are problems.

Sometimes the women raise their voice, get upset, argue, experience stress, and have conflicts.

That happens in every home. We say that's OK. When it happens we work with it. Our job is to figure out how to have the women express their opinions in respectful but open ways.

We want to work with the whole person, the angry side as well as the happy side, and help them be who they want to be. We had to learn not to overreact to wild statements and to recognize positive behaviors. After a while, the women appreciated our calmness and the peace and serenity in their day.

I don't blame the women for their behaviors. That may have been the only way in the past for

them to get the support they needed.

We can have opinions about whether institutions work for us as a society. But they did not work well for the women at Elm Street. They tell me that every day.

Some of the women need support in self-care—bathing and teeth brushing—in meal preparation, and in doing their laundry. Some need help in crossing the street, seeing the doctor, and in making safe, healthy choices.

Mainstreaming in school has made a tremendous difference. Today people with developmental disabilities can stay in school until they are 21. They may require one-on-one aides, but all can learn. People with special needs have unique

Family-style dining, communal food purchasing, preparation, and clean-up are part of the Elm Street staff's program to make the residence a "home" and not a "facility."

interests and will tell you about them, but you have to listen carefully.

I can remember one parent saying, "My daughter doesn't like such and such kind of music." I knew she did, because she kept telling me that she liked Elvis.

So we bought her Elvis tapes and got Elvis pictures and when it was her birthday we had Elvis wrapping paper. Pretty soon she had four or five hobbies and interests. She loved male singers so we took her to the Festival on the Green. We kept expanding her horizons so that instead of being depressed or sad or upset she had something pos-

itive to look toward.

These interests can be identified in institutions, but they don't have the staff or resources or time to expand on them. We take the time to focus on them so they have a life that is full.

Supporting the home takes five full-time workers plus substitutes for vacations and sickness. We have a few community volunteers and some Middlebury College volunteers, like the women's ice hockey team which has adopted the home. They will take the women to the movies and help with social events.

Each person has her own room and does

what she can around the home. Several can do quite a bit of cooking and cleaning. Most can help a little bit.

Our normal shifts are either 24 or 36 hours, because it's too hard for residents to adjust to new staff every eight hours. Working a long shift is a big commitment. It's very demanding, but it is also wonderful. You know exactly what you have done at the end of the day, and there is a joy in watching staff do something they love.

When I started, people with developmental disabilities worked in sheltered workshops away from the rest of society. But everyone can do some work in the community. That was the idea behind the creation of the counseling service's Employment Associates program in the 1980s.

Four women at the home have excellent jobs and love their work. One is washing dishes at Middlebury College and works 20 hours a week. She was trained by the Counseling Service's Employment Associates, but she works independently now.

Another woman has worked independently at Geiger 20 hours a week for over 10 years bagging and boxing clothes for shipment. A third woman cleans 10 hours a week at the CPC plastic company. An Employment Associates employee stays with her. A fourth woman volunteers in the clothing room of the community action agency.

Do the women have a happy, fulfilled, and interesting life?

We constantly ask ourselves these questions and when we review our program annually with the women, family, and guardians.

As manager I look at several criteria. Are the women safe? Are they making their own choices? Are they seeing family and friends? Are they getting good medical attention? Are the women getting to their job and being supported in what they want to do?

If they want to be in Special Olympics are they getting there? If they want to be with friends and go to the movies are we helping with that?

This is a home for women, but we hope they interact with whomever their friends are. That could mean dating or hanging out. We talk about safe relationships and supervise relationships as needed. No one from a group home has ever married, but people have relationships. Some are

Protection of the manatee, pets, Patsy Cline records, snowshoeing, Special Olympics basketball and swimming, Festival on the Green concerts, movies, sewing: helping residents pursue their interests is essential to a rich home life, Shappee believes.

deeper than others.

Friends can be someone at work or through church. Beverly, one of our residents, knows the difference between me, being paid to manage the home, and the couple who invites her to their home every Christmas eve.

And we ask if the group setting is working for them. Sometimes a group home doesn't work over the long term. The women might want to be in a smaller setting like an individual developmental home, which is much more like a foster home, or in a supervised apartment.

Some of the women can't always tell us how they are feeling, but their behavior shows us if they are content and happy. We often hear from par-

ents or guardians that residents were sad and depressed before they came and that they are blossoming now.

I don't think we will ever go back to institutions, but we as a society have to recommit to the idea that we will support people who have developmental disabilities. So we have to keep people aware of what budget cuts mean.

Many of the women here don't have families. And for older families care for an adult child may not be workable. If these women were not getting services they might be without basic medical care and living at risk.

We have absorbed some budget cuts and are now at the bone. We can't cut staff, because

"We can have opinions about whether institutions work for us as a society. But they did not work well for the women at Elm Street. They tell me that every day," says Shappee.

we do not have the option of not having someone here through the day and at night. It's not safe.

When I get discouraged, I look to people who do inspirational work. I'm reading Vernon Jordan's book, *Vernon Can Read,* which is wonderful. I have just read Rosa Parks's autobiography on her expériences during the Montgomery bus boycott. I read about Jimmy and Rosalyn Carter

helping with disease prevention in Africa, and I get inspired by them.

The people of Middlebury and Addison County make it very possible for me to do this work here. The community is respectful to all of us at Elm Street.

Our neighbors are friendly and helpful. We have one neighbor who says, "Please call me if

there is ever any problem." When I hang up the clothes she waves to me and says, "I like what you do."

That goes a long way with me.

Beverly Goes Right to Your Heart

Beverly came to the home in the early '90s after she had lived with a family and had been in an institution in southern Vermont. Her guardian—her parents are deceased—thought Elm Street would be a supportive environment for her.

When she came she was very quiet and fearful. The staff did not push her to talk but tried to create a safe and warm atmosphere. It took several months to get her to speak at the dinner table.

Everyone needs time to process new situations. Beverly needs more time than the other women to grasp new opportunities. She sees them as scary.

She apparently had not had many everyday experiences. When we asked her to blow out the candles on her first birthday cake, she was very frightened and ran into a corner. She later told us that she had never had a cake with burning candles.

When Beverly first came to Elm Street, she spent days at a private home where a woman nurtured her, built her confidence, and discovered some of her interests, like a love of music.

Music is an avenue into her heart, and she sings and dances along with Patsy Cline in her room. It's hard for her to sing outside her room, but if you go into her room, her world, she will sing for you.

Beverly now works five mornings a week cleaning at a local plastics manufacturing plant. A staff member from Employment Associates supervises her. It took several years before she had the confidence to be able to go out, but she now loves her work.

Her housemates have been very good teachers and have helped her be less fearful. They

Beverly came to the home with little confidence and little exposure to everyday events—her first birthday cake with candles was frightening. With the support of staff, community members, and housemates, her warm personality has emerged.

were constantly telling her, "It's OK. You can do such and such. We will help you."

Tammie is her closest friend and encouraged her to try Special Olympics, where she competes in soccer, swimming, and snowshoeing. This has given her a lot of confidence and now she goes to a gym two days a week to work out with weights and swim.

When Beverly feels safe, she has a wonderful, warm personality. She can look at you and say something that goes right to your heart. And she appreciates her friends in a beautiful way with lots of hugs.

93

Sheltered workshops have been replaced by work in community settings. Four of the five women at the group home work: cleaning dishes at a Middlebury College dining hall, preparing boxes at a clothing manufacturer, volunteering in the clothing warehouse of the county's low-income advocacy organization. Beverly, above, cleans at a plastics manufacturing plant.

Marian Greenberg

Coordinator, Emergency Services,
Counseling Service of
Addison County

Finding Hope

In 1988, Marian Greenberg began working at the Counseling Service as the one-person, part-time staff of the Youth in Crisis Program. She left the program in 1996, worn out by the non-stop scramble to find and maintain funding for an 11-member staff and non-traditional programs that served as many as 200 youth. Today, as the Counseling Service's coordinator of emergency services, Greenberg faces similar demands. Emergency services must be staffed—the team consists of a coordinator (Greenberg), seven master's-level crisis clinicians and substitutes, and two psychiatrists and two advanced practice psychiatric nurses who are on call—24 hours a day. Much of their emergency counseling is over the telephone, which is not billable. As a result, the program annually runs a $50,000-plus deficit, which is made up by cost shifting from programs with a surplus, community donations, and United Way support.

Some people believe that you have to be about to jump off a bridge before you would be eligible or want to use the crisis service. In fact, people call who normally function very well but who have hit some distressing situation. That could be financial stress, really difficult parenting concerns, losing a job, having family members who are gravely ill or learning that you have a life-threatening illness, or adjusting to situational depression.

People also don't realize how much focused prevention we do or that we organize community crisis debriefings or that we are available to family members, clergy, or anyone who has concerns.

Referrals come from across the community: family members, the family doctor, clergy, school counselors, the police, the emergency department at Porter Hospital. The most common referral is from a counseling service therapist. In that case, we have baseline information and are pretty confident when we make an assessment. We also cover for counseling service programs when they are backed up or have therapists on vacations, so we know these clients as well.

Other people are brand new to us and call because they have seen our number in the phone book. Usually the initial conversation happens over the phone. If there is any question whether they are safe we will have them come to our office if it is daytime or meet us at the emergency department at Porter Hospital if it is night time.

We don't have crisis beds in the community or a psychiatric hospital unit nearby, which can create problems. We don't have the option of sending people to the hospital at the drop of a hat, so we might check in every three hours through the night for several days with someone if that person wants to stay out of a hospital—in Rutland, Burlington, Berlin, or Brattleboro—and is working to resolve the issues with us.

We have no interest in putting people in hospitals and will work with a person as long as they can stay safe. One unintended benefit of not having a nearby psychiatric facility is that the emergency team gets much more involved in prevention and ongoing therapy.

We had over 4,000 calls in 2002. Some were acute. Some were simply requests for medicine refills. Most were in-between.

Over this last weekend, the on-call clinician had 29 calls. A great many of these calls involved a young person having delusions. The clinician worked with the family, the state hospital, the police, an area hospital with psychiatric capacity, and people in the community. During these discussions there is always the need to balance an individual's safety and the safety of people around them with that individual's rights. At what point do we consider doing involuntary hospitalization? At what point do we divulge information to other family members?

So there were multiple phone calls and issues to figure out.

Ninety percent of the time people go to the hospital voluntarily. But some people state they are going to harm themselves and are so compromised by a thought disorder or are delusional or paranoid or so severely depressed that they are not able to work with you or voluntarily go to a hospital.

Three or four times a year, we have to get a court warrant from a judge, generally the Addison County District Court judge, to take a person into custody so they can be evaluated by a psychiatrist. Before a judge will approve involuntary hospitalization, mental health and/or law enforcement must document that the person is not safe and appears to have a mental illness.

Major crises can be the opportunity for change. It takes a lot of courage, especially for someone not used to using emergency services, to pick up the phone and say, "I need help."

When people call they are usually motivated so you can do a lot of good work in a very short time. This is mentally challenging and can be emotionally difficult, but it is also a privilege to be able to help someone through a very difficult time of life.

The Counseling Service's emergency service team is available 24 hours a day, responding to over 3,000 calls annually. Crises can be the motivation for personal change, but the counselor must first understand and stabilize, if not resolve, the person's distress, says Marian Greenberg.

There are boundaries in professional relationships, but the relationships are still very intimate. You talk about things that people don't talk about in other places.

To be a good crisis counselor, you need the ability to think on your feet. And you can't be overwhelmed by other people's distress if you are to be a calm and rational partner. However, you also need to allow yourself to empathize and feel compassion or you probably won't be much help.

To some extent good counseling is an art. You need to be knowledgeable about differential diagnoses and treatments, but you also need an intuitive sense of what people are really saying to you.

There is no one style that works. One person on the emergency team is a nurturer who is very clear about the issues and is very careful about not fostering dependency. But this clinician still communicates incredible concern.

Another clinician has a great sense of humor and knows when and when not to use it. This person is great at helping a person see where they got strength in the past to manage a situation.

And we have another team member who is more businesslike and sets very clear boundaries about the limits of the emergency team. But this person does a terrific job finding what the problem is, what resources are available, and helping people use their strengths.

I see myself as someone who is empathic, curious, calm, and clear about the need for the person's safety as the bottom line.

My job doesn't sound like fun to most people. To a large extent you are autonomous, and it can be isolating. But we constantly support each other in informal consultations and at staff meetings.

And there is the satisfaction of enjoying your colleagues and in learning all the time. And I'm committed to community mental health. There is something special about it. We see the whole spectrum of the community—all ages, every socio-economic group, every type of diagnosis. And we see people as part of families, social groups, and communities and try and support them there.

Departments across the Counseling Service periodically explore new approaches, learn about them, and use them. Sometimes external situations impose changes.

For example, the Counseling Service used to be able to serve people for a long time. Now managed care has placed constraints on long-term treatment. As a result all clinicians have gotten more training in short-term therapies. That training has also been helpful to the emergency team, where most of our contacts are short term.

Short term means whatever insurance will pay for, generally six to eight initial sessions, although we can make a case for additional sessions. We have gotten better at getting to places a little more purposefully and better at not encouraging dependency. But we also lose a lot in not having the flexibility to work long term with people, especially trauma survivors.

So something gained, something lost.

Another change has been clients' expectations toward drugs. There is so much publicity, even television advertisements, saying take this pill and you will feel better. So more and more people are coming into therapy wanting medication or they are coming in already on medication.

As crisis clinicians we cannot prescribe medications. We have to go through a psychiatrist or psychiatric nurse or refer clients to their family doctor. I think all physicians prescribe antidepressants, but I don't see too many people who throw pills at things.

It would be so nice if medications would do the trick. But medications alone are not the answer for many people. They may need psychotherapy as well and can benefit from support organizations, such as hospice, WomenSafe, and mutual aid groups. And they may need help with housing, vocational, and parenting issues.

Good clinical skills start with education, but counseling is in the doing. Here you need role models, mentors, good clinical supervisors, and the sense to know when you need a consultation from a psychiatrist.

Over time, I have learned to tune into certain phrases or clusters of phrases—"My mind is just going," "I'm pacing"—that lend themselves to a proximate diagnosis.

At the same time, I don't jump to conclusions as quickly. I'm aware of other problems, such as a substance abuse problem, that people may not mention or conceal. So I listen carefully and ask.

I have also become more and more aware of the problems people face in getting help so I work more diligently to find places for them.

My nightmare call is the person who calls and says, "I have a gun on the table here," or "I have six open bottles of pills."

It's just so delicate. You don't want to question or challenge someone's suicidal intentions with "you-really-don't-want-to-do-this." You have to first acknowledge their incredible distress and that they are feeling really hopeless. Even if there is only a very small part of them that wants to stay alive, you say, "Let's work with that very small piece and see how big we can make it right now."

I have a checklist of questions in my head at this point. I want to know what their suicide risk is. I want to know what support they have in their life. Are they alone? Do they have a particular plan for themselves and an intent? Can they remember a time when they felt some hope?

Do they have parents or children that they want to stay alive for? Do they have pets? You'd be amazed at how many people are staying alive reportedly because of their cats.

So I want to know all these things, but I'm not going to know them unless I can engage them. It might be around something they say, like they love their kids.

So what are their names, and I say it must be really hard to be parenting when you are feeling so low. So you communicate concern.

Then you need specific information.

What's different? What are the situational stressors that are making things feel worse now? What made them pick up the phone at this moment?

Some people who are very articulate think they are doing a terrible job in explaining their plight, because they feel so different and isolated and believe that no one can understand them. With some people you can quickly start figuring out whether they are safe. Others are so ambivalent or frightened or bound up with emotion that it is a longer process.

With pills, I might say I'm sending the ambulance and the ambulance will take you to the hospital. There you have at least a reasonable chance in getting them medical help no matter what they have done.

The gun is the nightmare situation. There's a lot of talking and getting to the point where you can call the police safely. Getting them to put the gun in another room. Buying some time. Getting them to think about family or children if they have them and reminding them what suicide means and guilt tripping them sometimes.

And you try to get them to remember times when things didn't feel like this. What did it feel like the last time you had hope? If this person has clinical depression you remind them that the worst time to make major life decisions is when you are really depressed, and that depression is treatable.

So those calls, maybe 25 to 30 a year, are nightmare situations for clinicians. The crisis team and our psychiatrists are very supportive in debriefings, but some therapists try working on the team and find that emergency work is not their cup of tea.

Naomi Smith

Executive Director, WomenSafe

We Want Women to Be Safe

A group of social service workers in the community started the Addison County Battered Women's Project in 1980 in an attempt to reduce domestic violence, primarily abuse against women. The project, originally under the umbrella of the non-profit Addison County Community Action Group, provides a variety of services today: a 24-hour hotline; community, legal, and medical advocacy; education and outreach; support groups; and supervised visitation of children. Naomi Smith has been executive director of the organization, renamed WomenSafe in 2001, since 1999.

Education and coordinated community responses are key to reducing domestic violence and abuse, which affects from a third to a half of all women during their lifetimes, says Smith.

About 30% to 50% of women will be abused at some point in their life. This violence and abuse can take many forms—physical, psychological, financial, emotional, sexual. What links them is the abuser's intent to gain and maintain control over a partner.

Ninety to 95% of domestic violence is perpetrated by men against women. Domestic violence happens across heterosexual, gay, and lesbian communities at comparative rates. If the abuser doesn't get help, the abuse usually increases in frequency and violence.

Abuse is largely a learned behavior, much of it stemming from an historical belief that a male has the right to control a female.

In the 1700s, English common law had the "rule of the thumb," which decreed that a husband had the right to "chastise his wife with a whip or rattan no bigger than his thumb, in order to enforce...domestic discipline."

In the United States, courts continued to uphold a man's right to punish his wife violently until 1871. The court then ruled that:

The privilege, ancient though it may be, to beat her with a stick, to pull her hair, choke her, spit in her face or kick her about the floor or to inflict upon her other like indignities, is not now acknowledged by our law.

It hasn't been that many years since women had few powers in our legal and social system. Not until the 1920s did women get the right to vote. Not until the 1970s could a woman get a loan on her own without her husband co-signing.

About half of batterers come from families with a history of domestic violence, but it would be naive to think that domestic violence could be contained there. We can't separate Addison County from what's happening in the rest of the world and the messages we get every day. Listen to the war talk and the attitudes around September 11. "No one is going to do this to us." This is consistent with a macho image at the individual level that you don't fool around with me.

Popular musicians and rap groups have appalling lyrics that talk about hurting or killing their wife or girl friend. We have sports stars who are convicted of domestic violence. All those things contribute to an attitude that condones abuse.

Last year (2004) WomenSafe staff and volunteers worked with over 575 women and fielded 1,945 crisis calls from people who were clearly experiencing trauma from domestic violence. Staff members had 849 individual meetings on top of that where we provided housing, employment and financial information, and peer support. Then we have a support group once a week. Staff members also had nearly 800 general information calls on our hotline.

But that's only part of the picture. The U.S. Department of Justice estimates that just over half of simple assaults between intimate partners are reported. Slightly less than a quarter of rape/sexual assaults are reported, largely because of the embarrassment victims feel in discussing the incident with police and in court proceedings.

The Centers for Disease Control and Prevention have released a study that estimates the annual health-related costs from domestic violence at more than $5.8 billion.

It's hard to tell if domestic and sexual violence

is going up or down, because our reporting and responses have changed so much. Twenty years ago, police called on a "domestic complaint" used to tell the perpetrator to take a walk around the corner and cool off. Now the police are more thorough in responding to those calls.

The feminist and women's movement has been instrumental in many of these changes. Unfortunately, most of the major changes have followed violent deaths. And there has been a backlash against the feminist movement for this activism, which reflects the male/female double standard. If a man stands up and protests injustices, he is powerful and brave. If a woman stands up, she is pushy and a bitch. But I see that much less of this attitude today than I did in the past.

Some women leave a relationship seven or eight times before they are able to leave permanently. This has a lot to do with the tactics that batterers use to draw women back: the kids will suffer; if you leave I'll kill myself and/or you; I promise I won't do it again.

And a battered woman who tries to leave and be safe often needs many services. She may need help finding new housing, and this has always been difficult, especially today where the housing vacancy rate is less than 1%.

In the 1970s, domestic violence programs started developing emergency shelters. We don't have a domestic violence shelter in Addison County, but we can refer women to six shelters in the state, Burlington and Rutland being the closest, as well as to safe homes in Addison County. Shelters usually look like a home and are very homey. They're not like some homeless shelters with rows of beds.

We are also connected to a national and Canadian shelter network. If a woman has family support in Texas, for example, we can help her connect with a shelter there. If she needs to go across the country for safety reasons we can also help.

The length of shelter stays has increased considerably over the last five or six years because the housing vacancy rate is so low. The Department of Children and Families/Economic Services has a program that supports women in emergency housing. Because housing is so difficult to find, the legislature has increased the length of payment for the program from 28 to 56 and now 87 days.

So housing is a big issue when women consider leaving.

She may also need counseling, financial and legal help, child care, respite care, and counseling for the children. Some women can be disenfranchised in many ways and may not have the skills to access all these services.

And each situation is so different. What works for one woman may be potentially fatal for another. For example, we will assist women in getting relief from abuse orders. These court orders, which can require that the batterer have no contact with the victim, can be helpful. But the order, which is another affront to the batterer's power and control, only increases the danger for some women.

And some men who have been involved in the criminal justice system are less likely to pay attention to a court order. They aren't intimidated by it. On the other hand the threat or the reality of a court order can have a huge affect on someone who has a good reputation in the community.

Many times women are much safer staying in the home until they can pull a lot of things together. She can monitor his moods, his behavior, and get a sense of where he's at. When she is not liv-

ing with him, there can be stalking and surprise attacks. Most serious injuries happen at this point.

Women in our culture generally feel that they are responsible for the relationship. They are the nurturers and their batterers are telling them that it is their fault. And sometimes families don't understand the dynamics of abuse and blame the woman, too.

Batterers often strongly believe that they are completely justified. If she had behaved, if she had my dinner ready, I would not have had to hit her. It takes some women time to process and understand that it wasn't their fault.

Batterers can break down women's belief in themselves. "You don't know anything." "You're stupid." After a victim hears it enough, she can begin to believe it.

We always do safety planning, but we can't tell women what to do, because we haven't lived with that batterer. I ask women, "What does your gut tell you?" I want them to know that we believe in them as a person who can figure these things out, because she is the expert in the situation.

And we usually have more than one opportunity to discuss the relationship. Sometimes a woman will call and won't be ready to talk. Six months later she will call and be completely ready and want to come to a support group.

It can be excruciating for family members, particularly concerned parents, to watch their child in a relationship with a really scary person. Parents may not have a lot of faith in our process and want us to "make her see the light" and do something.

But I think we are successful because we develop a level of trust. We're not going to tell a woman what to do. We will listen and help her to make her own decision because that is the safest way for her and her children.

WomenSafe's board oversees programs and staff that responded to nearly 2,000 crisis calls and worked with nearly 600 Addison County women in 2004.

There is not a lot that we can do about changing entrenched beliefs in the short run. We keep educating people and hope they will change.

For the past 15 years batterers who have violated relief of abuse orders have faced a choice—jail or a 27-week Domestic Abuse Education Program (DAEP). In the program batterers have to accept responsibility for their behavior. Each week they talk about a different spoke in the power and control wheel: intimidation, emotional abuse, isolation of the woman, use of children, use of male privilege, economic abuse, coercion and threats, and minimizing, denial, and blaming. They also have a seven-week component on kids and how to parent.

Approximately 40 men go through the Addison program every year. About five years ago, the Department of Corrections started a year-long intensive education program within correctional facilities for men convicted of domestic violence.

Some batterers will be repeat offenders, but judging the success of these programs is difficult. Batterers who have gone through the program will bruise a woman where it can't be seen or can be explained. Or physical abuse could be combined with emotional or psychological or financial abuse. A batterer, for example, may try and prevent the woman from going to work or back to school. He may give her a black eye to embarrass

her from appearing in public or not take care of the children to sabotage her efforts to improve herself and become more independent. And a batterer may complete DAEP and return to an environment that tolerates domestic violence, so we need a coordinated and consistent community response—police, courts, social service agencies, and schools working together.

But many people don't fully understand this. So we are constantly out in the community talking about these issues. Our number of calls increased last year, which I hope stems from our community education.

What has changed over the years is the availability of a range of services and our understanding that ongoing support is essential. We used to just help with that initial crisis, finding emergency shelter. Three days of rest in a shelter and I wouldn't recognize some of the women.

Some would say this was the first night they had slept without worry. Their faces would lighten up, and they were sure that they would never go back. But once they faced the harsh reality of living on their own as a poor single mother some would go back.

~

We haven't felt the budget pressures yet that other organizations dependent on Medicaid and Medicare funding are facing, but it could happen. About 30% of our $244,000 budget (2004) comes from state grants. About 32% of our budget comes from federal grants through the federal Violence Against Women, Victims of Crime, and Family Violence Prevention acts. Given the conservative administration in Washington, we could face cuts in this funding.

The remaining 38% comes mainly from the United Way, general contributions, in-kind donations, small grants, and Middlebury College student fund-raising events.

We don't charge for our services, and I can't imagine that we would ever be able to charge. I can't tell you how many women come here and say, "I have no money. He took my pay check or welfare check or food stamp card." Controlling financial resources is part of the batterer's strategy to keep the woman from leaving.

So programs like ours are typically accessed by poorer women, because we're available and are free. Women with more resources have more

options, whether it's private therapy, counseling, legal advice, or support from family and friends.

Legal services are a major need. Women will go to court for a relief of abuse order or a divorce or child custody. The batterer will have a lawyer. She can't afford one. Without legal representation it is likely that she will lose. WomenSafe can help women feel more comfortable speaking up in court, but we are not lawyers.

We have a small grant from the federal Domestic Violence against Women Act that supports Legal Aid attorneys. However, the Legal Aid attorney who is responsible for domestic violence cases in Addison County is based in Rutland and is also responsible for Bennington and Rutland counties. And he can devote only 40% of his time to this project.

I don't see the availability of legal services changing in the near future.

We also need to study the need for longer-term transitional housing that is rent subsidized and gives women a chance to get on their feet, but that's a long way off, if at all.

Success in decreasing domestic violence boils down to resources, training, and education. If the state's attorney or the police don't have adequate staff, that lessens our response. Some judges are outstanding. Others don't seem to understand the ramifications of their decisions on families.

We are trying to reach out to the community to find out where the gaps are. Six or seven years ago, we had a huge gap in education for children. Education is the long-term key to changing beliefs, and our goal is to be in every school in our service area. We have been contacting classroom and health education teachers and have been in

all the middle and high schools with our healthy relationships curriculum.

We get very positive feedback from students and teachers about the program itself. With high school kids we do a pre- and post-test. They invariably considerably increase their knowledge of dating violence and healthy relationships. Women's studies in college, Title 9 sports programs, all those things contribute to making a difference for women.

We are making progress. I see young men today where the equality of the relationship is amazing. At the same time, some young men believe that women are there for their benefit and use. In one study, 38% of college-age men still didn't think their actions were wrong when told the statutory requirements for rape or assault.

Certainly, I don't mean to say this is true of all young men. A small percentage of men perpetrate these crimes against women. And I am very optimistic about how far we have come over the last 20 to 30 years.

We are much more aware of the need for a much more coordinated community response. Addison County is noted for its cooperation among agencies, and we are working even more closely than we have in the past.

And most people are letting go of the old stereotypes about our work. We are not men haters or out to break up marriages and relationships. Our name describes our mission: we want women to be safe. It doesn't matter whom they choose to be with.

Wendy Lynch

Board Member, Counseling
Service of Addison County

We Err on the Side of
Giving More Services

*As one of 10 state-designated community counsel-
ing services, the Counseling Service provides mental
health, substance abuse, and developmental services
to all Addison County residents regardless of their
ability to pay. Wendy Lynch has been part of the
CSAC community for nearly 25 years—first col-
laborating on programs with the Counseling
Service as a special education teacher in the diversi-
fied occupations program at the school district's
Hannaford Career Center and from 1994 to 2004
as a board member. She was president in 2001–
2002 when the board grappled with program-
threatening budget deficits.*

Staff turnover in county mental health agencies has been 20-plus percent in recent years. Pay that
doesn't keep up with inflation, long hours, and burnout are some of the causes. Staff and community
members are recognized by board president Wendy Lynch with service awards at the annual meeting

My first involvement with the Counseling
Service was in the late 1970s when I met
a woman who was developing programs for people with developmental disabilities. We both
thought that the community needed to provide a
work component for these people, specifically
people who didn't have anything to do once they
completed school. I was working with special
needs high school students, and some were just
staying at home after completing school.

We worked together in developing a sheltered workshop, which isn't a politically correct
term now. We called them opportunity centers.
People could gather there and work on subcon-
tract jobs, but the center also placed people in
jobs in the community. Most people in the com-

munity thought the program was great, especially
the parents. This was something that they had
needed for their children.

About nine years ago (1994) I became a
board member. I was recruited by a friend and
colleague who was also a special education
teacher and was about to leave the board. I think
the board wanted to replace her with someone
who had a similar background and knowledge.

One constant over the years has been funding crises. The minute I went on the board, there
was a financial crisis when the state cut our funding.
Basically, mental health agencies are underfunded
so these crises are repeated again and again.

Sometimes the cause is external when the
state cuts our funding during the year and may
make the cut retroactive to the start of our fiscal
year. The issue may be a change in Medicaid case
rates or how we must bill for services. Sometimes
it's a combination of external changes and internal
problems.

Funding for mental health agencies is going
to get worse and worse, so over the last two years
(2001-2) we have spent a lot of time looking at
how we can become more efficient. We have gotten better at identifying our internal problems, but
we have to become more creative in capturing
more funding and getting unpaid bills paid.

Our new information system helps here. Our past system wasn't up to what it should have been. But the complexity and coding of billing is just amazing. It's a constant struggle; therapists say they sometimes have to resubmit bills three times.

We have just completed a new building to be the home of our administrative and youth and family services. And we are thinking about building a second adjacent building to house the remainder of the agency's programs in the next four or five years. This will save on rent and consolidate our services, which are spread across many buildings.

And we are investigating a loose confederation with two other counseling services to share personnel and expensive systems.

In fiscal year 2001, when I was board president, we had to lay off people twice because we were facing a $400,000 shortfall in an $11 million budget. Our executive council that includes the executive director, director of human resources, medical director, the CFO, and the directors in charge of children's and adult outpatient services looked at where we could cut, consolidate or change full-time to part-time positions.

The executive council was very careful about not reducing whole positions. This is still not great. You may get paid for half-time work, but you're working almost full time. Or you're cut to a quarter from a half. In some ways it's bad, but the agency didn't say, like some corporations, you're gone.

One lesson from that experience was the importance of having a CFO that you know and trust and who can closely track revenues and expenses. This was something we were lacking then. But it's hard to find CFOs for the money agencies like ours can pay, and it's hard to find a person who knows how the state of Vermont funds mental health.

Our financial problems are shared by all counseling agencies—payments don't cover the cost of services. That's been true for several years. Our auditor says every agency doesn't face the severity of our recent problems, but this could happen to any agency at the drop of a hat.

Over 90% of our revenues comes from the state, mainly through Medicaid, with some grants and contracts. Our CFO has some state projections on how much we will be able to bill Medicaid when he builds a budget. But it all depends on how much the legislature appropriates.

We have never been able to count on more money for a program. When there is good news it is always a surprise. And Medicaid doesn't pay the full cost of some of our programs, such as adult outpatient counseling. This service has not made money in recent years, but we feel, unlike some other county counseling services, that this is part of our mission and we can't drop it.

This service helps everyone, not just those who can't afford a private therapist. In the past you could have seven or eight one-on-one sessions with a counselor. Now for the most part we must have group sessions or require greater client contributions.

Our 24-hour hotline and emergency crisis team had 3,000-plus phone calls last year. We lose money on this service, because phone consultations generally can't be billed, but we are mandated by the state, because we are the designated counseling service for the county, to provide the service.

We felt so fortunate two years ago to be able to hire a child psychiatrist to work along with our two adult psychiatrists. But because of our financial problems one of our adult psychiatrists resigned so we could keep our new child psychiatrist. Compared to other counseling services, the state said we were overstaffed, which is absurd because the need exceeds what our two psychiatrists can meet.

Our services for the developmentally disabled are almost completely funded by Medicaid. We get a capped payment based on the client's needs and have to live within that regardless of how much service we provide.

Staff who give direct service to children and families feel we're not doing enough. Some programs, such as autism or outdoor-based therapy, can go after grants. Other programs, such as outpatient counseling, don't have that option of using grants.

While other counseling services have eliminated programs that are not money makers, we have not. Our executive director looks at funding trends, and we try to balance losers and gainers so the agency as a whole isn't losing money.

People aren't aware of all the things that the Counseling Service does. One reason is that people may still be reluctant to seek help for mental health problems. An old misperception is that counselors will be too personal and snoop into your private business. Or they will take away your children. Those views come from people who don't use the service rather than from people who do. I'm sure there are some conflicts, but most people welcome the help.

It's not as much a problem today, because people's lives are touched by mental health programs and issues in so many ways. Nearly everyone has had a friend or family member who has had problems.

The range of counseling services in Addison County is exceptional. Almost to a fault, the agency doesn't draw any lines in terms of one's ability to pay or in following guidelines on who should be seen. When I talked with the Commissioner of Mental Health she said that we err on the side of giving more services rather than on the side of being a tight financial unit.

One board expectation is that members will have a proactive attitude about mental health. We have had some members who have bordered on the attitude that taxes are too high and who constantly asked how we could slash programs. They didn't fit in or have the patience for the way an organization like this is run.

We are the safety net for the community.

Our needs are constantly changing, so we don't have a 10-year plan. We find out what we need from what our programs are telling us. Schools are saying, for example, that they need more counselors, because kids have more behavior problems. We have had programs for these families since the kids were very young so we have seen the growing need for several years.

The hiring of the child psychiatrist was important. Schools and parents wanted evaluations. In the past, our adult psychiatrists would have handled it or referred it outside the agency.

Another issue is that our wages have fallen far behind inflation, and we have major problems in hiring and keeping people. Some staff leave to be school counselors or move to other state or private agencies where the pay is better. At one time many counseling service staff were part-time, had a partner, and didn't need a full-time job. But non-competitive pay is becoming more of an issue and our annual turnover is now about 25%, which is similar to turnover around the state.

The board is trying to address this issue, but the state usually fixes the amount of new money for salaries so there is little we can do there. We are exploring other benefits, like internal staff development programs, that could improve working conditions and hopefully increase morale.

The best case would be to get back on our feet financially, have a tighter rein on all of the financials, and then add back some positions. But the whole billing thing is so crazy. First, we are underreimbursed for what we bill. And we have the reputation for going the extra mile for clients. But if we work harder we aren't paid more. The state caps what it will pay.

It's like special education, where federal mandates come down to the state without any funding. The state doesn't pay for its share, and the local community has to pick up the cost. In downsizing Waterbury State Hospital and closing Brandon Training School, the state thought they would save money, but I don't think that has been true. We have been penalized because we have done more and tried to serve these people in our communities.

If I had a magic wand I'd like money that comes without all kinds of strings attached. Less paperwork would be number two. And I'd like to see more direct service done by people who are well trained and experienced. Clinicians would get decent salaries and not have to move up to management to make more money.

In January (2004) I will have been on the board for 10 years and will probably step down. I think it's good for others to come on, but it's not easy to find members. Most people who serve have had some contact with the mental health field—it could be through their family, friends, or themselves. We brainstorm and think these peo-

ple would be great and find they are already on two other boards.

We might approach 10 people to find one member. That's definitely true with lawyers. We have probably asked more than 10 lawyers recently and are having a hard time finding one. In one case, the husband was a lawyer, but the wife served instead. And we had a lawyer, but he took a job with a state agency and had to leave because of a conflict of interest.

And there are people's time constraints. We meet once a month for two hours, 4:30 to 6:30, and members are on at least one committee—outreach, fund raising, executive committee, development—which meets at least once a month.

Half of the board's membership—board membership varies from 12 to 15—is supposed to be people who have received services either directly or indirectly through family members. Then there are people like myself who are in a profession, special education, that overlaps.

We're not as savvy on financial issues as business people. Dealing with the financials can be overwhelming and it takes at least a year to become comfortable with them. This is not an easy board to be on, because we have so many services and different types of problems.

Some boards seek members with deep pockets, but the Counseling Service has always been ambivalent about fund raising and until recently has never had a development person. The agency would try fund raising and then would be part of the United Way and give up the right to fund raise in certain parts of the year.

This approach has changed because of our financial problems. For the past two years we have had a part-time development person who has raised money to keep programs alive. Beginning

Counseling Service board members oversee programs for children, adolescents, adults, and families that serve over 2,000 county residents annually. Board members hold their annual meeting at the Legion Hall before pitching in to serve a buffet supper.

in the spring of 2003 we will have a full-time development person.

How much the board will be expected to do if we have a capital campaign for a new building has not yet been decided. Some people don't mind being on a fund-raising committee, but others say they didn't join the board to ask people for money. That's not how they feel they can contribute.

As a board member, I have enjoyed working with a group of people who problem solve. Being on the board has also helped me learn more about all the Counseling Service's programs in the community. And it's been satisfying to have some input in programs, such as special education, where I have some knowledge.

Over the years, I've always been impressed

by the staff that comes to board meetings. They are really the strength of the organization. So many of them could be doing something else that is less demanding and pays better, but they are committed to community mental health.

Bob Thorn

Executive Director, Counseling Service of Addison County

Shouldn't We Be Able to Take Care of Folks Who Are in Pain and Suffering?

Bob Thorn came to the Counseling Service in 1979 to direct the agency's new housing and support program for people with developmental disabilities. Recognized around the state for its innovative and comprehensive programs, the Counseling Service provides services to children, adolescents, adults, and families. As executive director, Thorn faces the administrator's ultimate challenge, ever-growing community needs at a time of tight or declining state and federal support.

Medicaid reimbursement makes up over 80% of the Counseling Service's $12-million budget. Responding to increasing community demands at a time of growing state Medicaid deficits and tight reimbursements is one of executive director Bob Thorn's most pressing challenges.

In a rural mental health agency we do it all. We're the safety net. We're not here to make a profit. We're here to meet the needs of our community.

People who can't afford private services get pushed to us. The very challenging and difficult get pushed to us.

The U.S. Surgeon General's 1999 Report on Mental Health estimated that two-thirds of people with mental health disorders do not seek help because of a lack of insurance coverage, an unwarranted sense of hopelessness about the prospects of recovery, or the stigma still attached to mental illness. Who really knows, because these people are not coming forward, but I believe that figure is accurate for Addison County, too.

Studies do show that many people with psychological problems go to their family doctor. In fact, more people are treated for psychological problems by general practitioners than by people trained in the field. Doctors who have the right experience can often provide the best treatment. Sometimes being identified or labeled as having "some mental problem" creates a whole series of problems.

Seeing the family doctor fits with the idea that people should be treated in as normal a setting as possible. But sometimes people would be better served by an agency like ours where we have a psychiatrist and clinicians who can do an evaluation, who are much more current on medications, and who can make referrals for other services, such as case management, family counseling, and assistance with employment and housing. Studies also show that people with depression who receive both medication and psychotherapy have much better outcomes.

Are people getting the best service that they can get from their family physicians? Sometimes and most often, yes. Sometimes, no.

The agency has a reputation for aggressively trying to meet people's needs and then trying to find funding. We're at the top in many measures of services per client and are first or second in the state in children served per thousand. Some of our programs for kids have become statewide models, such as the Parent/Child Center, which was started by a community-counseling service collaboration, and our autism program. In fact, the

Department (Department of Developmental and Mental Health Services) has been concerned because other agencies say, "Addison County does this. Why can't we?"

We have more counselors in schools than any agency our size and a full range of interventions for school-age children. We have services where we deal with problems in the home and work with the whole family. Or we see someone briefly and offer ideas to manage problems

Some agencies don't operate that way. I have heard other directors say, "If they don't want to pay us for it than we're not going to do it." We tend to overextend ourselves to preserve what we see as mission critical services.

We're overextended, but we're still reluctant to cut back on services. We probably have the best services for people with autism. But that has hurt us financially, because autism services have never been adequately funded. We also have a child psychiatrist, which is a much needed resource, but this, too, is not adequately funded.

We're pretty good in hourly cost comparisons with other agencies, except in children's services, where we are a little higher. The state only requires B.A.-level people for some school services, so most agencies have hired B.A. people. We have tried to maintain a good core of Master's-level clinicians in the schools.

Nearly all agencies have eliminated or significantly reduced their outpatient counseling and treatment program, which works with people with a broad range of problems, including depression, anxiety, substance abuse. Outpatient counseling is a money loser because Medicaid reimbursement doesn't cover costs and we serve everyone regardless of ability to pay.

We've been reluctant to shrink this program, but because of our budget problems we had to cut our outpatient department from 14 clinicians to five. We have no problems with private practitioners picking up more of our outpatient business. Many area clinicians have worked for and gotten a lot of their training here. They are good people and some will donate two hours a week for people who can't afford to pay. They do what they can, but that's not their job. It's our job.

There is going to be a whole group of folks which is not going to get served. Some people with Medicaid won't get seen because reimbursement rates are too low for private therapists. The working poor, who have jobs and families but can't afford health insurance, may not seek help.

That said, I don't think any county in Vermont works as collaboratively as Addison in providing services. Part of it is the people. Part of it is our shared values. But we as an agency are providing services that we can't sustain with current funding.

Medicaid payments make up about 80% of our budget. But in some areas, like psychiatry, emergency services, and substance abuse treatment, Medicaid rates don't cover our costs or those of any other counseling service. Agency directors have thought about writing a letter to the state saying that we won't provide emergency services, which you mandate, if you are not going to fund them adequately. But that would just be a bluff. We can't be in this business and not have emergency services to deal with people in crisis.

Legislators say, "We have put $100 million of additional money into mental health in the last seven years." But only a very small amount of that new money, about 7%, went into existing services and the rest went into new services. The state has a pattern where they fund the "new thing" and funding for existing programs starts eroding or is outright reduced.

When the state was closing Brandon Training School in the 1980s we could get lots of money for development services. Community and rehabilitation treatment programs, which mainly serve people who were at the state hospital, were hot when they wanted to downsize Waterbury State Hospital. Children's services have been receiving a lot of attention recently.

In its defense, the Department walks a fine line and is in the middle of many different pressures. You have the advocacy groups, legislature, the secretary of human services, and governor all saying, "Here's what I want you to do."

The problem is that there is a finite amount of money in the mental health system. The commissioner says, "Tell me what your priorities are. You want me to change the rate on psychiatry. Fine. Where do you want me to take the money from?"

They do try and work with us, but that's the reality. Any system that is inadequately funded, no matter how well defined, will fail.

We meet with local legislators before each session. They need to recognize that their constituents care about these issues, and we have not been great in telling their and our story. It's hard, because clients of mental health services don't always want to speak up. People are more educated about mental health today, in disclosing they have an illness, and in advocating for themselves, but we still face a lot of stigma and ignorance.

The governor and legislators are interested in their political careers so if you have a loud enough voice they will support you. But it really should come down to values. What is your vision on how we relate to each other as human beings and how we care for our vulnerable populations? We are a very wealthy country. Shouldn't we be able to take care of folks who are in pain and suffering?

Our end product is quality of life. That's the measure, and we've been terrible at measuring outcomes. That's been part of our problem in our lobbying for greater funding.

We've seen what we do as more of an art than a science. To be successful in maintaining and gaining adequate support we have to become much more outcome oriented. National organizations are trying to define outcome measures, but a good complete set doesn't exist. Everyone asks clients if they are happy with services, but that's not enough.

In developmental services, a big measure is employment. Is someone employed? Are they getting a competitive wage, minimum wage or better? Are they in a meaningful job or in the old sheltered workshop model of putting nuts on bolts and then taking them apart? Is it integrated? Is a person with a disability next to someone who doesn't have a disability?

We use those measures, and I think our employment program is the best in the state. But part of me says that you can never adequately measure the value you bring to someone's life. In a small community, people will tell you that so-and-so staff person saved their family or saved a depressed husband's life.

It's a lot like Jimmy Stewart in "It's a Wonderful Life." We never get to see what many lives would be like if we weren't here. But there is no question in my mind that many people are grateful. It's not just to the Counseling Service, but to the people we have in our community.

My main agenda when I was president of the Vermont Council for Developmental and Mental Health Services in the late 1990s was to build coalitions. We identified 21 advocacy groups, many of whom had never met together. We would shoot ourselves in the foot because advocacy groups sent contradictory messages to the legislature.

I said we had to find common ground and move forward with one voice. That approach has been surprisingly effective with the legislature.

My other priority was increasing salaries, because salaries, which are already low in the mental health field, weren't keeping pace with inflation. Annual staff turnover in mental health agencies was averaging 26% statewide. The scary thing was that the numbers were increasing very dramatically, and it looked like it could get far worse. (Turnover in 2005 remains at that level, and recruitment is becoming even more difficult.)

Unfunded state mandates are another stress. The state and federal government recently created new privacy laws and data sets, which require collecting, entering, and transmitting service and demographic data to them. Complying with these mandates—new software and staff time—costs us over $10,000 a year.

None of these requirements seems bad individually, but cumulatively they have had an impact at a time when managed care has already increased the complexities of billing. We have had to hire a full-time person to get authorization for service from managed care companies.

Managed care revenues are probably under 10% of our total budget, but our margin of survival is so thin that missing 1% can be enough to break us. Managed care will delay payments and find any loophole to make a denial. You have to fight and hammer at them all the time.

The bottom line is that every dollar spent on administration reduces someone's services.

But our financial squeeze is not just the result of funding and mandates from the state. Our health care costs for 210 employees have gone up $500,000 over a 2.5-year period; nearly 10% of our $12 million budget (2003) now goes for health care.

I got into the mental health field with the idea of making the world a better place. Now margins are so tight that it's difficult to make this "business" work. Boards are hiring directors to run the organization who are just money people without a clinical background.

My struggle is to find a way to keep the organization financially healthy and do it without losing its heart. It would be easy if I could just cut what isn't making money. But what is the impact on people's lives? It's worth the effort and sweat to figure out the very best ways of keeping essential services intact.

Politicians don't want to be the ones who come to the table and say this is what you can't have. They say continue to provide high-quality services, but this is all the money we can give you.

Even the Department doesn't want to put themselves in the middle, because they have all these advocacy groups pushing them. They cleverly position themselves so they don't have to make choices. So it really puts it on the counseling services to make these decisions, and we shouldn't be the ones to do it, not if the issue is unfunded mandates.

In the past we have emphasized putting "people first" and cutting non—human-related services with the legislature. We've also emphasized the multiple impacts of these cuts. Some families are served by SRS, by us, and by other

Please don't cut support for programs that provide essential services to needy people who have no other safety net is the annual message of the Counseling Service to visiting county legislators.

service agencies. With all of these services getting hit, we're going to see a very dramatic impact on some families.

Part of me thinks that it is very unfortunate to see services on the decline today, but the pendulum swings. I don't know when or how far, but it does swing. I know how bad it can get and it is worth the fight to tell people that we can't risk going too far backwards.

We can only go so far, and we will have class action suits again, like the ones in the 1960s and 1970s to get people out of institutions. Many states are under court orders now to improve their services and are at risk of losing their federal funding.

Vermont truly is a leader in mental health services in this country. That's a scary thought because there is so much more that we can be doing.

Critics will say that we are always asking for more money. I agree. Our role is to advocate for the people we serve, but people aren't getting services beyond what they should. Yes, money isn't wisely spent in some cases. That's not our doing. Rules tell us how people must be treated.

At what point do you say enough is enough? We're a rich country and we can afford to take care of our vulnerable fellow citizens. I don't think that we are anywhere close to saying that we have enough.

Just as we have a dialogue about a legal minimum wage, we need a community dialogue about core mental health services.

Do you want emergency services available to everybody? Do you want preventative treatment? Do you want to intervene at early ages? Do you want to provide services if someone is homeless with severe depression or schizophrenia?

I'd also like to see us take a much more holistic view of health and well-being where we have a single entry point for hospital, mental health, and social assistance programs. People would only have to fill out one application, not applications for every service.

Wouldn't it be wonderful to have an advocate say, "Here is how health care and social services can really assist you. This isn't a lifetime endowment of services. It's what we can do to empower you, assist you through medication or minimal support, help you find a job and keep your family intact."

Agencies wouldn't be looking to generate fee-for-service dollars but to identify the best care and support for that person. I love that idea.

When we redid our mission statement a number of years ago we recognized the benefits of community outreach and prevention. We are now offering educational programs, for example, for people in mid-life, but we don't have any funding for them.

The criterion for getting treatment and Medicaid payment is that the person be in crisis. As funds tighten, the definition of crisis has become more and more acute. That's the nature of most of our funding. You need to be in crisis to get served.

What scares me the most is that we face increased demands for health care when health care costs are already a crisis for any business or organization. In addition, Social Security is not adequately funded to meet obligations to baby boomers.

I don't know that anyone has the answers. I see much more intense competition ahead for resources for health care and social services, especially after September 11, when no legislator will want to vote against an increase in military spending.

My goal for this agency isn't very ambitious. I would like to be able to sustain the services we currently have, meet the needs of our community, and preserve the spirit of our agency. I'm struggling to do that.

Chapter 6

Growing Old

**People Hate to Give up
Their Independence**

THE HIGH COST OF GROWING OLD

Halfway through a 45-minute Power Point presentation on "Section 1115 Demonstration Waiver: A New Long-term Care Program for Vermonters," the commissioner of the state's Department of Aging and Disabilities flashed a solid black pie chart on the screen.

Global Medicaid Long-term Care Budget Estimated FY 2004 $128,000,000

That one chart summed up the immediate funding horizon for the state's and Addison County's long-term care providers. There would now be a single pot of Medicaid money that would provide equal access to long-term care options—nursing home, home, and community-based care. This proposed equal-access provision would be a dramatic change from current practice where qualifying low-income Vermonters were "entitled" to nursing home care but had to apply for a limited number of waiver slots for services that would enable them to remain in their homes or receive community-based services.

The 25-odd representatives from the county's long-term care organizations—nursing home, home health, adult day care, residential care homes, and the area agency on aging—could do little but squirm. Not just because the folding chairs in the basement meeting room of Middlebury's Congregational Church were granite hard, but because their funding was being tweaked again and the stakes were high.

A swing of several patients in a daily census could mean financial comfort, nose-barely-above-water survival, or bankruptcy. Everyone knew of nursing homes, residential care homes, and home health agencies around the state that had recently downsized, were struggling to survive, or that had gone under. One had to look no further for proof than the second row where an anxious administrator and three board members of the Helen Porter nursing home sat. The nursing home, now in the black, had lost about $900,000 in a projected $6 million budget three years earlier (2000) when long-term care funding had been tweaked to favor home and community-based services and the nursing home's daily census dropped abruptly.

Everyone favored giving Vermonters more choice and a more balanced system of long-term care, but money was on the table and emotions and long-standing institutional differences were close to the surface.

The state has no obligation to support institutions that are not meeting the needs of consumers in a changing marketplace, argued the executive director of an adult day care center that had benefited from funding changes.

The state must provide transitional support for essential services before they have massive losses, said the administrator of the nursing home, speaking from first-hand experience.

These fault lines were familiar to the commissioner. There would be work groups in the summer to work on the proposal's details, he said, and time for additional comments before the plan would be submitted to the federal government at the end of the summer.

But like it or not, the status quo wasn't working, and there would have to be change, the commissioner said. Vermont, like other state governments, simply couldn't afford annual 8% increases in its Medicaid budget. From 1990 to 2000, Medicaid spending on the state's nursing homes had increased from $45 million to $84 million. With the number of Vermonters 75 and over projected to increase from 35,000 in 2000 to 60,000 in 2025, the state had to curb the cost of long-term care.

Very simply, home and community-based services cost less, in some cases a lot less, than the $50,000 to $60,000-plus annual cost of nursing home care. The state was now supporting the long-term care of about 3,200 low-income Vermonters, about 2,200 in nursing homes and the rest in home and community-based settings. Shifting Vermonters to less expensive home and community-based services would allow the state to serve more Vermonters while remaining within the $128 million budget.

In the past, there had been more demand for waivers for home and community-based services than the supply, about 1,000 slots. As a result, some Vermonters had to enter nursing homes when they were unable to get the services, such as personal care, adult day care, and home modifications, that would enable them to remain in their homes.

What went without saying during the com-

PRECEDING PAGE: Addison County's adult day care center serves 170 people annually in its six-days-a-week, 12-hours-a-day program.

How can the Department of Aging and Disabilities control rising costs and best serve the long-term care needs of low-income Vermonters? The department and Commissioner Patrick Flood, here at a community hearing, believe that the most efficient allocation of Medicaid funds is 60% for institutional nursing homes and 40% for home and community-based services.

missioner's presentation was that nearly everyone, if they had the choice, would choose to remain in their own home or in an assisted living or enhanced residential care setting that provided more privacy and independence than a nursing home. And while the commissioner assured the long-term care providers, especially the nursing home, that their current residents would be grandfathered in, the future was clear.

With a new push from the state, nursing home enrollments would most likely continue to decline and less expensive home and community-based care would increase. Vermonters wanted to stay in their homes, and the state wanted to continue its efforts to help them stay there.

In 1996, the state legislature had begun to channel more resources into home and community-based services with its passage of Act 160. This law required the Agency of Human Services to expand services and improve independent living options for the elderly and for younger people with physical disabilities. More specifically, the Act required the Department of Aging and Disabilities to shift $20 million in Medicaid funds over a three-year period, 1997–2000, from nursing homes to community-based services.

And after three years, the share of Medicaid money spent on community-based services had grown from 11.5% to 18.5%. This was a marked improvement but far short of the Department's goal to spend 40% of long-term public funding on home and community-based services.

Act 160 was but the first step. Seven years later, this demonstration program to create equal access to long-term care services was the second step. While approval was not a fait accompli, the federal government favored proposals that expanded coverage while controlling costs—the federal government pays 63% of the state's Medicaid budget—and the five-year demonstration project could begin within a year, the commissioner said. (The U.S. Department of Health and Human Services approved Vermont's demonstration project, the first in the nation, in the summer of 2005, two years after Commissioner Flood's presentation. The program will begin October 1, 2005.)

If it alleviated any fears, Addison County, the commissioner said, already had achieved a far better balance of services than other areas in the state. Some imbalances remained, but there wouldn't be as much systemic change as some people thought. Reassurances aside, nearly every agency and health care service is heavily dependent on Medicaid funding—two-thirds of the community nursing home's budget, for example, comes from Medicaid.

~

Private long-term care insurers have a numbing list of projections that argue, in essence, that your Golden Years may bankrupt you and that you'd better have insurance. The Health Insurance Association of America warns that three out of five people over age 65 may need some form of long-term care in their lifetime and two out of five may spend some time in a nursing home. The National Council on Aging estimates that the cost of institutional care for a family member would drive seven out of 10 families below the federal poverty level within four months.

Their hammered-home message: if you don't qualify for Medicaid you'd better be very wealthy or have long-term care insurance. But as everyone in the room knew, very few people have long-term care insurance and those who do often have limited coverage.

If the funding unknowns in the state's proposal were "scary," they were simply part of the ongoing struggle that the agencies already faced in cobbling together resources to meet changing needs. The commissioner, though, was right. Addison County's end-of-life services are among the most comprehensive and balanced in the state. In fact, the county had already exceeded the department's goal to have 40% of its Medicaid funding support home and community-based services and 60% support institutional nursing home care. Addison had already reversed those numbers, with 61% of Medicaid funding in the county allocated to home services and only 39% to nursing homes.

Programs at Project Independence, the county's non-profit adult day care center, have long been a state and national model for other rural providers. Project Independence and the home health agency have aggressively used funding from the state's Act 160 law to provide services that enable many nursing home–eligible residents to age in their homes.

A network of private home caregivers and the volunteer hospice service further support residents in their homes. The nursing home has rapidly reinvented itself with new services, such as an expanded rehabilitation center and a new Alzheimer's unit, to replace the loss of traditional long-term care patients.

In this chapter, Joanne Corbett, the executive director of the adult day care center, describes the evolution of the center's programs and the public's misconceptions about the limits on the lives of the elderly. Finding services and the right program for elderly parents can be a nightmare. But once found, they are a godsend, says Louise Beil, who has cared for a stroke-ridden mother and father.

A vital part of any community is the network of neighbors, volunteers, and private caregivers who provide essential services—from picking up groceries to providing end-of-life comfort. Edith Miner, a dairy farmer's widow, describes how she began caring for neighbors 20 years ago and continues today.

"Nursing home" is often a dreaded two-word phrase. Amy Curtis, the social services director at the community nursing home, discusses how families grapple with their guilt in placing a member in a home and how residents struggle with their loss of independence.

A good life should have a good death. What does that mean, and how? Rev. Diana Scholl, Porter Hospital chaplain, Catherine Studley, the director of the county's hospice program, and Edie Corse, a hospice recipient/volunteer, end the chapter discussing their experiences with illness and dying.

Joanne Corbett

Executive Director,
Elderly Services, Inc.

It Was a Whole New Way of Thinking

Project Independence began in 1981, an outgrowth of concerns of the Counseling Service of Addison County that area residents needed an adult day care center. Started as a free service in the basement of the Methodist Church with five participants, Project Independence now serves over 170 area residents a year and is nationally recognized as a model center for its innovative and comprehensive programs. Joanne Corbett has been executive director since 1990 and the guiding force in Project Independence's expansion and its successful campaign to raise $5 million to build a permanent home. This state-of-the-art, 16,000-square-foot center opened in the spring of 2005 after this interview.

Addison County's adult day care center, Project Independence, has long been recognized both within the state and country for its innovative and comprehensive programs. The center, the largest program in the state, is the only program that is open 12 hours a day. Joanne Corbett has been its executive director since 1990.

Staff tells me the center had a different clientele in the 1980s. It was a healthier group without the frailty and dependency that we care for today. It was a more social program as opposed to the medical-social program today. There were a lot of field trips, almost no toileting needs, no bathing needs, almost no incontinence, and almost no dementia.

In 1988, Project Independence instituted a sliding scale fee for the first time in which people were asked, in an honor system, to pay what they could, from $4 to $30 a day. Most people paid $4 a day, including transportation.

When I came in 1990, there was a sense that we have a great program and a great agency.

There was wonderful good will toward Project Independence and this agency, Elderly Services.

I'm a social worker, but I have been director of a few different programs and am very into finances and budget. So I talked with the board and staff about the fact that we had a number of well-to-do people who were paying $4 a day. Staff wages and benefits were pitiful. I had been reading about adult day care, and there were places that were getting $30 a day.

So I started talking to the board about getting more serious about having a fee and scholarships. The board wanted better revenue and better wages,

and they agreed.

Under the fee plan, residents who could not afford the full fee of $30 a day completed a financial aid application. The center then offered scholarships based on a family's documented need.

At that time, the Robert Wood Johnson Foundation (the nation's largest health care philanthropy) was publicizing an adult day care initiative, called Partners in Care Giving. The first wave of grants, from 1988 to 1992, created 12 new dementia-specific adult day care centers.

In the second wave of grants, the foundation wanted to apply Part I's lessons to 50 existing

"I believe very strongly in getting old people out of the isolation of their homes and into a center like ours. That's a huge battle in a society where once you get old and frail you don't want anyone seeing you using a walker or getting in a van in your wheel chair," says Corbett.

centers that they felt had a strong track record, vision, and a commitment to marketing.

It was a very competitive process. I decided to apply, because they wanted to teach the directors how to run their non-profits like a business. Robert Wood Johnson didn't want you to become too dependent on the government, because a new administration could decide to change the Medicaid funding regulations. In some centers, Medicaid funded 90% of the participants.

At the beginning of the program they said your focus should be on trying to attract private pay. The private-pay market will not go away. The government-funded market can go away with a change in policy.

So we were chosen. We were the only center in Vermont. There was one in Maine, two in Massachusetts, one in Rhode Island.

We were all nurses and social workers and wondered what it meant to run your non-profit like a business. The wonderful thing was that the foundation hired a medical school in North Carolina to administer the project with a staff of nurses, social workers, and a doctor. It was and continues to be a very inspiring combination of compassion and a commitment to the highest-quality program.

They believe that you should think about what families and the elderly want, develop a product, be a staff that is incredibly attractive in its caregiving, have a space that is appealing, hours that work, provide a clean place and meaningful activities. If you offer a topnotch product, there are middle- and upper-income people who want their family members at home and who will be happy to pay for adult day care as part of their plan.

You should develop a product geared to the highest-paying customers and then make sure that you have enough income so you can offer scholarships to the lower-paying end. This was all very appealing, because we have a real mixed income clientele in our county. There is a very professional, upper-income segment that we can appeal to on a private-pay basis, and there are many poor people.

We made a strategic planning decision then to become an adult day care that cared for the really frail and at-risk. We were well situated, for example, to take people who had oxygen tanks and catheters because we had a program coordinator who was a RN. We welcomed other people, but they weren't our first priority.

Our attendance, which had been 15 to 20, dropped to around 12 for about a year after we abandoned the honor-system fee and instituted a fee with scholarships. Some people just left. And

Over 200 community volunteers—bridge and Scrabble players, story tellers and readers, historians, musicians of all ages—supplement a staff of 60-plus at Project Independence.

there were some fairly healthy people who really didn't need adult day care. They could go to the senior center and the senior nutrition sites.

So we had to rebuild the program and attract a new clientele. My goal was to average 25 people a day at the end of the project in four years.

In four years, we were averaging 40 people a day. Our average fee had gone from $4 a day under the sliding scale fee to about $25 a day in 1997. That included round-trip transportation, meals, nursing, and any personal care you needed with toileting, incontinence, mobility, feeding, and activities. The only thing it didn't include was a shower or medical escort to the doctor. Those were extra.

With new people, there was a case-by-case figuring of the rate. To make it affordable for lower-income families, we offered financial aid.

We were definitely the cheapest thing in town. Transportation and five hours of care were typically $15. That's about $3 an hour and nothing for transportation. In those years if you tried to hire someone to stay with your parents it probably would have been $6 an hour for an elder care sitter.

During this time we were also doing a lot of outreach and marketing with training and help from the foundation. They had quarterly conferences with the 50 directors and sent consultants here each quarter. They told us to concentrate on building strong personal relationships with professionals—doctors, home health nurses, and physical therapists—who work with elders.

Their version of marketing is to figure out what elderly people and their families want and then offer it. Instead of saying, "We have these hours, these activities," we say, "First, tell me a little about your father."

Then our response would be tailored to them as an individual. If they said, "Dad likes to play chess," then I would say, "We will find a chess player to come in and play with your father." As opposed to saying, "We have bingo on Monday, Wednesday, Friday," and then their response would be, "He won't fit in."

Once you're immersed in it, it seems so obvious, but it was a whole new way of thinking.

So we have really ballooned over the last decade. We had agreed with the Congregational Church that we would never have more than 30. Then we rearranged the agreement to 35, then 40, and that's it.

We rented about 3,000 square feet on the bottom floor of the Charter House, the former parsonage, and used part of the second floor for offices. By 1996, we had reached our maximum of 40.

We decided to open our center on Saturday in 1993 as a way to serve more people. We had been operating a field trip one or two Saturdays a month. At first we had a small waiting list and were able to fit people in when there were cancellations. But the list kept getting bigger and bigger until we had 25 families on it. So we started a second program from 2 to 7 in March of 1997.

Now we're open 7 to 7, Monday through Friday. And 7 to 3 on Saturday. It's taken three years and now both programs are full, and we have a waiting list, which peaked at 23 in the fall of 2002, most of the time.

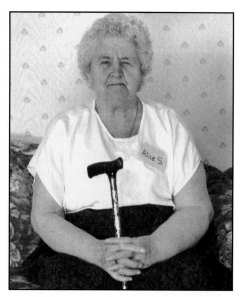

Many families are not aware of the range of services—home health, Project Independence, friends, neighbors, church, and Meals on Wheels—for the elderly. Creative use of these resources will enable many people to remain in their homes and out of nursing homes, says Corbett.

In a typical week, we have 140 participants. In an average day, we have 70. We have 20 people who attend both sessions, which we didn't anticipate. We have had families take people out of the nursing home and bring them home once we stayed open until 7.

We have a lot of extremely disabled people who continue to live at home because their families can have 10 or 12 daytime hours to themselves. Some families will pay for help some nights of the week, but not too many people can afford help every night. It's very rare for people to have private, long-term care insurance

The Robert Wood Johnson project definitely transformed our organization. (The project

stopped in 2001.) Our budget was $150,000 when I came. Now it's $1.5 million. The staff was 8. Now it's 65 (2005).

We're now the biggest adult day care center and the strongest center financially in the state. No one else is open 12 hours a day, and we were the first to be open on Saturday.

Historically we have had a pool of overqualified, idealistic people, attracted in part by Middlebury College, and have been able to create a uniquely qualified staff. We also have 200 volunteers, many of whom have retired here because of the College. The whole state of Vermont is like that in a way because it attracts artsy, higher-income people who might have volunteering in their background.

And I am very aggressive with fund raising. I think many directors aren't that confident about fund raising. They feel that there is no one in the community to raise money from.

Our private fund raising has been small in the past, about $50,000, compared to our million-dollar budget, but it's a lot compared to other centers.

Our fund-raising program for our new center was by far the biggest campaign that an organization like ours has ever undertaken in Vermont.

In 1998, the board and staff decided to buy land and design a new building. We initially thought we might raise $1 million. Some board members were worried that this was too ambitious. Others, including myself, wanted to think big and beautiful.

We settled on a goal of $4 million in 1999, amended it to $4.5 million in 2002, and to $5 million in 2004. We have spent six years raising $5 million, which has taken patience and the perseverance to hold out for our vision. We have had a $1 million foundation gift, four gifts of $100,000

Listen to your clients and then develop programs—from chess games to naturalist talks, from bingo to field trips, from music appreciation and sing-alongs to hand massage and sit-down exercises—that respond to their interests. Tailoring programs to individual needs has, unfortunately, often not been the approach of adult day care centers, says Corbett.

plus, 400 gifts of $1,000, and many gifts under $1,000, many of which were $5 to $50. As of December 2004 we have raised the $5 million and will be able to concentrate on supporting the operating expenses of our new building without the burden of a mortgage.

When our new permanent home opens in the spring of 2005, we will be able to serve 80 people at a time, double what we can do now. We have designed the center to look like an old farmhouse—a very big farmhouse as it will have 16,000 square feet, two dining rooms, a great room with a cathedral ceiling and fireplace for activities, a music library and book library, several bedrooms for resting and possibly for respite care in the future, sun

Project Independence's new 16,000-square-foot center roughly quadruples the center's program and office space and can serve 80 at a time. The five-acre site includes a pond, a semi-wild meadow, walking paths among gardens, a golf putting green, and a whiffle ball field.

rooms, examination rooms for doctors and therapists, porches, and a greatly expanded kitchen.

We have a five-acre site and the building will be like a school for the elderly, with computers, crafts, and recreation areas. There will be paved walking paths among gardens, a semi-wild meadow, a golf putting green and whiffle ball field, and a small pond for birds and frogs.

Our designation as a national model by Robert Wood Johnson made our capital campaign possible. As we have in the past, we will be sharing our vision and design with others in the field of adult day care.

Unfortunately, Americans go from, "My mother is 88 and living alone and she's fine," to "She's now fallen for the third time, and it's time for a nursing home."

I'm very frustrated at people's lack of knowledge of the 100 different ways you can put together a package of services to keep them home. I have seen all the creative things that siblings do, systems they create, how they use neighbors and church members.

So many times when I talk with a family, they say "I wish I had known about you three years ago when this was going on with my father."

When I speak to groups, I always ask, "How many of you have heard of us? What have you heard about us?"

Mostly I hear good things, but I will hear things such as, "Everyone there is losing their mind." "You have to be really, really sick to go there." There is a grain of truth in all of this, but it's not the whole truth.

We have many extremely healthy 85- to 100-year-olds. Some physically healthy people are here simply because of depression and isolation and the fact that all their friends are dead.

We would like to have more people like them so they would have a bigger peer group. I believe very strongly in getting old people out of the isolation of their homes and into a center like ours. That's a huge battle in a society where once you get old and frail you don't want anyone seeing you using a walker or getting in a van in your wheel chair.

Most people who come here have been strong-armed into it by their families. I do a lot of educating of adult children about when it's time to take responsibility for lovingly forcing their parents to try something new.

It takes an extreme set of circumstances for us to say that we can't provide care. Generally, people have to be able to get in and out of the van in a wheel chair. But we have had some dying people who are in a recliner for most of the day. We often provide care for people up to the day they die. They are weak, but they can be dressed and transported.

What would lead us to say we can't care for your relative anymore?

We had a gentleman in his 60s. Handsome, strong, vital. He had Alzheimer's and had claustrophobia since he was a little boy. We cared for him for a year and a half, but he needed one-on-one staffing. Sometimes, it was two-on-one chasing him around the village of Middlebury, because he would not stay inside.

He began hitting and punching and running out in front of traffic. It was dangerous for him and our staff. After months and months of chasing him into traffic—his wife did not want him on any kind of sedatives—we gave her 15 days' notice to either try a sedative or we couldn't take care of him anymore.

In her case, she decided on an Alzheimer's unit of a nursing home in the northern part of the state.

Another time to think about a nursing home is when the care is no problem for us, but it is for the home caregiver. We have an 87-year-old woman here eight hours a day who lives with her 89-year-old sister. That 89-year-old is frail and legally blind and is trying to care for her sister who has very involved dementia. I'm saying to the daughters maybe we should tell your mother that she must put her sister in a nursing home.

The older sister is saying, "No, no, never." And the daughters are concerned because they don't want their mother to die while she is caring for her sister. Sometimes there comes a point when I will try, as they say in therapy, "to give them permission" to put their relative in a home and not feel guilty.

Most adult children assume that Medicare covers our services. They are very disappointed when they learn that the program only pays for hospital and doctor expenses. So that is something that, unfortunately, I have to clear up right at the beginning.

Since its creation in the mid-1960s, Medicaid, a program for low-income people, has paid for nursing home care. If you qualified medically and financially, Medicaid would pay for a nursing home for the rest of your life. That was the beginning of the enormous boom in the nursing home industry.

Unfortunately, a family could be tearing their hair out taking care of grandma at home, but Medicaid wouldn't cover any home or community-based services. When I came, Medicaid had just started a tiny, tiny waiver program to pay for home and community-based services like ours. We had three people on it out of 30 participants. Private payers paid what they could, from $4 to $30 a day, and we had to fund raise the rest.

If you look at our profile today (2005), about 60% of our people are supported by Medicaid or the Veterans Administration. This has made it much more possible to keep elderly people at home. Our fee is $12 an hour. Medicaid and the VA pay us $11 an hour. With scholarships, our private-pay participants pay on average about $7 an hour.

We make up the difference with help from the United Way, grants from communities, and our own fund raising.

As an agency, we were fully supportive of the state's Act 160 (passed in 1996) and its goal to support the elderly and infirm who want to remain in their homes. Ninety-seven percent of Vermonters in surveys say they want to continue to live at home even when they are sick and disabled. So it's important that government funding regula-

tions aren't pushing people into institutional care as they have in the past.

From the standpoint of families and consumers I don't think anyone can argue but that Act 160 was very good. Prior to Act 160, it was first-come, first-serve for the few Medicaid waiver slots, and there was a long waiting list. We had people on the Medicaid waiver list for a year or two in the early part of the 1990s. Then they went into the nursing home, because the family couldn't wait any longer for help to keep them at home.

This new system is very, very responsive to people in the greatest need and at the most risk. The whole point of Act 160 was to slow the growth curve for nursing homes, which it did, but not as much as it had been hoped. But it has been revolutionary in helping lower-income people remain at home and in supporting community-based services.

We've never paid good salaries or really good benefits. We've always operated like an underfunded agency and made the best of it. We have never had anything like the guaranteed inflationary rate increase that nursing homes had.

So those of us who have been chronically underfunded feel that the system was skewed toward nursing homes. Nobody likes hearing that nursing homes are hurting. But adult day care centers, agencies on aging, community care homes have always been squeezed and have always had to have bake sales and try to raise money every way that they could.

Home health services and Project Independence's adult day center have allowed
*Eloise Beil to remove her then 92-year-old father, Carlton, from a Staten Island nursing
home and care for him in her Vergennes home.*

Eloise Beil

Caregiver for Elderly Parents

He's Worth It

*Eloise Beil of Vergennes has had 25 years' experi-
ence dealing with the frailties of aging parents. Her
mother had her first stroke in 1976, followed by a
series of mini-strokes leading to her death in 1992.
Carlton, her educator-naturalist father, retired at
65 from the Museum of Natural History in New
York and then began a second 25-year career
organizing nature programs for the park system of
Staten Island, where he grew up.*

*Eloise moved to Vermont in 1988 to work at
the Shelburne Museum and later at the Lake
Champlain Maritime Museum. In 1999, Carlton
had a serious stroke, plunging Eloise and her two
sisters into a frequently frustrating search for compassionate, affordable, and effective care, first in
New York and then in Addison County. (The interview was conducted in August of 2000.)*

My father had his stroke in January of 1999.
He was fine right up until then. Two weeks
earlier he had walked two miles to the hardware
store because he was too impatient to wait for a bus.

After his stroke he was in a nursing home on
Staten Island for a full year, because I didn't know
about the services in Addison County. For three
months in the spring of 1999, they did intensive
rehab, which meant that he saw a speech, physical, and occupational therapist daily.

The price tag on all of this was horrifying,
$8,000 a month. Medicare paid for the first 100
days, then stopped. And it appeared we faced
more than 100 days of care.

The care center said that with his level of stroke he would never be able to live unassisted. There was a remote chance that he could recover enough to live at home with assistance. The odds were much better that he would have to be in an assisted living facility or nursing home.

In that case we needed to fill out a Medicaid application before his financial resources were expended. I believe he wouldn't have qualified for Medicaid until he had only $3,000 in assets left. We'd been talking for seven or eight years with New York City Parks and the commissioner for Staten Island about Dad's house becoming a historic house museum. It's a French Huguenot stone house built in the 1680s that was once owned by Frederick Law Olmstead, the father of American landscape architecture.

We wanted to sell it to New York City Parks Department and hoped to arrange for my dad to have the right to live in it for the remainder of his life. But in the meantime we were spending every cent that he had in savings, money that he inherited from my mother's parents and from a family friend who he cared for. With these savings, we wouldn't have made it through a second year.

After about six months, my two sisters—one lives next door to Dad on Staten Island and the other in Queens—and I met with the therapeutic team. Their assessment was that he was massively disabled and that any effort to get him to walk was fruitless. They said he would not be eligible any longer for physical, occupational, or speech therapy. They'd just let him regress. It was never stated explicitly, but that is what happened.

We thought we'd just have to make the best of a bad situation. The staff was truly compassionate in many ways, and they truly were fond of him. But there was a conspiracy of silence about his

Therapy has improved Carlton's speech, which can be word-by-word, haltingly slow or burst forth in sentences. Vocal exercises have also strengthened his swallowing muscles and enabled him to eat solid food.

progress. Their staff wouldn't provide any physical therapy, but we weren't permitted to have an outside person come in even though we were now paying out of his savings for his care.

I tried to get them to coach my sisters on therapy, so that they could work with him. None of it would happen. His comprehension was absolutely fine. He could speak, but there is a lot of hesitation, which is typical of people with brain damage.

At Thanksgiving we brought him home for the day. Even though he wasn't supposed to eat normal food, he ate an entire Thanksgiving dinner without any problems. I understand that bits of food probably trickled into places where they weren't suppose to go, but, by God, he had a good time.

After the Christmas home visit, he was so demoralized. I couldn't stand what was happening and said I would look into what can be done in Vermont. Early in January there was a snow day and I was home from work. The first number I called was Addison County Home Health. I got Sharon Thompson (clinical director) and she said, "Oh, we have a great track record working with families of stroke victims. We can have a home health aide come to your house, a physical therapist, an occupational therapist, and a speech therapist. We have a list of houses that do residential care where he could live with from one to three other people in similar circumstances with someone who is a trained nurse's aide."

I just couldn't believe it. And I think I was

absolutely typical in not knowing of these services.

Sharon sent me to Jeannette Brassard, who ran a care home in Lincoln. The transition from Staten Island was to be made to her home, not to mine. She had two women already living in her home who went to Project Independence six days a week. So I made an appointment with Joanne Corbett (Project Independence's executive director).

Based on my experience in New York, I was very hesitant. "Are you sure you can do this much?" Right from the start, Project people said, "Oh, he likes natural history. Well, we'll have to make sure that we plan the natural history programs for the afternoons that he will be with us." And, "Oh, he likes playing chess. Well, we'll have to find some volunteers who like chess and be sure to schedule them."

There was this immediate partnering on a very individual level. It was everything that I would have tried to do by myself and here was somebody else with networks in place.

I had heard that facilities don't like to let go of private-pay people, because they pay higher rates. Sharon Thompson gave me incredible moral support in this. She said, "Remember you're not asking them for permission, you are telling them that you are going to do this."

I called the social worker and she was horrified. Very abrupt, rather hostile. She had been so supportive, and I really wasn't expecting that.

I think she truly believed that their home was the only option.

They insisted that they had to approve a care plan from the new facility before they would release Dad. Jeannette Brassard is wonderful, but she was not setting herself up as the director of a "facility."

Choose an activity: bingo, shuffleboard, cards, sing-a-longs, group exercises, field trips, music appreciation. Carlton's favorite activity is chess. Community volunteers from 11 to social security age, college students, and an occasional Project Independence participant provide the competition.

Then I would call Sharon Thompson and she'd say, "You don't need to have an approved plan. You are the family member."

What they hold over you is they will never take your parent again if you check out without their approval. This was scary because this home was far, far better than other homes we had looked at.

Charlie, a friend who lives in Burlington, and I drove down on President's Day weekend and picked up my dad and brought him back. Charlie and my dad have always gotten along. Charlie is wonderful with elders. He's Native American and elder care is very, very much a part of the culture.

Jeannette Brassard was going out of town for the long weekend so we brought him to my house to stay overnight. The house was very familiar, because both my mother and father had spent summers with me.

At this point I didn't have much confidence in myself and wasn't sure that I could handle it. The nursing home should have been coaching and training us the whole time to do simple things like getting him in and out of a wheel chair and into a car. But they have a policy of learned helplessness for their own self-protection. "Moving a disabled person is too specialized." Every resident to them is a potential lawsuit.

Dad was only at Jeannette's Monday, Tuesday, Wednesday, and Thursday before he came back to me on Friday. But I learned so much from her. She was so matter-of-fact and shared all kinds of stories about what it's like caring for stroke victims at home.

Jeannette was herself recovering from a stroke and hadn't realized that some of her strength had not come back. With Dad she had to do a lot of the physical lifting because he was so weak from atrophying. She couldn't manage as a one-person caregiver and recruited another person to help.

Three days into his time this second caregiver had a stroke, leaving Jeannette alone. She was so far out in Lincoln that home health aides could not get there the first thing in the morning to help get him up. It just wasn't going to work.

Project Independence's 10 wheel chair–accessible vans are crucial to the Center's outreach efforts and travel to every town in Addison County as well as to Brandon, Charlotte, and North Ferrisburgh. About 80% of the center's participants are picked up by the vans; family, friends, and the limited county bus system transport the rest. Carlton Beil, who is picked up at 8:30 and returns home by 7:30, attends the adult day care center six days a week.

I thought I was going to have to find another care home. Even from having him in Jeannette's place for only four days, I knew more about what I was looking for. And I was beginning to think, "You know, he's so comfortable at home. I'm not looking forward to driving an hour three or four nights a week to sit in someone else's living room."

And I love cooking for my dad. It's one of my great pleasures. He loves to eat. I love to cook. It's a perfect match. So we brought him home here to the front parlor, which we had converted into my parents' bedroom years and years ago. I found out on Wednesday that I was going to have to bring him home and on Thursday the staff from the Lake Champlain Maritime Museum said, "We'll build you a ramp as a thank you to your dad for all the volunteer work he did last year for us." So the buildings and grounds crew came over Thursday afternoon and finished it on Friday.

Friday evening I brought him home and we had a ramp. That's the barn raising, quilting bee. That's life in New England. That's life the way it is supposed to be.

He came home the last week of February, and he's now been home six months.

Jeannette was the one who was smart enough to say, "He's still got an active mind. He's going to need to go to Project Independence every day."

I started out sending him five days a week to coincide with my work week. Monday and Thursday mornings he had appointments with his home health physical therapist, speech therapist, and occupational therapist. So he would only go afternoons on those days.

After several months, I realized that two days of the weekend sitting here, reading the newspaper,

going on errands with me, and hopefully having a friend drop in wasn't enough. He needed that community of like-minded people that he had become part of. So he started to go on Saturday as well.

Project Independence costs just under $2,000 a month for six days a week. The project van picks him up about 8:30, and he gets home around 7:30. By the time I even thought to investigate long-term care coverage he was too old to qualify. Project Independence does give him a scholarship of about $200 a month.

I haven't had him sign up for showers, but I'm thinking about it. We do sponge bathing everyday, and he is strong enough now to stand at the kitchen sink to wash his hair. His occupational therapist and physical therapist both have agreed that if I can retrofit the shower here with a shower stool, there is every reason that he could sit and take a shower here at home.

We're still using a portable commode in his bedroom until he is able to take a few more steps. Stroke victims have a natural tendency to move as economically as possible because of their muscular weakness and their fear that their legs will give out. That's counterproductive, because you don't strengthen your legs that way. Dad tends to stay in a crouch and scoots over real quick.

That's the nursing home syndrome. They teach them to do as little as possible, be as passive as possible. So, I have been coaching him to stand straight and take the time to straighten up and pull your leg back. He's moving so much more normally. It's just a treat to see. But it takes time.

I still do a tube feeding every morning, but he has regular meals at Project Independence. The home's recommendation was no food by mouth, because he might choke because of aspirating food.

Within three months of continuous speech

therapy in Vermont, his swallowing problem was upgraded from significant aspiration, which is a quite high risk, to trace aspiration, which is almost no risk. All because somebody coached him on vocal exercises three times a day.

The nursing home made an arbitrary decision to stop speech therapy. He would never taste another decent meal in his life because he was easier to manage if they just plugged a tube into his stomach. He has nothing else to look forward to but his meals and his newspaper and a visit from his kids. And they were going to take one of those three things away!

We don't talk about goals frequently. That would be a real mistake. When he is particularly successful I will say, "You know daddy, my goal for you is to walk across the room just holding onto my arm."

And he will say, "Don't be in such a hurry."

I've been waiting five months! Who's hurrying?

At some point my dad's abilities will decline further. When you are 92 years old you're headed one way. If he becomes even slightly less physically able, my strength might not be enough. If he becomes slightly less intellectually able, home care may not be an option for us. So while things are going really well, I also feel a real need to be looking into next options in terms of a residency program.

He has at times spoken to me with concern about how much work it is for me to take care of him and that he's sorry.

I tell him that I was only issued one dad. He's the one, and he's worth it.

By-the-book, can't-do-it-here care in a New York nursing home frustrated Carlton Beil and his three daughters. Addison County providers' individualized, let's-give-it-a-try approach has lifted father's and family's spirits, says Eloise Beil.

Long-Term Care Coalition Mini-Grants: May 2000

Act 160, a 1996 state law designed to shift some Medicaid funding from nursing homes to home and community-based care, required that health care organizations in each county form long-term care coalitions to improve communication and cooperation. Coalitions received "flex" funds from the state, roughly $10,000 to $20,000 a year in Addison County. This funding has mainly been used for "mini-grants" to meet the immediate needs of low-income residents.

$175 FOR ADULT DAY SERVICES: Recipient is blind, insulin-dependent diabetic who is suffering from depression and is on dialysis. Day care will provide medical monitoring, socialization and emotional support and will allow recipient to remain in her own home, avoiding nursing home placement. Application for Medicaid is in works.

$28.20 FOR A CANE: Recipient is on Medicaid waiver. Her cane was run over by a car and she cannot walk without it. Medicaid cannot cover the purchase of a new cane and recipient's income is very low. Not having a cane compromises her independence.

$360 FOR ELECTRICIAN: Recipient's 220 line into home broke, cutting off electricity to the water pump and furnace. Recipient is an insulin-dependent diabetic with heart problems, high blood pressure, and ovarian cancer and has had one leg amputated. Other funding is not available and heat and water are essential to recipient's continued ability to remain in her own home.

$500 FOR CAREGIVER: Recipient has short-term memory loss. Needs one-on-one caregiver to assist with shopping and medications. Caseworker is looking for funding for ongoing care, but without immediate care recipient would not be able to remain in her own home.

$500 FOR CAREGIVER: Recipient is on dialysis and needs someone to transport and remain with her while she is being treated. Elderly daughter has done this but recently fractured her shoulder and is unable to continue. Without service, recipient would no longer be able to remain with her daughter.

$581.85 FOR FUEL AND ELECTRICITY BILLS: Very elderly recipient has had unusual expenses that have caused her to get behind on bills. Recipient's furnace broke, her pipes froze, and then she got sick and had to go to the hospital. CVEO won't assist until recipient receives shut-off notice and recipient would go without food to avoid that. Funds will allow her to catch up and avoid putting her health at risk.

$35 FOR WHEEL CHAIR REPAIR AND $10.73 FOR SOCK AID: Recipient is on Medicaid waiver and because of multiple sclerosis requires a wheel chair. He was donated an electric wheel chair that is in need of repair. He cannot put on his own socks without a Sock Aid. Equipment and repair will allow him to maintain independence. No other funds available.

$400 FOR RAMP: End-state Alzheimer's patient unable to walk. Could not remain at home unless elderly husband had daily respite provided by day care. House had stairs that made wheel chair use impossible. Ramp cost $1,200, most of which family was able to cover. With ramp, recipient can remain in day care and continue to live at home.

Edith Miner

Home Caregiver

People Hate to Give Up Their Independence

When Edith Miner was growing up in rural Vermont, children who cared for elderly parents were the norm, not the exception. Today, extended family caregiving is more often the exception—a victim of greater job mobility, the time demands on two-income families, and parental resistance itself. Some relatively independent elderly do not qualify for home health services but still need some assistance, such as visits by private caregivers like Miner, to remain safely in their homes.

I got into personal home care through the Vergennes Area Rescue. I had been volunteering there, and a friend on rescue asked if I'd be willing to help her on a job in West Addison. I said, "Well, I'd do what I know how."

No one in my family had ever done anything like this. I grew up on a farm in Basin Harbor and milked cows for 43 years, a lot of those years with my husband. So I guess I'd relate my interest back to rescue where you are helping people.

This woman couldn't drive and couldn't live independently. We did everything: the housework, got her lunches, gave her baths, took her to town to get her hair done.

She had a niece on Staten Island and a nephew in Florida, but she didn't have any family nearby. She was 89 and very frail, but this was her home and she was determined to stay there.

The going rate for home care in 1980 was $4.50 an hour. She was very rich and could afford it.

Demand for private home care is growing, says Edith Miner, who works with two families and refers frequent callers to other caregivers.

At times she was crotchety and didn't like the way things were going in the world. But you have to expect that and learn to go around those corners. She was fairly healthy right up to the last and would sit in her chair, look out the window toward the lake, and smoke.

It worked out real well. I had the time. My husband had passed away, and I had leased out the farm. And I knew a lot about body functions from rescue work so I was comfortable with that.

I probably spent 10 hours a day with her, four or five days a week. That first job lasted eight and a half years until she died at 97.

Most jobs end with death. I might be idle for a month or so and then someone calls and says, "We need some help with mother or father. Can you help us out?" It's all word of mouth or home health will recommend me.

I've never encountered any state licensing or training requirements. They might be good for someone who is just starting out, but people know that I can do what has to be done.

I didn't interview for the job I'm on now because I have known the family for ages and ages, but I usually meet with the whole family. I let them know who I am and what I do. I want them to ask me any questions, and I want to see if the patient will be reluctant to have me around.

People hate to give up their independence, and you have to make them feel comfortable with you. I say I'll do whatever they like, whenever they like. That's a big, big item, especially with people who have been really independent.

I am comfortable with all kinds of patients. Alzheimer's patients are a challenge because they can change from day to day, week to week. They have their own little world, and you're trying to get inside it.

You have to be prepared for everything. You can't disagree, and you can't tell them they have to do something, because that is just a no-no.

I'm a little more tense with cancer patients. My husband died from cancer 26 years ago, and I have taken care of a lot of cancer patients. But I want to make sure that I keep the patient comfortable, so I'm more alert. If you have been with a patient long enough you can almost feel what is going on in their minds and can help them relax.

You have to be as compassionate and honest as you can. If they're down, you try and cheer them up.

To me honesty means not getting into things you shouldn't be in. Patients and families have things they don't want you poking into, and you can get very close to patients.

Patients give friendliness back to you. I can't explain it. It just makes you feel good when you have helped somebody through hard times.

A lot of the people I have worked for have lived alone, but I like to have family around and sometimes the husband or wife or children are in the house and provide some of the care. This lady who I'm with now had lived alone until I started spending nights with her 10 months ago.

She's 79, and I'm 74. We have known each other for years. She is able to get out and do her own shopping and does volunteer work at the hospital every Tuesday morning. She has lots of friends and they bring her lunch or go out to lunch together. She goes to church and sometimes to coffee hour after church.

She has two daughters who live nearby who call her every day. Her son in New Hampshire calls her two or three times a week. She has another son in Connecticut and he calls her a couple times of week so she gets a lot of phone calls from family. She has a Lifeline that she can use during the day if anything happens.

I generally go from 7:30 to 5:30 seven days a week. She has usually had dinner. We sit in the evening and I get her a glass of water or let the dog out. We watch TV until around 10, and she goes to bed.

She is frail and doesn't eat well unless you keep at her. If she gets up at night and needs me she will call. The family just thinks it is better to have someone there.

She was pretty good until this last spell when she couldn't breathe and had to go to the hospital. I wonder how she will be when she comes back. Her lungs are very bad, and she catches pneumonia every time she gets a cold.

On home care jobs, you're like family. I keep a record of everything that I do. If I see a drastic change, I like to have the family come in and observe what is happening. Then we have a conference, and the children will say, "Mother or Dad, don't you think you should be doing this?"

I have been with so many sick people that it is not hard to determine when they need to see the doctor or be in the hospital. The family knows that I have done this for so long, and I know a lot about the body from rescue.

If she gets bad enough she may have to go to a nursing home, but I'd still visit her to let her know that I hadn't deserted her.

I never dreamed when I started 22 years ago that I'd be doing home care now. But I didn't know how big the demand was. I know 12 to 15 women in the area who do private care, and I'm told there are more than 50 private caregivers in the county. Most or us are in our 50s and 60s with grown children so we can leave home. I'm probably the oldest home caregiver in the county.

Nobody realizes what you're giving up when you do home care. In the last 10 months, I have probably slept in my own bed half a dozen times. But I prefer to work nights, and at my age I don't go out at night anyway.

And I don't think anybody realizes how many people need some help. They may not have big medical problems and qualify for home health nurses and aides. They may just need someone to talk to and reason with. They may need some help walking or getting meals. A lot of people will just give up and don't keep themselves clean.

Medicaid will pay for long-term nursing care and some home care, but a lot of people don't want to go on Medicaid. They think it is degrading, but when it's a necessity they do go on. Medicare won't pay for home care at all.

Private home care can be $100 a night and not many people can afford that. I usually charge $10 an hour. If that is way out of reach, I will sometimes work for a little less. Most girls charge $12 to $15 an hour and some charge more for nights.

You can tell in an interview what the situation is in a home. It's more satisfying to know that you're not draining them of everything they have. Many people are very poor, and they appreciate somebody coming in and helping.

None of the people I have cared for have had long-term care insurance, and all long-term care is very expensive. I have two friends in assisted living apartments now, they're paying $2,800 a month. Nursing homes are a lot more than that.

I have a long-term care insurance policy that will pay $80 a day for home care and for nursing home coverage. It covers some medications and hospital care. After I sold the farm I got some money, but it wouldn't take long to eat that up.

I pay a little over $1,300 a year. I'm going to hang onto it if I possibly can. My son and daughter-in-law live with me, and they say they won't send me to a nursing home. So I might end up being a crotchety old biddy at home.

It's too bad that more of the insurances don't pay toward home care. None of us know where we are going to end up and if our money will hold out.

Amy Curtis
Director of Social Services,
Helen Porter Healthcare and
Rehabilitation Center

It's Impossible to Predict What Life Will Send Our Way

Nursing homes aren't what they used to be. No one has seen that change more closely than social worker Amy Curtis, who started at Helen Porter Nursing Home in 1993 just as the home had expanded from 50 to 118 beds. A decade ago, Helen Porter was primarily a long-term care facility. Today, with more community services and Medicaid funding that enables people to remain in their homes, Porter provides a variety of services—short-term rehabilitation and respite care, hospice services, specialized dementia and Alzheimer's care—as well. What hasn't changed is a family's anxiety and guilt over placing a member in a nursing home.

People say, "Never put me in a nursing home." But they are thinking of nursing homes 30 years ago. Their perception is that residents are drugged or tied up or not tended to on a regular basis. They may think that residents just sit there and do nothing. That is not the case.

This view has changed a lot in my nine years at Helen Porter. We do a lot of short-term rehab now. People don't sit there and stagnate. There are activities, and many get back home or to a more independent setting.

We have changed our name to Helen Porter Healthcare and Rehabilitation Center. People still

Amy Curtis answers families' questions, big and small, about when it is time for a nursing home and how to ease the transition from individualized home care to group care.

refer to us as the nursing home, but it is helpful for people to see rehabilitation on the sign.

We started respite care about a year and a half ago. That has helped because people who are potential long-term residents have stayed from several days to several weeks and understand the kind of care that we provide. That makes the transition easier if the time comes when they can't stay at home.

And we have started a unit for dementia patients.

Whatever the circumstances, there is almost always guilt around the decision to place someone in a nursing home. Many times people have promised their family member that they would never put them in a nursing home. But circumstances change.

Some people aren't able to handle answering the same question 500 times a day from someone with dementia. Or the person may wander around all night when the family is trying to sleep. Or mom has a serious stroke, ends up with a feeding tube, is totally paralyzed on one side, and needs care around the clock.

It's impossible to predict what life will send our way.

When I started, there weren't that many options, which put us in a difficult situation as social workers. People were either too healthy for home health, which requires a need for skilled nursing or therapy, or home health couldn't provide enough coverage for the primary caregiver to work full-time or part-time.

We referred many people to Project Independence's adult day care center in Middlebury if they weren't appropriate for here. But their program only ran from 9 to 2. They have expanded their hours with a second shift and Saturdays and that has helped keep people home longer.

The biggest change in the last five years has been the Medicaid waiver program of Act 160 (a 1996 state law that diverts money from nursing homes to support home and community-based,

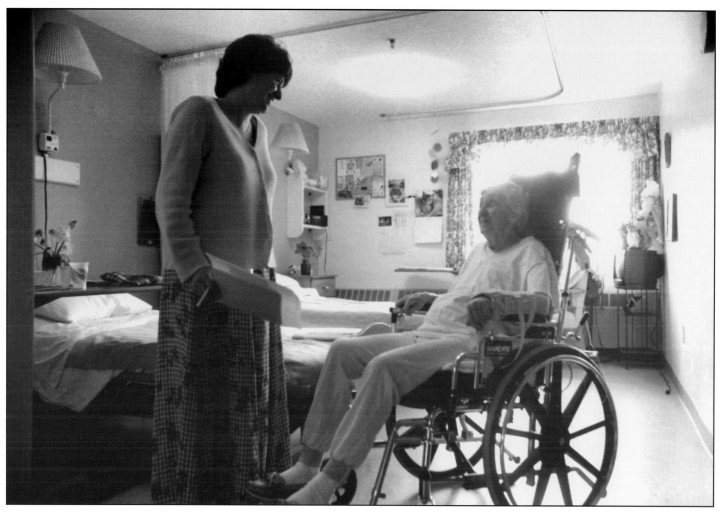

Helping residents adjust to nursing home life—sharing a room, missing familiar surroundings, adapting to a new routine—is one of Curtis's daily challenges.

long-term care services). This program pays for services to meet the needs of level 2 or intermediate-level care people who need moderate assistance with daily living activities in order to remain at home. All Addison County's 2002 waiver slots—95 home-based waiver slots and 15 enhanced residential care slots—are full much of the time. (On October 1, 2005, the waiver system will be replaced by a demonstration program that entitles people who physically and financially qualify to receive home and community-based services.)

People are pretty tuned into what is in the community today. Case managers at the Agency on Aging, Home Health, Elderly Services, and places like that are doing a pretty good job of keeping people informed of their options. By the time people come here this is usually the right decision.

We have always tried to discourage people from prematurely placing a parent or spouse or family member in a nursing home. We provide level 1 and 2 care here. A level 1 resident requires skilled nursing and/or therapy. They may have a feeding tube, a trach, need daily injections, dressing changes, or physical, occupational, or speech therapy.

A level 2 resident may or may not be able to walk but requires 24-hour care. Level 2 residents need moderate to maximum assistance in activities of daily living and/or decision making. They might have lung problems and can't bathe and dress without extensive assistance. They might not be able to follow directions, because of memory or physical impairment.

Someone who is able to bathe and dress fairly independently doesn't meet level 1 and 2 criteria for admission.

I encourage everyone to come in before they decide if nursing home placement is right. It's a huge change coming from a home, and I want

Vermont's over-75 population is projected to double in the next 25 years. How many beds will Helen Porter, the county's only nursing home, need? No one knows precisely. Home and community services have expanded dramatically, but Helen Porter, which has recently downsized from 118 to 105 beds, will be needed to serve those whose needs can't be met at home.

people to be fully informed.

It can be very disturbing if you see a resident on the floor on a mattress or sleeping on the couch in the lobby. If you have any questions, ask me. The person may have dementia and if they are not harming themselves or are not disruptive we let them do what is most comfortable.

You may see someone eating breakfast at 11 a.m. If people want to sleep in, that's fine. If they don't want their lunch, we will give them a snack after lunch. You have to be flexible.

I want people to come in at 7 at night and

know that what you see is what you get. When people are disappointed, I try and work through their concerns. Sometimes the family needs to adjust. It's a huge adjustment when a spouse or family member has been providing immediate one-on-one care, and now care is provided by aides who care for many people during their shift.

What is most difficult for a new resident is sharing a room with someone that they don't know at all. Some adjust right from the start, and there are never problems. Some people attend activities the first day and seem very happy. Two

About 90% of Helen Porter's residents are admitted following hospitalization, typically at Porter Hospital, a 100-yard wheel chair ride. Medicare will pay for up to 100 days of rehabilitation in a nursing home following a hospital stay of at least three days.

weeks later it hits them that they are going to be here long term and they're upset.

Some people never adjust. We have a lady with dementia who has been here for over three years who looks for a ride home every afternoon.

But we know her very well and talk to her about the visits of people who mean a lot to her.

We tell families to bring up any issue no matter how small. And we get all kinds of calls: mother is missing a blue scarf; mother had tomatoes with

her supper last night and doesn't like them; father needs new batteries for his hearing aid. People trust us to handle tiny little concerns.

We also always address larger questions, like end-of-life decisions. We ask during admission if the resident has a living will and has given a family member or someone else power of attorney concerning health care and financial questions. We find out family and resident wishes around resuscitation. Most people don't want resuscitation unless they are younger or if they are in great shape and are in here for rehab.

Most residents have had so many losses that they are ready to die when the time comes: "Let me go." Particularly if people are very religious or they have experienced someone else going through a long ordeal at the end of life.

We respect whatever a family or resident wants. We had a woman who was so brittle that chest compression would probably fracture every rib, but she wanted to be full code if she stopped breathing. She is fully alert and oriented, and she knew what that meant.

It wouldn't be pleasant for the nurse, but we have to respect the resident's wish.

~

Like most non-profit nursing homes, most of our residents, about two-thirds, are on Medicaid. Medicaid pays about 85% of the daily room rates. To be Medicaid eligible, single people must have resources, like bank accounts, CD's, stocks, below $2,000. Single residents can keep their house up to six months if they think they will be returning home within that time. This requires a doctor's signature.

Single long-term care residents will eventually have to sell their home unless someone else's name is on it or it has been transferred three or more years before they have applied for Medicaid.

A married couple can transfer about $84,000 ($95,000 in 2005) to the spouse who is in the community and be eligible for Medicaid as long as the resident doesn't have more than $2,000 in his or her name.

Today (2002), a shared room is $198 in the long-term care section ($215 in 2005). We have six private rooms at $210 per day ($225 in 2005). A room in the subacute unit, which is for people in the rehab program or who require skilled care, is $235 a day ($275 in 2005).

People assume that Medicare will take care of long-term care. They don't understand that Medicare only pays for skilled follow-up care at a nursing facility following a three-day hospitalization. Medicare will then pay for up to 100 days of care.

We have to validate each week that recipients continue to need skilled nursing care or services like daily, physical, occupational or speech therapy. We have to project how long residents will be covered and tell the resident or responsible party.

At 5, 14, 30, 60, and 90 days we assess the level of our services. We may get reimbursed at five different rates during a resident's stay. Depending on services, Medicare coverage could be $150 to $400 a day. After Medicare, recipients have to qualify for Medicaid or pay privately or through private insurance.

Not many people have long-term care insurance. We have one person who is coming who has a policy that covers $85 a day. We get one or two people every six months at the most. I am getting many calls now from people 50 to 60, who are purchasing long-term care insurance, asking what we charge a day.

About 12 to 14 residents are private pay.

I can't imagine that the state would reduce our Medicaid reimbursements further, but you never know. Some funding has already been taken away by Act 160. People come here when they require more assistance than what they are able to get in the community, and we are getting paid less

to take care of them.

The state has increased our daily Medicaid reimbursement because we were losing thousands of dollars, but that took a lot of work on the board's and Neil's part (Neil Gruber, home administrator).

You need a soft spot for older people or people with chronic health issues to work here. It breaks my heart when I see an old person struggling to take care of themselves in the community. I wonder if anyone is taking care of them.

For me that's depressing. Coming here isn't. I can be totally exhausted or stressed, but I am immediately happy when I see the residents. It's hard to explain. Ever since I was little my mom said I was drawn to older people. I feel that it is a blessing to get to know these people so intimately.

Everybody has something that they love. This is something that I love.

My greatest frustration is not having the time to talk with residents more. I started in 1993 about a month after the new Helen Porter opened. We went from 50 beds in the old nursing home to 118 beds, and there was a huge file of people waiting to come in.

Coming on board when we had about 50 people and getting to know every person until we reached 118 was wonderful. Helen Porter was a long-term care facility then and nearly everyone came in for the rest of their lives.

The pace began to pick up several years after I started. Like other nursing homes, we started doing more rehab and got our own in-house physical therapist. But even when we had a lot of admissions, we knew residents were going to be here for a while and got to know families and res-

Amy Curtis's greatest frustration is the lack of time to get to know residents as the pace of admissions has quickened and the length of most stays has shortened.

idents very well.

Today, it's a different pace. We may have two or three admissions and discharges in a day. That used to be a month's activity. We may have as many admissions and discharges in a month, 15 to 20, as we used to have in a year.

Our director of nursing has been on a campaign that if you have an extra five minutes, sit down and talk with people. It doesn't take a lot of time to make a difference. Maybe it is because the world has changed so much and everybody is always in a hurry. It's a nice change when some-body sits down and talks with you.

Staff sometimes feel they need permission to do that because there are so many things to do. You almost feel guilty if you sit down and talk with someone rather than fill out all the forms that document what you are doing.

Sometimes with staff I have to say, "Write it down. If I have to do one more thing now, I'll burst." Everyone is in the same boat, though.

But I do a pretty good job of leaving things here. When you start you are so excited and want to help everybody. It's hard to leave that here, go home, and have a normal life. But I have learned that you have to let go if you are going to stay in this job.

A couple of years ago I worried about the new Medicare payment system and all we had to learn. Now I believe that we have been through so many changes that we can deal with whatever comes our way. I don't get anxious anymore, because health care is going to change for the rest of my life.

Rev. Diana F. Scholl

Chaplain, Porter Hospital

I'm Not an Angel of Death

Porter is one of the few small community hospitals in the state to have a full-time chaplain. Since 1998, Diana Scholl has been the chaplain as well as the staff person for the hospital's ethics committee and a member of a community grief and bereavement-counseling group.

Hospitals and doctors get very focused on the medical side and haven't always been on the cutting edge of body-mind medicine or body-mind-spirit medicine. Middlebury has an active alternative medicine community, but Western medicine is still heavily oriented toward drugs and technology as the answer. This can leave little room for the whole spiritual side of healing.

Doctors mainly see me functioning around end-of-life issues. I have resisted that. I'm not an angel of death. A common understanding is that if you open your eyes and the chaplain is there, you say, "Oh, God! Am I dying?" So a lot of what I do is educating people that my role is broad: to be there at the birth of a child when you're happy and want to thank God for His blessings and to be there at difficult times.

I'm here as a support person to bless and bring that spiritual energy and force of goodness and love into your experience, whatever it is. If your spirit is peaceful and calm, whether it comes from stress reduction, prayer, meditation, family support, our caring staff, or whatever, you will be able to accept better the healing from your medicine.

I try to see myself as clear a slate as possible

Rev. Diana Scholl encounters people at their most vulnerable—sick, tired, anxious, and in the hospital. She tries to be a thoughtful and calming listener for all a patient's concerns.

and to be as much a presence of God as I can be. I believe that whatever way you come to God—Buddhist, Jewish, Hindu, charismatic Christian—is OK and fine. That is how God is speaking to you and how God will work whatever healing is possible.

In the Christian tradition we have an understanding that each person is the peace of Christ. So I pray that not only will I bring the peace of that divine energy to this person, but that I will see the Christ in him or her.

I say that prayer every time I go into a room. I hope it puts me in the right frame of mind and that I won't see the patient as the "grizzled old fellow who is going to throw you out of the room," as I was told about somebody last week.

Well, guess what. We had a wonderful conversation.

I always check with the nursing staff or social worker to find out if there is anyone who could use my visit or another chaplain's visit, someone who could use a listening ear, some good kind words, some cheer. I listen for patient and family problems and watch for cases that are difficult for nurses.

Some patients are combative or very demanding. They are constantly ringing that bell. That translates to me, "Maybe that is somewhere that I can spend some time and get them coffee or water or a blanket and take some pressure off the staff." Maybe it means that I spend 10 to 15 minutes sitting with a person.

I also watch for the hardest cases. If someone has just been given a cancer diagnosis, I always try to see that person. I also try and see people with heart disease or chest pain and younger people who are in the hospital.

Many times a person has their best face on for the doctor or nurse, but the person who comes in to clean the floor sees the tears. Sometimes I think

Western medicine is still heavily oriented toward drugs and technology. Everyone needs an oasis of sacred space for the spiritual side of healing in the midst of this technology, Scholl believes.

nurses feel that younger people don't need as much attention, because they are healthier. I look at it that younger people are not used to a hospital, probably don't like it, and need attention. If they're very young, I try and see the parents.

I also watch for those who don't have a lot of support or family or friends and connect these people to their local church and pastor, because we look to their church to provide some support

when they go home. If someone has really good church support, family, and friends, I might just say, "Hi," and put my time elsewhere.

Most people want to talk about their illness. Sometimes the illness has been sudden, and they need a way to process and understand it. Chaplains are the one people who have no needles or horrible medicines. We are there to bring you a sense that someone cares about you as a person. It matters to everyone, but staff don't always have the time to show it.

I had someone the other day who asked, "What are you going to do to me?" I said, "Nothing. I am the chaplain. I'm here to see how you are and make you smile."

And she said, "Oh, good."

Patients are in bed, almost unclothed and in the most vulnerable position they will ever be, and this stranger is asking what's going on in your life. The only way any of us will share our feelings is if we feel comfortable with that person. And I have a very short time period to make them feel comfortable with me—the average hospital stay is four days. Out of those four days I might only see the person a couple of times at most unless they are high on my list.

Sometimes I hear a lot of fear and anxiety—what is going to happen to me or to people that I love.

Most people in their 50s have rarely been in the hospital, maybe to have a baby but probably not much other than that. Maybe they broke something, but that is usually in and out. The first signs of vulnerability of your body can be very frightening. It doesn't matter how old you are.

Some people with chronic illnesses are in all

the time. They are exhausted and disappointed and tired of being sick. So you listen to their exhaustion and try to help them find some energy and cheerfulness.

Sometimes people say they are fine and that there is nothing that I can do. Those are the hard ones, because you are not fine if you're in the hospital. They often have the most need, but they are not willing to look at what they need.

I have a lady on the floor now and all she wanted to ask was, "Why did God do this to me?" That is really a rhetorical question, and she knows that I don't have an answer. So I talked about how most of us have had something happen in our lives that we know is not logical.

This morning I felt that I should not have engaged in the discussion, because there is no answer to the "why" question. But I have to separate my own views and attempt to respond to her concern. For me, "why" doesn't lead to anything positive. It usually just leads to anger or loss of energy.

The Bible says the rain falls on the just and unjust and the sun shines whether you are good or bad. It is just the way it is. But people have different theologies. If there is a loving God why does He do this to me? So there is something wrong with God. Or that means that God is a pretty nasty character or doesn't care two hoots about me. So it reveals more about the theology of the person.

I have a very different theology. To me, God is with you through your life regardless of what happens. It's frustrating, because I don't have the time for Bible studies and patients are sick and have medicine running through their brains.

She was being honest in expressing her wonder, her doubt, and her search. I talked with her, but in the end I felt that I talked too much. I should have kept quiet, because it is a common question that we all ask. I ask it too, even though I don't believe that God works that way.

Chaplains have probably one of the highest levels of stress among medical professionals. Doctors and nurses are compassionate people. They have to put that needle in your arm, and you're going to hate it but they have to do it. They have that level of separation.

A chaplain has to maintain professional boundaries, but I have to let your concerns and needs and fears and anxieties and deepest desires be present and felt. That is the only way that they are going to get resolved.

When I pray with you my goal is to articulate your concerns and give them sacred space and holiness and to help you feel that God's love is present and that it is going to be OK. In the end that is what we all need.

This can be exhausting when you're working with families who are trying to make some sense of what is going on and are trying to make life-and-death decisions.

I do a pretty good job of leaving work at work. That requires that I keep my own spiritual discipline up, because I believe that God is in charge. It's not me.

I pray for all the staff, the patients, and their families when I come to work and to do the best that they can when I leave.

In the future I hope that we will have a place where people can go and find some spiritual refreshment, some quiet and calm. Everyone needs to have a little oasis of sacred space in the middle of technology. So I hope we succeed in our capital building campaign. There is a chapel or meditation room in the plans. I bring it up often enough; the architect says it is still in the plans.

Catherine Studley

Executive Director,
Hospice Volunteer Services

Dying Is the Most Profound Process

Hospice Volunteer Services was established in 1983, a grassroots effort of area clergy, residents, and the home health agency to help the terminally ill die at home. Much like hospice nationally, the local hospice has grown dramatically—from 30 volunteers who attended 11 patients that first year, 1983 to 1984, to 84 volunteers who served 50-plus patients in 2003. Studley directed the non-profit program from 1992 to 2002.

When hospice originated in the mid-1970s, there was sometimes an adversarial relationship with doctors. Hospice sometimes sounded like it was placing blame and pointing fingers. This was unfortunate.

A lot of that venom has been taken out of the relationship. In the years I have been involved in hospice I have seen it dissolve more. Hospice has really become the specialist in end-of-life care. Physicians don't see it as an intrusion and as a taking over and are now able to view it as a partnership. They maintain control of their patients, but much of their work is done through the home health nurse.

Physicians still struggle with when to let patients go, when to advise patients that maybe they have gone as far as they should with treatment. I don't think it's malicious or self-serving in the sense that my ego is involved. Sometimes it's just really hard for them to stop trying.

Hospice tailors its services to the needs of the dying and their families. A full team could involve a hospice nurse, social worker, home health aide, a homemaker, clergy, and hospice volunteers providing 24-hour care. Patients, with rare exceptions, can die at home with these services, says Studley.

And a lot of times patients push doctors. "I'm 38. You have to find something else out there."

Physicians are also somewhat tentative about making referrals to hospice for terminal patients who do not have cancer, such as cardiac and Alzheimer's patients. In some cases, physicians are uneasy about certifying that a patient has six

months or less to live. There are very formal criteria that can be used to evaluate a patient with those diseases. I wouldn't say it is easy, but it's possible. And it can be done as a partnership between the physician and hospice nurse where they evaluate the patient together.

People who have an array of problems and end up seeing five physicians often feel that nobody is looking at the total person. So we continue to have a problem with late referrals.

We have a very diverse group of hospice volunteers, people from 16 to their 80s. Our first 16-year-old completed training this fall. Her grandmother died in her care with her mom. Some time we will have a teenager whose parent is dying. I would exercise some caution with a person her age but that would be a perfect placement for her.

We have about 65 volunteers (2002). Six to 10 are men. We have working people, retired people, people who have home businesses and homemakers.

Their motivations really run the gamut. For some people, death and dying are very foreign, and they have made it into middle age with little personal experience. But death interests them. It's a curiosity. It's something they don't want to be afraid of so they want to get a little closer to that experience.

For other people, hospice has worked in their family or they have seen it work in somebody else's family. This motivates them to become a volunteer.

The training program is about 24 hours spread over nine weeks. The Hospice and Palliative Care Council of Vermont tries to ensure that our training programs meet a minimum standard. We must also meet Medicare eligibility requirements. We contract with Addison County Home

Health to provide nursing care, which Medicare pays for.

Occasionally I won't certify someone to work with patients because I feel they are not emotionally stable or I am not comfortable with their motivation or their ability to be non-judgmental. And I have had volunteers who are not physically able to provide personal care, but they have many opportunities for bedside vigil in the last stages of life where personal care needs are minimal.

Volunteers who go on feel a little apprehensive until they get some experience. Then they just recognize what everybody else recognizes. You do the best you can.

When a volunteer is on an active case, we ask for at least two hours a week with a maximum of 10 hours a week. As patients require more care, volunteers might spend the night, but we try not to let people get overwhelmed.

We try and help volunteers relax and understand that there is a team of people behind and with them. People will challenge them with questions and concerns that they can't answer, but they don't have to. The most important thing is to respond honestly and ask for help from the home health nurse or social worker or me.

Hospice sometimes has a reputation for being overly verbal and having a prescription for dying where you have to share your every feeling. I remind people that communication and connecting with people can often happen without a lot of talking.

Dying is the most volatile and profound process that people can go through. From day to day you will not find the same person, so I tell volunteers to always be open. There may be profound or deep reflections, but you can't walk in with that expectation. That can happen by just doing things together.

People who stay are able to tolerate the fact that some people will only be acquaintances. With other people they will make a profound connection.

~

Our case load in Addison County runs about 50-plus patients a year; most people are over 60. The majority of the people have terminal cancer, but there are other diagnoses.

Most referrals come to us from the home health agency after the agency's hospice nurse and a social worker have visited a patient and family. We also have referrals from Porter Hospital, usually from the social worker. Home Health also now has a hospice contract with the Helen Porter nursing home where all components of hospice care are provided there. And a patient or family will occasionally directly request our help.

I'm comfortable that we're serving the people who need us, because we collaborate closely with Home Health. They provide the outreach and a safety net so we know that we're not overlooking people.

To be eligible for hospice you have to meet medical criteria. You must be terminally ill with a life expectancy of six months or less and must not be undergoing a potentially curative treatment for the disease. But because we are a free service and independent organization we have always had some flexibility. (Hospice's $112,000 budget in 2005 came from bequests, donations, fund-raising, investment income, United Way and town support, and an arts auction.)

A nurse may come to me and say, "I've a patient who is very, very sick with a recurrence of cancer. She has two little babies and can barely get them bathed and in bed." This person is technically not hospice, but we could provide volunteers to help her get her children to bed.

Home Health gives me a sketch of what has gone on: who this patient is; logistical information; something about the disease, when they were diagnosed and subsequent treatment; something about the family structure, how tight or how loose a support network they will be providing; and the general plan and goals for this family.

Home Health may have only visited once or there may be an in-depth report if they have been following the patient. I then visit the home, meet the family, and talk with them about what hospice volunteers might be able to do.

Families typically have several concerns and questions. Families are not always comfortable having strangers in their home for the purpose of caregiving. This is a difficult exchange that can take time, so these relationships often start on a more social level.

However, we rarely have a personality conflict between a volunteer and a family. One skill we try and cultivate in volunteers is an ability to adapt and respond appropriately to different families.

There are families who express their needs and receive help with great graciousness. The hospice relationship can also be very problematic and uncomfortable for some families. In some cases we make an introduction and let the relationship develop on its own.

Some hospice directors coordinate volunteers from their office and don't visit homes. By visiting, I feel that I am able to see what a volunteer and patient might have in common that would give them some starting ground for their relationship.

Another concern is that the hospice team, in its full form, can be quite overwhelming. If you become significantly ill you're talking about the

A panel discussion at Hospice Services' 2003 annual meeting examined ethical issues in end-of-life care and the proposed Vermont Death with Dignity Act. More than 90 community members filled the basement meeting room of the Congregational Church for a respectful airing of divergent opinions on how family, friends, doctor, and health care providers can best meet the emotional, spiritual, and physical needs of the dying.

hospice nurse, social worker, home health aide, potentially a homemaker, clergy, perhaps myself, and then the volunteers.

The bottom line is that people are free to choose just the things that are going to be helpful. They can decline a visit from a social worker or clergy or myself and choose only to see the nurse. But potentially all those things are available.

We try and be sensitive to that and do as much as we can for a family with as few volunteers as possible without taxing the volunteers beyond their ability. If we have a case that is quite short, maybe a month, with a husband or wife who wants to continue to work, we might have five or six volunteers. We would cover big blocks with home health aides and homemakers and volunteers so the person could continue to work. That would require a lot of volunteers.

Families often underestimate their own abilities and grow into them as they feel the hospice program's safety net is truly there for them. Families often do much better than they predict, but part of the initial conversation about goals is developing a backup plan

Not everyone chooses to stay at home. There is a respite house in Williston, which serves our community. And we have contracts with Porter Hospital for short-term intensive pain control and with Helen Porter nursing home for short-term relief for caregivers.

There is also a provision for 24-hour home care when a patient is very close to the end and the family is about to "crash." We can provide 24-hour care so people do not have to go into the hospital in the last 12 or 24 hours of their lives. We can provide extreme vigilance on pain control during this time. This around-the-clock care could last for 72 hours.

It's very rare that we would lose control at the end, and a patient would end up in the hospital. We have the resources when people want to die at home.

I recently had a referral for a man who was 57. When I met him, he said, "Well, I must be a lot sicker than I think I am. Because all of you are coming around and trying to put all this stuff in place."

Part of my response was the time to meet volunteers for the first time is not when you're really sick and near death. At that point you want people around you that you are familiar with and that you trust. You want people who have had an opportunity to get to know you when you were more whole, more yourself.

That's the point of introducing people earlier rather than later even though they might only visit once every couple weeks. They have an opportunity to know you in a different way that means they will be really, truly valuable to you when you need them.

A sense of trust develops quickly because we have a really skilled team, but a longer time would permit an even greater rapport and trust to develop. I'd guess we could profitably double the time with patients.

The gentleman understood that, and I told him that he didn't have to feel compelled to be any sicker than he actually was.

What seems very clear is that in the future we will be working with people for much longer periods of time. Hospice has been this service at the end of a person's life. That mission or restriction, I think, will be broadened, and we will be adding palliative care earlier than six months' certification.

This palliative care for people with serious life-threatening illnesses will allow us to work formally as a team with a much larger array of patients. We have already been doing some of that, but I think it's going to expand.

People who are very sick are still having treatment. These patients want traditional hospice services, such as pain control and symptom management, that make hospice intervention unique. So every hospice program will have or is developing a bridge program for patients who technically don't qualify for hospice.

Another concern is the aging population. We will see more and more people signing on to hospice. I wonder what we will do when we have two partners who are aged and dependent and their extended family is not close. Are we going to need additional personnel to help people to stay at home?

Right now you can usually count on one spouse to do some of the caregiving for the other, but that may not always be the case.

Most people prefer to die at home, but only slightly more than 20% of Vermonters do. About a quarter of Vermonters die in nursing homes; 40-plus percent die in hospitals. Edie Corse, like many hospice volunteers, became a volunteer after hospice services enabled her husband to die at their Starksboro home.

Edie Corse
Hospice Volunteer

The Last Summer
We Caught 148 Trout

Edie Corse became a volunteer, like many volunteers, after hospice services enabled her husband to die at home.

We got the word the day after our 39th anniversary that it was lung cancer. Tye was 61, and that's not very old.

When he was first diagnosed, we were just devastated. It can't be. We had all these plans for trips when he retired from the fertilizer company. Bus companies have lots of several-day tours that aren't too expensive. We didn't have any special places in mind, but we'd probably shy away from cities because we're not city people.

We found out in September of 1995 from Dr. Unger about the cancer. We went through radiation and chemo. At one point, things looked really good. The tumor had shrunk and his lungs were clear.

In December of 1996, Tye went for his bimonthly X-ray. When Dr. Unger came out you could just tell that something had changed. In a period of two months, one lung had completely gone. There was no air in it at all. There was a tumor at the top of heart, and they couldn't operate.

He said, "I'm sorry that I have to tell you that it is very terminal."

I said, "What time frame are you talking about?"

And he said, "Maybe two months."

Then Dr. Unger said, "I'm going to put you in touch with Maura, a hospice nurse."

And I said, "Is that Maura McClure?"

And he said, "Yes, it is. Do you know her?"

So I told him. My husband and I worked at a ski area (Mad River Glen) on the weekends, and I had told a co-worker about my husband when he was first diagnosed. He broke down and said, "When the going gets rough, and it will, I want you to call Maura, my wife, she will help you."

So Maura came and we met Catherine (Catherine Studley, executive director of hospice). Catherine is like the Rock of Gibraltar.

My husband was a private person; I'm more outgoing. I told Catherine before she came up to the house, "My husband might not be very receptive to this."

But we had a connection with Maura and with nearly everyone who came. Catherine was the only one who we didn't.

She said, "We'll take care of it." So she came and was so bubbly and pretty. And I said, "Oh, my gosh. He is going to fall in love with her."

She met Tye and saw the fish on the wall first thing and asked him, "Oh, do you go fishing? And you probably hunt, too?"

He said, "Yes."

And she said, "Oh, my husband hunts, too. We will have to get some pointers."

It opened the door.

Going to the nursing home was not even a question. And the hospital was out of the question. Tye was deathly afraid of going to the hospital.

I told him that he would go to the hospital over my dead body. I will take care of you myself. Then I know you are getting cared for.

I had heard so much about hospice and the care that people had from them. My problem was that I had too much pride, and I wanted to keep doing it myself.

Catherine told me that it might come to the point where I would need somebody. Maura did, too. She said don't be afraid to call.

The paperwork was like three sheets. They took care of it all. They asked questions, and I answered them.

Tye wasn't bedridden until three days before he died. For the last year and a half, we did a lot of fishing to keep his mind off things. We'd get up at 4 in the morning and drive up to Morrisville and fish the Lamoille. Getting up early was no problem for Tye. He grew up on a farm in Fletcher and worked on a farm in Charlotte for many years.

That last summer we caught 148 trout. We kept a few for ourselves, but we gave most of them away.

Up to the very end, he was able to be out here in the living room. We didn't go for rides for maybe a month before he died. He couldn't stand the pain from the jarring.

According to my diary, hospice came 23 times. It was mainly Maura. She said, "Never hesitate to call," and would come every day if I needed her. No set time. She was only 10 minutes up the mountain road and would stop on her way home.

Catherine would also stop to check in.

I have one son, who lives a mile away, and he would help when I needed to do errands. It bothered him at the end when he had trouble understanding his father, but I told him to try and just understand one word and then another and pretty soon he could understand what his father was saying.

I have another son in St. Albans, and a third son and daughter in Tunbridge and a second daughter in New Hampshire. All the kids were very attentive and were constantly calling. At the end, some were calling daily.

Tye was totally at ease with Maura, because he knew her husband. At that point he was resigned to the fact that this was going to be the end. What was the sense of denying it?

Hospice has a team if you need it, but I only had a volunteer come once.

I had been staying up all night with Tye, and it got to the point where I was so exhausted that I was afraid I wouldn't be able to take care of him when he needed me.

I called Catherine and she had a volunteer up here that night. That gave me a chance to get a night's sleep. Up until then I had my neighbors come in if I wanted to go grocery shopping and didn't want to leave him alone.

And the hospice minister, Gary Lewis, came one time. My husband wasn't a churchgoer, but I said, "Honey, I think we should have the minister come."

When Gary came, I said, "I have to tell you something that I did."

He said, "What's that?"

I said, "I got to thinking last night that I don't think my husband was ever baptized and so I did it. But maybe you want to do it over again."

By then he was real near the end. I just wet my hand and I laid it on his head and I baptized him. I said his name and I said, "I baptize thee in the name of the Father, Son, and the Holy Ghost."

"Well, I'm not going to," he said.

I said, "Oh? I'm not a minister."

"That doesn't matter," he said. "You were acting as God's agent. It would be defeating the purpose if I were to do it over again."

Tye was afraid of going. But I told him when the time comes you don't have to be afraid. God will give you an inner peace and you won't be afraid.

He died February 23, 1997. It's been more than five years now, and if I have any questions I just call Catherine.

Little crazy things will come up. I will feel that I'm not doing right emotionally. I'm more comfortable talking to her than my son. Probably some of it is that she is a woman.

Like I'm anxious about going on this trip to Michigan. She said, "Go! Have a good time. You're due."

She just gives me courage. If I just want to call it quits, she says, "You can't quit." She makes me feel good about myself and capable that I can carry on.

I have no regrets about what I did. I took care of Tye to the best of my ability and hospice helped me as much as I needed. In hindsight, I probably would have had them come in a little quicker so I wouldn't have been so tired.

My husband would have really liked to get to know these people. Once he did he was on his last legs and didn't have time to have fun with them. He could have relaxed a little more had we started a month earlier, and he could have given Catherine's husband some hunting tips.

I decided to become a hospice volunteer when my husband was sick. I had always wanted to be a nurse, and I ended up being a nurse but not quite the way that I thought.

That would be one way that I could give back to hospice. I talked to Catherine because I wondered if I could do it.

I've been a caregiver for a neighbor with Parkinson's for the past four years. I go over and help her with household chores, hang the wash and sometimes I cook meals and take them to her. Sometimes I'm just there for moral support and for her to have someone to talk to.

I don't want to accept anything because I know she is on social security. I tell her that I have to go to Middlebury anyway and that this isn't a special trip just for her, but she is very independent and insists on paying me $5 or $10.

I told Catherine that I thought I was too tender hearted to be a volunteer. I didn't know if people broke down if I could control my feelings.

She said, "I think you would be wonderful." She always bolsters me up anyway.

But whenever they were having the training program, I was always busy. Last fall everything just fell into place, and I took the course. If I had any questions I would just come out with them.

The training gave me confidence, and I felt like Catherine was right over my shoulder saying, "You can do this."

I've only been on two cases so far: my sister-in-law and a person in Bristol. I didn't know if I could do it emotionally, but if they all go as smoothly as these first two, I'll be all set. I know some cases are going to be a lot more difficult, but I have learned to take one day at a time.

When a situation gets trying, you just have to put your feet flat on the floor, sit up, and take a deep breath. That gives you a boost.

So far, it's been very satisfying. You feel that you are helping somebody in difficult situations. You're giving them moral support, letting them know that they are not alone, and that there are people who care.

Chapter 7

Listening to the Community

That Two Hours Flies by Awfully Fast

Responding to the Community

Hospital Faces Crisis Needs $50,000 Drive Gets Underway

Porter Hospital faces a crisis. The equipment it has used for twenty-five years for the people of Addison County is worn out or out-of-date or both. Running the hospital with that equipment is like trying to run a modern interstate bus company with a few old trolley cars that couldn't travel twenty miles an hour downhill....

One gets more for his money in a hospital than anywhere else. $6 a day or 25 cents an hour is less than it would cost to have your lawn mowed or your dishes washed. Yet for this amount the patient is bathed in bed, fed in bed—three eight-hour shifts of constant care, linens changed from one to a dozen times a day (incidentally, linens only last one-fourth as long in a hospital as a private home). No one can buy as much anywhere for a dollar as he can in a hospital. This is another reason we should give our money to Porter Hospital as it goes farther than anywhere else....

The hospital needs $50,000. That's a whale of a lot of money. That's a terrific amount of money from a small county like ours.... The replacement of equipment is a once-in-a-generation matter. The former equipment installed in 1925 when the hospital began to function hasn't been replaced since. That's about twenty-five years. You ought be able to afford a big donation to give yourself a first class hospital nearby, once every twenty-five years.

And when YOUR sickness comes or YOUR accident happens—and no matter how well you are or how careful, you can get chopped up pretty badly by modern power equipment—it's nice to have a hospital close by. Not thirty or thirty five miles away, but close by....

You've read and so have I in newspapers, "The patient died on the way to the hospital." Maybe it wouldn't have said that if the hospital had been nearer.

That banner headline from a 1949 fund-raising newsletter and the story's subsequent exhortations to give generously have a familiar ring today. Most non-profit community organizations, working on thin margins, depend on volunteers, the goodwill of their community, and on the annual fund drive and capital campaigns. And in most cases, community members strongly believe that there is no care as good as local care.

What is striking, besides the chatty language, is the writer's assumption—perhaps justified given that the hospital had never had an intensive countywide fund drive before—that one gift would take care of the hospital's needs for the generation to come. Little did the writer apparently envision how rapidly health care would change in the next 25 years.

In fact, the life of that successful fund-raising campaign was less than eight years. In 1957, the state Health Commission refused to renew the hospital's license because of fire and safety violations; Porter was granted a temporary license, as

were nine other community hospitals.

This fund-raising brochure, "To Reach New Heights," had a distinctly different tone—community health care was changing rapidly:

People were rapidly becoming conscious of the advantages of hospital care over home care when Porter Hospital opened 32 years ago. The new age of medicine had not yet dawned and hospital insurance plans were still unknown. Neither the hospital's founder nor any of his contemporaries could possibly have foreseen the amazing developments that, in a single generation, would make their liberal planning wholly inadequate.

Cosmetic building surgery was not enough. Porter needed a new single-floor wing to consolidate care on one floor, instead of three inefficient floors. Outmoded wards needed to be replaced by single- and double-bed rooms. In addition, the wing would contain a new operating room, emergency room and a delivery suite with the hospital's first labor room.

Creating a "modern, functional hospital" would cost $360,000, with $300,000 to be raised by a community fund drive.

Porter had largely been created by three gifts, totaling $100,000, from William Porter, a Middlebury native, College trustee, and prominent international banker. The College, which owned the hospital until the early 1940s, when it transferred ownership to a college-community corporation, had covered Porter's operating deficits in the past. Maintaining the hospital should

PRECEDING PAGE: *Porter Medical Center's annual meeting is informal and neighborly, but the questioning concerning the hospital's future is sharp and detailed.*

148

now be the community's responsibility.

Fast-forward to 2000. Porter launches a 75th Anniversary Campaign with a $4 million community goal to support the proposed $14 million North Project expansion. Hospital rooms were no longer $6 a day. A private room in the medical-surgery unit was now $774, a semi-private room (two or three beds) $715; a bed in the intensive care unit $1,209; and private and semi-private rooms in the obstetrics wing, $715 and $643, respectively. As a nation we were spending far more on health care than the fund raiser of 1949 could have imagined—from $82 per capita in 1950 (roughly $500, adjusted for inflation) to approximately $5,000 in 2000.

But the fund-raising themes are similar. Times have changed; we need your help.

The creation of the county's community hospital and these fund-raising efforts are specific to Porter Hospital, but with minor differences they are repeated in the history of community nonprofit organizations everywhere. An individual or group of community-minded activists sees a need—a free clinic, programs for teen mothers or the elderly, an emergency ambulance service—and creates a program on a shoestring. Start modestly in a church basement or rented space with lots of volunteer help. Outgrow that space and move into new quarters. Ideally, leapfrog again into your own building.

While the bulk of an organization's funding might eventually come from federal and state programs and private insurance, local support, how-

The escalation in health care costs can be seen in Porter Hospital's expansion. The original 22-bed hospital and nurses' home, above, were built in the 1920s for under $150,000. A wing was added in the late 1950s at a cost of $360,000. A new birthing center, operating rooms, and reconfiguration of existing space will be completed in 2006 at a cost of $16 million. Major medical equipment has similarly increased from the four-figure cost of early X-ray machines to today's six- and seven-figure investments in magnetic resonance imaging systems and CT scanners.

ever financially modest, remains essential to an organization's well-being.

In this chapter, two community activists, Anne Ginevan and Peg Martin, discuss their experiences in listening and responding to community needs. Three board members, Joe Devall, Louise Sandberg, and John Myhre, reflect on the challenges that volunteers face in overseeing increasingly complex health care organizations.

In the last commentary, Peter Newton, the administrator of the Middlebury Volunteer Ambulance Association, discusses the growing challenges facing an all-volunteer organization.

Anne Ginevan

Community Listener

You Have to Make Things Very Practical

Anne Ginevan has worn many community hats —volunteer, board member, program director, and legislator—since she came to Middlebury in the early 1970s. She was the director of Project Independence, the community's adult day care center for its first five years, 1978 to 1983; director of the United Way of Addison County from 1983 to 1998; and one of Middlebury's representatives in the state legislature from 1997 to 2001. She has been a member of the board of Helen Porter Healthcare and Rehabilitation Center since 1998.

First, be a good listener. Second, keep your eye on the big picture. Third, have broad community representation on your boards. Those are some of the lessons Anne Ginevan has learned in 30 years of community service.

We moved here in 1973 from Pittsburgh when my husband was hired by Middlebury College. I had been working in student personnel at the University of Pittsburgh and there were no comparable positions here. So I became very involved as a volunteer with several organizations, first with the Porter Hospital auxiliary. That was my introduction to this community and health care in general.

Porter was a small rural hospital then with only a few doctors and not many specialties. If anything serious came up, you went to Burlington. I also volunteered at the counseling service and was on its board.

In the late 1970s there were no services for the elderly. Children and adults with mental illness were being cared for, but we were not addressing the needs of the elderly. The director of the counseling service attended a national meeting and came home with an idea to start an adult day care center, which was a very new idea.

The board talked about it at some length and decided that a center had potential. In 1978 I left the board and the counseling service hired me to direct the program, Project Independence. I hadn't worked with elderly, but I enjoyed administration and thought it would be a challenge. We started with five participants in the basement of the Methodist Church.

As word of the program spread, we expanded to serve as many as 20 people a day and 70 to 80 people over the course of a week. When I left in 1983, we were a federal Medicare demonstration project with on-site mental health services.

What I learned from working at Project Independence was that you have to make things very practical for Vermonters. People know what their needs are. But sometimes people don't immediately understand how you can help them meet those needs.

When Project Independence began I visited homes to explain the program. Some people were very hesitant about coming. They'd say, "Why in the world would I want to leave my chair right here?"

We had to provide what they wanted. And the most important thing for many frail people was a hot cooked meal at lunchtime. This was something they couldn't do easily for themselves, either because a spouse had died or they lacked interest in cooking. Their diets definitely suffered as a result.

People would come and eat. If we could get them involved in other activities then we had accomplished something.

And we had to be honest. I had one woman who came the first day, looked over everything, and said very sarcastically, "Now where do I sleep?"

I said, "What do you mean?"

She said, "You got me here because you want me to stay here all the time."

I said, "Well, I don't know about you, but I'm going home tonight. I'm going to sleep in my own bed. I'll come back tomorrow."

She looked at me with big wide eyes, "You mean, I don't have to live here." Big smile.

I said, "No, you don't have to live here. You can't live here."

"Oh, then I'll come back."

You have to break through these barriers and offer them what they need at the level where they are.

Vermont has very definitely been a national leader in the expansion of programs for the elderly. Our success rates are higher in Addison County, because we have had a lot of grassroots support when we start programs. There is not very much top-down creation of programs here.

We are also known as a very cooperative county in delivering human services. People are not concerned about their turf so coordination and cooperation have really been exceptional.

More than once someone has said at statewide meetings, "Oh, you live in Addison County. You're different, because agencies cooperate."

On the other hand, I have seen times when some organizations weren't working well together, the hospital and the counseling service, for example. The hospital feels that when they refer to the counseling service that they never hear another thing about how Mr. or Mrs. Jones is doing. The counseling service responds that the information is confidential. So there hasn't always been good two-way communication.

There is tension now between Project Independence and the nursing home because of Act 160, which provides more money for services to help people stay in their homes and out of nursing homes. This has dramatically decreased the number of people in the nursing home.

As a result the nursing home has had some big deficits. As a member of the nursing home board, I'm in the thick of it. If we can't support a 118-bed nursing home, then how many beds does the community need?

Our unit for short-term rehabilitation of people coming out of the hospital is a wonderful new program. Creating a dementia unit and setting beds aside for respite care are other needs that we are responding to. Helen Porter is a wonderful facility, but I, too, would want to keep my mother at home until I couldn't any longer.

Most local boards do a good job of representing different perspectives. But once you're on a board your opinion becomes much less grand or your perspective becomes much less broad. You narrow your focus to what the organization is doing and you don't see as far outside the box as maybe you did when you first came on the board.

Maybe that's loyalty. Maybe it's just more education about what the entity does. Maybe you believe in it more, but you lose some perspective once you have been in one organization's camp for a long time.

There are some board members who ask tough questions. That doesn't lessen their feeling for the board. They want their board to be looking at all aspects of the problem.

When I was the director of the United Way, we used to talk about how we raised money for organizations that served low-income people, but we never had board representation from these recipients. So we asked the Addison County Community Action Group to recommend someone for our board. We had to supply transportation to the meetings so that she could attend and give her input.

She would listen to grandiose plans and finally would ask one practical question, which went to the heart of things. You'd say, "Right. This is not going to work because of this, this, and so."

These people do bring perspectives that you haven't thought about. Even if you don't follow the advice, at least you have heard it. My concern is that too many boards become ingrown.

Peg Martin
Community Activist

I Come at Community Needs from the Standpoint of Kids

Peg Martin has been a community activist and gadfly since coming to Middlebury with her English professor husband, Ed "Sandy" Martin, in the mid-1960s. She was instrumental in starting the county's first Head Start program, was a Middlebury representative in the state legislature for 10 years, and a consumer representative on the Vermont Program for Quality in Health Care. She is a past member and president of the board of Elderly Services, Inc., and is currently a town selectman.

Addison County can stand up well with any rural county in the state and be proud of what is here. We have a reputation statewide as a county that gets things done on a local level in a very pragmatic way.

There are still holes—personnel, facilities, money—and they will remain for the foreseeable future. But the county's reputation is deserved. When I was in the legislature (1987-96) and listened to what was happening in other places and states, I'd say to myself, "Wow, we have been doing that for a long time."

But when you sit here in your own little puddle you tend to look at what's wrong and say, "Oh man, we aren't doing anything." But Addison County does pretty well and works in a fairly cooperative manner.

There is a general recognition that it is OK to help people who are down. You don't have to blame them for being where they are. They are where they are, so what can we do about it? In general the county looks at its needs and then figures out how to do something about them. We haven't waited to be blessed from somewhere.

There is a reservoir of skills, talents, and knowledge at the College and people at the College have played a strong role. But there have always been strong community people who have been the backbone. People like Catherine Fitzpatrick, whose family has been around forever. She was raised in town and worked at the Chittenden Bank for years. She knew lots and lots and lots about people and found ways to help when help was needed.

Someone like Ken Perine, who's a native son. His dad was affiliated with the College, and he runs the bank (the National Bank of Middlebury), which has always supported the community. Peter Hicks, president before him, had little pots of money. A check would arrive in someone's mail with a note that said, "We think that you can use this."

Someone had left money to the bank, and he had aegis over it. When Peter found out about needs of a family he could send them some money. There are funny ways that these things happen in a small community.

I have generally come at community needs from the standpoint of kids, because it's very hard to beat up on kids. Right now I'm part of a small group, the Dr. Wayne E. Peters Society. We are an informal Vermont non-profit corporation and are looking for ways to perpetuate Pete's respect and care for kids and families.

There are about a dozen of us who worked with or knew Pete (a longtime Middlebury pediatrician). Paul Berkner, Pete's son-in-law and a pediatrician, is president. I'm vice president. Pete's wife Natalie is treasurer. Lerin Peters, their daughter, is secretary. Sandy, my husband, does the news releases. Jim Daily, CEO of Porter Hospital, is a member.

We have tried to determine the overriding immediate needs of kids in Addison County. The group doesn't see itself raising funds or directly providing services but facilitating the emergence of these services, possibly through existing agencies.

The first need we came up with was expanding dental services for kids. This is a grim scene. Besides anecdotal reports, there are Medicaid statistics on dental utilization. There were 4,146 children in Addison County eligible under the Dr. Dynasaur Medicaid program to receive dental services. But less than half, about 45%, received dental services. We know that there are other folks who are eligible but who are not identified. About 31% of the 3,211 Medicaid-eligible adults received dental care.

Access is a piece of the problem. There is a shortage of dentists in the state. Another piece is persistence of parents. They may not know that their children are eligible for this program. And some kids may not need treatment, because they are doing wonderful things today with sealants to reduce cavities.

The Department of Health was soliciting grants for ways to increase dental access for Medicaid-eligible people. I wrote a grant (2001), and we got $11,000 of our $17,000 budget from the dental division of the Department of Health to do a planning process with local dentists and community health leaders. We have another $2,500 that was donated in memory of Dr. Peters. We will have to raise the rest.

We are hoping to pull together the Open

Peg and Sandy Martin have had their fingerprints on many community health care programs over the past 30 years: Head Start, the adult day care center, the Dr. Pete Society, and the Vermont Humanities Council book discussion series on health care issues.

Door Clinic, the local Department of Health office, all the various clinics which supported the grant application, and come up with a plan. Our thought is to hire a half-time person for six months to look at how we would want to do this.

It turns out that we need to provide services for adults as well as for kids, because adults' needs are so great. Theoretically you could have the same dental clinic for adults and kids but you might have different waiting rooms for each group. Kids need to feel comfortable and at ease and that doesn't happen in an adult waiting room that is not kid centered.

Another possible initiative is looking at the stigma around mental health care. How do you get counseling to a kid who really needs help? Perhaps we need to get counselors into pediatricians' offices and integrate counseling into existing practices.

Paul has talked with the person who is in charge of children's services at the counseling service (Counseling Service of Addison County), and she is interested. The possibility is that they might work out of Paul's office; no one will know if you are coming in for counseling or something else.

It could be something that simple that makes a difference.

Joe Devall

Chair, Porter Hospital Board

They Were Looking for Someone with a Business Management Background

Joe Devall was an admitted newcomer to the financial, medical, and community issues facing Porter Hospital when he became a board member. Like many board members, Devall sought to apply his life experiences—as an insurance agent and president of an insurance cooperative—to the hospital board room. Determining if, when, and how business principles should be applied to the operation of a non-profit community hospital has been a continuing question. He was on the board from 1996 to 2002 and was chair, 2001 to 2002.

Bob Stetson, a neighbor, was chairman of the hospital board back in 1996-97, and he asked me if I would serve on the board. Until then my only contact with the hospital had been some minor outpatient surgery on my thumb.

They were looking for someone with a business management background who was used to working with numbers and financial statements. The insurance business is a numbers business.

What struck me when I first went on the board was how the medical practices that the hospital owned didn't have a focus on profit and loss, and the hospital was losing a lot of money on them. In the insurance world, we want to treat our policyholders fairly, but we are also very much aware of when we are making or losing money. And when you're not making money, you try and figure out why you're not making money.

Community board members face a steep learning curve in understanding the health care system and in applying operating principles from their business livelihoods, says Joe Devall.

Doctors are not bottom line oriented. Their job is to make you well, to save your life, and to give you as good a life as possible. That's how they've been trained.

And physicians just don't want to be measured. They don't want to meet certain goals, so many patients a day or a month. They argue that you can't compare someone who is seeing a lot of very sick patients with someone who is treating lots of sore throats. But if you are spending a lot of time with really sick patients, charges and revenues

ought to show it. I don't mean you should measure with one stick—here is the number of patients that you have to see. But many physicians don't want to be measured on revenue or expenses or the number of patients.

Overall, the hospital's buying private practices has worked out relatively well. We're not buying them just to make money. We have a big hospital up in Burlington and a good-sized one down in Rutland. We're in the middle here. If you live in Brandon it's about as easy to go to Rutland as it is to come to Porter, and if you're in Vergennes it's about as easy to go up to Fletcher Allen in Burlington.

The hospital administration felt, and I have no quarrel with this, that our location made it essential that we have close connections with surrounding primary care doctors. You can't tell doctors where to send their patients. However, everything else being equal we'd rather have doctors sending their patients to Porter.

When the hospital bought two pharmacies they thought they would be profitable, which they are now after several years of losses. But it's risky when you start getting into fields where you don't have any expertise.

It's not that different from the 1960s and 1970s when conglomeration was the rage. People got into all kinds of related businesses and lost their shirts. There is a parallel here. In the hospital, the patient has no choice but to take your pill at your price. Outside the hospital, the patient has lots of choices, and the competition is cutthroat.

As a board member it's easier to understand insurance than medicine. When I was Co-op president (Cooperative Insurance Companies in

Middlebury, 1993-2000), I could talk with board members about farm owners' policies. Some members would be farmers, and they understood risk and that certain buildings were more susceptible to collapse. Everybody has an automobile, so when you talked about auto insurance, accidents, and the cost of repairs, board members could relate to that.

As a hospital board member, none of us, except the physicians, understand all this stuff. You can ask questions. You can read files. We don't understand how a patient can be totally misdiagnosed, but a physician can.

Doctors probably get frustrated trying to explain something to a board member who doesn't understand the subject, the terminology, or the intricacy of the procedure. So they might walk away and say, "Why do I even bother?"

There is a steep and long learning curve being on a hospital board. I couldn't go to a 30-day school and learn everything there is. But you sit in meetings and you begin to get a feel for what is going on.

But there needs to be a place where a board member can go besides a Boston meeting once a year where you hear about things that might work in a big city but not in small rural communities. I've been to several meetings of the Vermont Association of Hospitals and Health Systems and have met with other board presidents. And you pick up some things that you could be doing if you had the staff.

Good formal schooling for board members would help, but somebody would have to pay for it. Does a board member pay or the hospital?

~

My impression is that the medical staff doesn't have much respect for the board or want much help from the board. The less the board interferes, the better. I get this sense from going to quality coordinating committee meetings and listening to staff. They just don't want to have to answer to very many people. I will say that the quality coordinating committee did develop a system that gives the board a better perspective on the quality of care.

Hospital boards have to rely on the management, and management can hide behind statements: you can't measure this; we don't have control over our revenue stream; we can't make people sick.

In insurance, if I'm a good enough salesman I can convince you to buy my product. In medicine it is not very easy to do that. Hospitals may not have the control over their revenue stream that an insurance company would. You can't compensate physicians for referring patients here the way an insurance company can reward agents.

And Jim (Jim Daily, Porter Hospital CEO) doesn't have as much control over expenses because hospitals have to staff for capacity even if they may only be half full.

The board has done a fairly decent job in strategic planning. The North Project expansion to build new operating rooms and a birthing center is an outgrowth of the strategic plan. Our operating room is not as modern as it should be. Our birthing areas are not particularly good and need to be updated. We need office space.

Technology changes constantly and if your facilities don't keep up then people go where that technology is available. That has definitely been the case where people have gone to hospitals that have birthing rooms and the mother can stay in one room.

We really do need this North Project and it's satisfying that we have reached our $4 million community fund-raising goal. Now all we have do is get a certificate of need from the state to build the $14-million expansion, which may not be easy.

Long term, Porter will have a problem trying to keep up with new technology. Trying to spread the expense of new technology over a relatively small base whether you are a community hospital or a small business is very difficult.

Our mission statement says that Porter should be a leader and catalyst in meeting the health needs of the community. I don't think we do as good a job as we could, because there is a tremendous amount of turf protection among all the health care facilities.

Nobody is very interested in my idea that Addison County should have an Addison County Health Board overseeing all these entities. We all have individual boards and CEOs and to a great extent we are all protecting and trying to expand our own turf. It would be a very high-level board that would have some jurisdiction over anyone that is administering health care.

But there are other ways we protect our turf. When I was first on the hospital board, the board discussed allowing some alternative medicine people to have a booth at a hospital health fair. One physician who was on the board at the time strongly opposed it.

My feeling is that some alternative medicine procedures may be good. Let the public make the decision, not a physician who says, "I know what is best for you." It was quite a discussion and they got their booth, but it was over a dead body.

Another controversy among the hospital and physicians in the community is whether we should allow midwives in the hospitals. A lot of women

Porter Medical Center has six governing boards. Between monthly and bimonthly meetings, board presidents, like Devall, meet for stay-in-touch breakfast meetings

who have babies swear by them. Some doctors aren't very supportive of midwives.

They argue what happens at 2 a.m. when the midwife has a problem and needs to bring the mother to the hospital. The supervising physician doesn't know the patient's history and can be faced with a dangerous situation.

That's a pretty strong point. As a layman am I going to argue with that? Probably not.

How often would such a crisis arise? I don't know.

When I became board president, I thought that by working with Jim and the medical staff that I could get a little more collegiality out of the

organization. That was a goal. But to be perfectly honest I think I failed.

The whole year was very discouraging. I always thought physicians put the patient and the care of the community above everything else. I have done 180 degrees on that after seeing how they fight over bringing in a new physician and credentialling doctors.

The board has to approve a doctor's application for staff privileges and to perform certain procedures in the hospital after a review and recommendation by a medical staff committee. We would get, for example, a podiatrist who wanted to do certain operations on the foot and the orthopedist would oppose the application.

Increased competition and financial considerations should not enter into it, but I think that is what often determines the decision in many cases, more than skill and competency. On the other hand if we credential doctors who have not done a lot of procedures and they make mistakes, the board would look like it had used poor judgment. But what came through to me was that doctors weren't as concerned about the skill as they were about the competition.

My feeling is if you're good you won't starve. If we have two very good surgeons, people will come here rather than go to Fletcher Allen or Rutland. If one is mediocre and one is really good, the doctor who is good is going to get the business.

One approach to all these problems is to recruit optimistic people for the board. If you have pessimistic people they will probably start out with a lot of pessimistic remarks about all the problems.

We're getting there. We have a new board member who is chair of the hospital finance committee. He wants to see information that will help the board make better financial decisions and is digging to get that.

And I have proposed a person who could represent the blue-collar community. Boards are normally made up of people who are managing businesses. I think the board and administration should hear from a person who is a consumer of your product. A person who is articulate and has a lot of good common sense in the blue-collar community would make a good addition to the board. That hasn't gotten off the ground, and I don't know why.

But you need two or three people who think outside the box. If you only have one, everybody else shoots that person down.

Another thing we can do is educate the public about trying to live forever. We are spending tons of money on keeping people alive when the quality of their life is very poor. I think a dialogue needs to be started about the doctor's creed to do everything you can to keep this person alive. That creed was written back when we didn't have all this technology and new drugs.

But I don't think the hospital would be very interested in that, to be perfectly honest. End-of-life care is where a lot of the money comes from to keep a hospital going. Lots of people would say I'm too cynical.

And lots of people would say they want that money spent when it comes to them. The American public has to start understanding that you can't live forever. You shouldn't have to walk around with this terrible guilt feeling that you decided that you're not going to do everything to keep a loved one alive.

If you have a teenager who needs a bone marrow transplant, I'd say go ahead and try it. If you're 65—and I'm 68—maybe not.

Louise Sandberg

Board Member

That Two Hours Flies by Awfully Fast

Louise Sandberg has been one of the community's most active volunteer board members over the past 20 years. Beginning with the Parent/Child Center of Addison County, Sandberg has been on the Interfaith Housing Board (low-income housing advocates), the Shard Villa community care home board; and chair and long-time board member of the Counseling Service of Addison County. Most recently she has been a member and chair of the boards of Porter Hospital and Porter Medical Center.

In 2002, the Middlebury Rotary Club, Middlebury Chamber of Commerce, and Vermont Bankers' Association recognized Sandberg's contributions with their community service awards.

Health care has changed so rapidly that it's a real challenge to be a board member today. What is our role as community members? Are we fulfilling our fiduciary responsibility to the organization and community? How do we work with the management, the community, and staff?

It's really a hard balance, and there can be a great deal of frustration and anxiety. Some hospitals have gone to almost all-physician boards, but I feel that it's important to have community input.

My first board was the Parent Child Center about 20 years ago. I was on that board for five or six years. After that I was on the counseling service (Counseling Service of Addison County) for about 10 years. Once you are on one board, it becomes a circle and you get asked to be on other boards.

When I started in banking at the Chittenden 25 years ago you could be your own social welfare agency. You could lend to people who on paper didn't look like they would be a good risk. I still have some of that flexibility, but my career has changed from personal lending to overseeing small business lending around the state. Being on a board is an opportunity to use your skills to give back to the community.

People go on boards to help, but there are no permanent "fixes" and it is easy to become frustrated by your lack of knowledge and consumed by problems and threats. But I am more comfortable now and believe that common sense is common sense no matter what the industry.

When I was on the counseling service board, the agency was having funding problems. The Brandon Training School had completely shut down and community mental health agencies were absorbing training school residents into the community and losing money.

The challenge was to figure out the right fees and structure. The analysis—looking at the financials, the balance sheet, and cash flow—was what you use in business lending. You have to think about the long-term impact on the agency when you say, "Yes, we are going to fund this even though it means we will lose money."

Unfortunately, the balance sheets of most agencies have eroded so badly that they can't make those decisions anymore. Their fiscal strength has been so depleted that if you make that decision you can jeopardize the whole agency.

And it is becoming harder and harder to build a margin to take those chances. If you have a good grant writer you can get grant money for specific start-up programs, but it is really hard to get grant money for ongoing programs. I can empathize with the state that there is only so much money. But when you are dependent on state funding, you have to lobby for more money.

～

Porter's mission statement says that we should be a leader and catalyst in helping determine and provide for the health needs of the community. I'd like to see a more unified approach to meeting community needs, so that each agency is not approaching them separately.

That's a huge challenge and it becomes harder and harder as agencies become more fiscally fragile. If you could pull the financial strain out, organizations would be much freer to work more cooperatively, because they wouldn't all be struggling for their survival.

Integrating services is possible, but it takes trust. Somebody has to ensure that whatever we do is done equitably, and that we eliminate and don't create more barriers. The long-term care coalition (representatives from area agencies working with people needing long-term care) was supposed to help do that. My understanding is that the coalition hasn't broken down many barriers, but it does create some communication among agencies.

Having an Addison County Health Board that would look at the county's health care needs and how to best deliver them makes sense. But we're not ready for it yet. We need to take some smaller steps first. People would be way too threatened by it now.

The authority piece would be tough. Other agencies are suspicious of Porter because we are so much larger. If Porter comes on too strong it won't work, because there is already a feeling that Porter is the big bully.

Porter has pretty good channels of communication with the home health agency. Project Independence (the adult day care center) and the nursing home relationship needs a lot of work. When the nursing home was having better years financially, Project Independence was in a very fragile state. Now it is reversed. So there is wall there.

I have organized a meeting for both boards. The boards got along great, but we didn't break down barriers at the administrative level. The administrations are facing such very different challenges that it is hard for them to step out of their institutional roles.

I worry that as we hear political concerns about the rising cost of health care there is tendency to blame the providers. If MRI use or whatever is going up, there is a tendency to shoot the provider. The hospital has to be at the table and talking about it. But we shouldn't decide who gets an MRI and who doesn't. That's society's responsibility.

Any solution will probably require legislation and that won't be easy legislation. And I don't know if we will ever have the political will to take those steps until we end up in a complete crisis in health care. Everybody knows that health care needs to be controlled, but nobody wants to say, "You can't have that MRI."

This question is indirectly on the hospital board's agenda every month. We deal with the effects of increasing costs, but sometimes we forget to step back from the daily crisis to look at the big picture.

Community boards can get caught up in the daily crisis and often don't spend enough time looking at the big picture, Louise Sandberg believes.

As board chair, you don't want members to be surprised by events at the hospital that are known in the community. We have to go over the financial piece. We have to approve the credentialing of staff. We need to talk about legislative issues so that we can be effective in lobbying. We need to talk about current issues, so that two hours flies by awful fast.

At the end of the meeting, we have mostly looked in the rear view mirror instead of looking forward.

My advice to the new chair is don't spend all the board's time talking about what is going wrong. Spend some part of every meeting with things that are going right.

My other advice is to build supportive relationships with management so that your disagreements are not viewed as a threat. Building that relationship takes a lot of time. I probably spent 6-7-8 hours in meetings every week. Add to that whatever time I spent on the phone with Jim (Jim Daily, president of Porter Medical Center).

It's a big commitment.

John Myhre
Board Member

Issues that Keep Me Up at Night

John Myhre, like many members of the Porter Medical Center boards, is well known in the community. Born and brought up in Middlebury, Myhre has been a Middlebury town selectman and planning commission member. From 2000–2002, he was chair of the board of the Helen Porter Nursing Home when the nursing home, faced with a rapidly declining census and institution-crippling deficits, was forced to reinvent itself. A name change to Helen Porter Healthcare and Rehabilitation Center reflected the many subsequent internal program changes: a reduction in size, from 118 to 105 beds; creation of new services, such as a dementia unit; and expansion of its rehabilitation unit.

Myhre and board members were traveling in largely uncharted waters then as they considered these and other program changes in an essential community service. At the same time, Myhre, as chair of the Ad Hoc Committee on Governance, was trying to bring coherence and consistency to the bylaws and roles of Porter's six boards: the parent organization, Porter Medical Center, Inc., and five subordinate boards—hospital, nursing home, ancillary services, management services, and the medical center auxiliary.

In 2002–03, he was chair of the Porter Medical Center board. That seat has confirmed his initial impression that our health care system faces challenges as far as the eye can see.

What is the role of a small community hospital and nursing home? That question is central to all deliberations of the Porter Medical Center board, says chairman John Myhre.

Seven years ago, I was asked by the chair of Porter Medical Center board if I would consider filling a vacancy on the Helen Porter board. I'm one of those people who seemingly can't say no. I was born at Porter Hospital and think the hospital and nursing home are an important part of our community. So I was pleased to be a part of it.

During board orientation, I was overwhelmed by the complexity of the business. And I was surprised, having been a business owner, how differ-ent a nursing home is from an entrepreneurial business model. The nursing home, subject to fixed-price reimbursement, has a limited ability to create additional revenues and increase profitability.

The second major difference was nursing home regulations, which are more involved than any business that I have been involved in. And I'm involved in a very regulated business right now—securities.

There are those who say that one board would be fine and that there are too many meetings. We're not General Motors; we're a small community hospital and nursing home with limited facilities.

I came in like a bull in a china shop, saying simplify, simplify. But now I don't think we have too many boards. The issues are so complex that we need a group that understands the nursing home's issues, which are very different from the hospital's. Porter Health System's issues (Porter owns for-profit pharmacies and other outpatient services) are very different from either of the other two.

In the past we wanted board members who were geographically dispersed and covered our market area and who had experience and expert-ise to contribute to a $50-million operation.

Now we are more sensitized to diversity—gender, ethnic, and social strata—within the board-room. I don't think we will ever be a mirror of the county, but we can probably do a better job of being sensitive to what the county looks like. It is easier to say what we want to avoid, which is a sit-uation where everybody knows each other and one friend suggests another friend.

What we also don't want is a situation where we have factions. We want to avoid that because we have so many people in our boardroom who have gone from one organization board to another organization board and now are at Porter. When we differ with other organizations these members are able to bring that other board's perspective to our meetings.

We have also learned from other hospitals' problems that we need to question everything. We need to have broad discussions in the full boardroom and not deal with important issues in executive committees and in offices.

What hasn't changed is the systemic stress in the health care system. The system will be stressed, certainly as long as I can see, and there isn't any way to simplify it. Probably the only constant will be our inadequate levels of reimbursement, whether at the nursing home or the hospital. There are not enough dollars to go around.

Health care is growing at some multiple of inflation because of new services, technology, and our appetite. Add the fact that we are getting older as a society.

That said, I have never seen the board's role as a "watchdog" of utilization. We are, however, concerned about health care use from two absolutely conflicting perspectives. We want Porter to be on the low end of utilization and to seek the most effective and cost-efficient ways of caring for the community. By almost any measure—the length of hospital stays, our hospitalization costs—that is where we are.

Because we are in that low-usage, low-cost quintile maybe we don't see utilization as a primary issue. But we have a conflicting challenge: How do we make sure that we are getting our fair share of health care revenue without increasing utilization?

We want to make sure that someone from our area thinks of the hospital as a quality provider when they are considering various surgeries or obstetrics. If doctors share privileges at hospitals in Burlington, Middlebury, and Rutland we want their patients in our market area to come to Porter. If too many go elsewhere, we ultimately can't serve the community.

We have had a presence in Brandon for years with doctors who considered Porter to be their hospital. Why did Rutland (Rutland Regional Medical Center) feel they had to build a multi-million-dollar outpatient facility there? Why do they need to regularly advertise in our local newspaper?

There have been discussions at the CEO level and their response generally has been, "We have special programs that you are not offering at Porter, and frankly Brandon is Rutland County and it is our duty to let people know about these services."

But it feels pretty close to home to see their ads in the local newspapers.

I can't think of a situation where we have said, "If we build it they will come." When we do expand services, we have to get approval through the state's Certificate of Need process.

Our birthing center and expansion of surgical facilities in the proposed North Project are a good example. Docs are saying that their patients are demanding a different type of experience from our traditional labor and delivery rooms. We are just not with it and a significant number of mothers are going to other hospitals.

In a perfect world the CON process would be helpful in determining market areas and services. But we haven't felt particularly well served by some state decisions.

Our boards are getting better at dealing with the big issues. Management prepares us better. We deal less with meaningless data and are getting more useful information. Our hospital finance committee has done a very good job massaging data into decision-making information. The nursing home administration has gone a long way toward providing board members information, whether it's ratios or critical indicators, that is helpful.

As PMC chair, the big issues that keep me up at night vary by the subsidiary. At the hospital, we are scrambling to get our arms around why our inpatient volume has recently been declining (2003). This is happening not just at Porter but hospitals around the state and New England. Is this a blip, a fairly quickly developed trend that will worsen, or will it stay where it is now?

We don't know the answer. We do know that our inpatient census has dropped 20% to 25% over the first six months of this fiscal year while our outpatient volume is on budget.

If this decline continues, we probably will have to structurally change the hospital—the number of beds and services offered. For the last two months, we have seen some rebound, but we will need to cut $600,000 to $1.5 million to break even on our budget of about $35 million.

And we really have little control over our pricing—I'm not saying that we should—but that is why health care is such a challenging business. We have three or four major revenue balls in the air. The state legislature determines Medicaid coverage, and well-intentioned legislators have lots of different options to spend money in good ways besides the health care system. Insurance companies tell us what they are going to pay.

We have some control over staffing and quality. We can't control the marketplace for nurses, but we can treat our employees well and pay them the most we can so that they feel they are being fairly compensated.

Any level of measurement shows that we are very strong from a quality perspective, but this is a

State policies, from Medicaid coverage and reimbursements to approval of facility expansion, directly affect the health of small community health care organizations. Gov. Jim Douglas outlined his health care views at the 2003 annual meeting of Porter Medical Center. Hockey fan Douglas received a shirt in appreciation from board chair Myhre.

critical-care, life-and-death business so there will always be issues. Doctors say nothing is more important to them than quality of care and that we need to trust them. We do trust them, but the ultimate oversight responsibility falls on our shoulders and we are not sure that the existing checks and balances make sense for us.

I suspect that more quality-of-care oversight wouldn't be the docs' first request to the board. They want the board to see that the hospital is well run and economically viable. They want us to give them the best facilities so they can provide the best care. And they want us to keep the staff happy, trained, and plentiful.

Porter Medical Center needs to be a positive influence with the other community entities, whether it is the counseling service or home health or Project Independence (the adult day care center). That doesn't mean we continually acquiesce to their interests or that we need to fill every gap in coverage. But as the largest health care provider we need to provide the best health care while still remaining economically viable.

There are organizations that we are "competing" with, such as the good folks at home health. The state is promoting home care because that is what most people want and it costs less. We support the state's emphasis on home care, but there will always be a need for a nursing home-type facility when home or community-based care no longer meets a person's or family's needs.

For the most part we do try to look at the greater good, but we think that there should be an accurate accounting of home care's true costs and some financial compensation when the state's promotion of home care harms essential community facilities, like our nursing home. And I'd like a clear appraisal of the costs of a day at the nursing home and the hospital and what the state, federal, and private insurers are reimbursing us.

I would hope that in the future community members would feel that Porter is responsive to their needs and offers quality and economically efficient care. We don't need a great enhancement of services as a community hospital, but our services need to be seen as good modern medicine.

Bigger hospitals will always be a threat. But I hope that if you walked down Main Street that community members would tell you they wanted to come here for 80% of what ails them, because Porter is small, personal, close, and good. As long as we have those characteristics, the future remains viable.

Peter Newton

Administrator,
Middlebury Volunteer
Ambulance Association

Volunteers Have Only So Much Time They Can Give

The Middlebury Volunteer Ambulance Association covers 11 towns: Orwell, half of New Haven, Ripton, Salisbury, Bridport, Cornwall, Shoreham, Whiting, Weybridge, Middlebury, and East Middlebury. When the ambulance squad started in 1970, replacing an informal service provided by funeral homes, initial training was a 16-hour Red Cross advanced first aid course. Today basic training is 110 hours. Several members now have paramedic status, a 1,000-hour plus program. Perceived community demands for increasingly sophisticated service and the availability of members now require, says Peter Newton, the association's first paid administrator, that the association constantly monitor the viability of an all-volunteer operation.

Newton, who took over as administrator in the fall of 1999, resigned in the fall of 2002 to work in the emergency department at Fletcher Allen Health Care.

Peter Newton, the association's first paid administrator, is part of a trend where all-volunteer ambulance organizations are hiring staff to help meet increasing responsibilities.

We have 49 volunteers now (2002) and one full-time administrator, me. We have nurses, college administrators and students, carpenters, insurance agents, former truck drivers, a retired chemist, a former owner of a chain of Midas Muffler shops, a retired real estate agent. About half of our members are women.

On our application we ask why people want to be a member. Some applicants have had a fam-ily experience with the ambulance and want to help other people out. Most people volunteer, because there is a really good feeling when you help someone. You may not necessarily save their life, but you make them feel better.

My brother John, who was a member, talked me into volunteering in 1989. I was just graduating from high school, and they were hurting for members. I was working as a carpenter and decided to check it out. That's how most of our recruiting is done. You know someone and try and get them involved if you think they would be good at it.

Normally people get hooked on it and stay. When people don't stay, it's usually because of the time commitment, 20 hours a month, and time away from the family.

Our membership is good now and we usually have no trouble covering our calls, but over the last 10 years we have had three big swings. When we have had 25 to 30 members with only 10 active volunteers, we had a hard time without calling mutual aid in Bristol or Vergennes. Sometimes they are in the same boat.

How far do we let membership drop before something drastic happens? That's what we were looking at when we started paying members $10 a call (April 2000). No one is in this for the money, but members looked at the time it was taking away from their family. And you have people who come in to the station to be on call and have to buy their own dinner.

Some people were against payment, because we have never charged for our time. Now that we have done it, I think they're glad we did it.

We still have problems on holidays and when people go on vacation. We're always in a recruiting mode. The usual life span of an EMT (emergency medical technician) is five years. In a big city, you're going to get burned out faster. We do a fair amount of calls, but it's not all day long like a big city. Spending so much time away from your family is the big issue.

In 2001 we had a little over 1,250 calls. In 1970-71, our first year, we had about 200 calls. There are not a lot of calls that get your adrenaline rushing. About 60% of our calls are for difficulty breathing and chest pain. Probably 20% are falls.

Rope, boat, and ice rescues are rarities but the association must train for them. Flotation suits keep rescuer and victim warm but their bulkiness makes maneuvering difficult.

Another 20% would be trauma related to car accident or some other equipment-related injury.

It's been a couple years since we have had a farm-related accident. We have had one person mauled by a bull and a couple people have been kicked.

We also started billing for emergency calls to the hospital about a year and a half ago. Service had always been free, but money just wasn't coming in from fund raising and our expenses kept growing. Bristol and Vergennes have been billing for years, but we were concerned what the public would think. Would the public still donate money to us if we were billing? But the public already thought we were billing.

We had been billing for hospital transfers since 1990. We were transporting patients to Burlington frequently and couldn't afford the cost of fuel and the wear on our rigs. We wanted to bill for transfers but not for emergency calls, so we created a separate entity, the InterHospital Transfer Service.

We have been well received in the community since we began charging for emergency calls. Since we are mainly billing Medicare and Medicaid we use their rates. A basic life support call to pick you up and take you to the hospital is $190 and $7 a loaded mile. An advanced life support call would be $290 plus additional charges for intubation, shock treatment, starting an IV or oxygen. In the past we sent a letter asking for a donation. Most of the time we would get $10 to $20.

Private insurance and Medicare won't pay if they think the call wasn't medically necessary or a true emergency. If insurers won't pay or people can't pay, we just write off the bill. That's probably 5% to 10% of the time.

Quite often we think it isn't necessary for the caller to go by ambulance. We get calls from people who have a cut hand or a bad toothache, but we're not going to question whether you need an ambulance. We simply go.

~

Five or six years ago our budget was $80,000 a year. This year, 2001-02, it was about $300,000, but about $117,000 was the cost of a new ambulance. Our budget for paying volunteers is roughly $40,000. We put away at least $40,000 a year toward a new ambulance each year. My salary is roughly $30,000. Our fuel budget has probably doubled. Our supplies are up.

We have three rigs and a rescue truck. We're starting a rotation where we replace each rig every eight to nine years and get a new rig ever two and a half to three years. We used to keep equipment until it was unusable and then have a fund raiser to buy new equipment. Now that we are charging for calls we budget for equipment. If there is something that will make life easier for us and the patient, we will get it.

Since we started billing we have stopped our semi-annual fund-raising letters, which used to

Since September 11, community organizations have intensified their training for acts of terrorism. In the spring of 2002, association volunteers, Middlebury fire and police departments, and Porter Hospital emergency staff responded to a "massive explosion" in the basement of the town hall and a separate school van accident that "killed" or "injured" about 20 people.

raise $75,000 to $80,000 year. We probably won't do any fund raising in the future unless it is for a new station or a water rescue boat or a new ambulance.

We are still asking each town for $1.55 per capita in support. We usually get between $800 and $1,200 from each town except for Middlebury, where we get about $13,000.

And we have about 1,000 subscribers to our ambulance service, which raises about $35,000. Some people use the ambulance four or five times

a year and have no insurance. For $35 a year we will transport anyone in your family to the hospital or other health care facilities at no charge.

~

Being the administrator was something that I really wanted to do and they were willing to give me the chance. For 20-odd years, Kathy Pomainville did everything as a volunteer and when she burnt out everyone realized how much she had done.

About 60% of the association's calls are for chest pain and breathing problems. Another 20% involve falls, such as this call where an elderly man fell out of bed and could not get up.

I like the job a lot, but it's hard being the only full-time person. With volunteers their job is their first responsibility. We have two, three, four meetings a month. The majority of our members attend, but people get "meetinged out," and it's hard to get things done without getting everyone involved.

I get pressures from two different groups on the squad. One group says we need to do whatever it takes to provide coverage. If that means hiring full-time people, we do that.

Another group says we need to do whatever it takes to stay voluntary. Some members feel that if we have to pay people to provide around-the-clock paramedic coverage they would rather not provide it. It doesn't mean that it's not best for our community and patients, but let's not do it if we have to pay someone.

Communities are generally happy with our service, but people are demanding more. They watch the TV shows and they expect we're bringing our magical drug box to make you better.

The public isn't going to accept that we didn't get there in time to save someone's wife, son or daughter because we're volunteers. That's not going to be good enough.

Sometimes we don't have enough people who can get free during the day, and we sometimes have trouble meeting our goal of having a three-person crew respond within five minutes. Nighttime coverage is still pretty good with volunteers.

We are going to ride this membership wave as long as we can. Payment has helped keep some members active, and people are also doing a lot more. I don't know what we would do next time to increase our staffing. Maybe we would have to pay people $20 a call.

I'd guess that within five years there would be at least a paid day crew with volunteers covering the nights. Within five to ten years, I envision a paid 24-hour crew of two with volunteers to ride with and supplement them.

I don't believe we are going to be able to stay an all-volunteer organization for very long. Volunteers have only so much time they can give.

Chapter 8

The Health Care System

We're Going to End Up with a Crisis If This Continues

The Business of Medicine

Health care today is often a good-news, bad-news story. Costly care and procedures that marginally prolong the life of a few may reduce the coverage and increase the cost of health care for all. Changing programs, regulations, and funding that are good for the community in the long run may be bad for individual organizations in the short run. New funding for health and home services enabling people to remain in their homes, a desired goal, can empty beds and decimate revenues of nursing homes. An unexpected outbreak of good health is good news for the community and health care costs, but may be bad news for a small community hospital operating on a thin edge between profit and loss.

That good-news, bad-news scenario was brought home very directly to the boards of Porter Hospital and Porter Medical Center at an early-winter joint meeting (2003). The good news for the community was that there had been an unexpected "outbreak of health" in the first quarter of the fiscal year and the 45-bed hospital had an average daily census of 14. What was good for the system, reducing hospitalization, the most expensive link in the health care continuum, was bad news and financially traumatic, a $490,000 loss, for Porter.

In the past, the hospital's positive "operating margin," roughly several hundred thousand dollars in a $40-million-plus budget, had offset losses at the affiliated nursing home and for-profit pharmacies.

Was this a temporary short-term outbreak of good health or was it indicative of a trend toward lower hospitalization rates that could have begun as much as a year earlier? Was the hospital a "victim" of the success of the county's strong home health agency that was keeping people out of the hospital?

Was the hospital losing market share to Rutland Regional Medical Center and Fletcher Allen Health Center in Burlington, which were both busy and advertising aggressively? Were doctors referring patients to these hospitals because of their convenience, patient preference, unhappiness with Porter? How big a factor was the departure of a hospital-employed orthopedist?

Given this uncertainty should the hospital go forward and seek state regulatory approval for a long-planned $14 million expansion? Would this shaky short-term census threaten the financial viability of the project and the likelihood of state approval? What would the 700 individuals and organizations that had pledged $4 million during a two-year long fund-raising campaign think if the hospital's boards delayed submitting a Certificate of Need application to the state until the financial

picture was clearer? If the expansion, which had already been trimmed from $16 million, was too expensive, what could be cut?"

Writ small, the joint boards' two-and-a-half-hour discussion was a microcosm of the health care debate. Many moving parts. More difficult questions than easy answers. Consequences that ripple far beyond the immediate organization.

Much like the Porter boards' discussion—they delayed submitting the permit application pending the next quarter's census and financial results (the daily census later rebounded)—our national health care discussion is also a series of good-news, bad-news paradoxes. We have cutting-edge medical care for individuals who can afford it, but, by many measures, an inefficient and inequitable health care system. In the midst of miracle drugs and life-saving technologies and procedures, many patients, especially those with chronic diseases, are choosing alternative treatments from acupuncture to herbal remedies. We retain a Norman Rockwell image of selfless doctors and providers while our health care institutions fiercely compete to protect and, when possible, to expand their market shares.

We have long since moved from the 19th century's nature-will-take-its-course home care to today's approach—aggressive use of technology, surgery, and drugs—that is far more costly, but is often no more effective, than health care in other developed countries. Government and private-sector efforts to control the high cost of this can-do, do-all approach have not surprisingly often resulted in near pitched battles among consumers, insurers, business, government, and the medical community intent on protecting their interests. These conflicts are brought home every day in national health care headlines:

Medicare Battleground for a Bigger Struggle

Is US Health Really the Best in the World?

Medicaid Costs Skyrocket, States Cutting Benefits

Doctors Withhold Services, Protest Malpractice Costs

Closer to home, Vermont's health care community has found that painless answers are elusive:

We have seen the failure and frustration of fragmented and limited approaches to managing our decentralizing health care

system. All the pieces of this machinery seem to be linked, and altering one component inevitably results in changes and adaptations in all the other components.

The time for a total approach is at hand. We must build the necessary structures to manage and prepare for the sweeping changes that seem likely to occur within the next several years.

That was the Final Report in 1992 of the Vermont Blue Ribbon Commission on Health. Translating the commission's recommendation—universal health care with a common set of benefits—proved far too complex for legislative action in the following session. More than a decade later, in 2005, the legislature, the governor, and health care community were still struggling to broaden coverage while containing costs.

In this chapter, two doctors, three administrators, and a medical anthropologist discuss the social, economic, and cultural forces that shape our health care at the community level and that lead to our best-of-all-worlds, worst-of-all-worlds health care system.

Family doctor Bill Fifield discusses the medical progress, changing patient expectations, and frustrations in practicing community medicine

today. Neil Gruber and Jim Daily, administrators of the community nursing home and hospital, reflect on the balancing act that both institutions face in being good community citizens while protecting their organization's financial health. Larry Goetschius, director of the home health agency, laments that our health care system has grown as a group of largely independent cottage industries that have not yet learned how to resolve their differences and work together for a common good.

Dr. John McPartland, a complementary medicine advocate, argues that an effective health care system must combine the strengths of traditional medicine in dealing with acute problems, such as heart attacks and life-threatening infections, with the success of complementary medicine in treating chronic problems, such as arthritis.

Medical anthropologist David Napier concludes the section arguing that the well-being of communities and individuals depends on the integration of health and social services. American health care, he believes, too often looks for quick technological and drug fixes without understanding the social dimensions of patients' lives.

Dr. Bill Fifield

Family Doctor

I'm Not a Businessman. I Want to Practice Medicine and See Patients.

Medical students are warned that medical knowledge is doubling roughly every five years and that much of what they learn will be challenged and may be discarded before their careers are over. But this exponential increase in knowledge is but part of the challenge in being a family doctor today.

Doctors no longer occupy the pedestal they once did. Many patients now want to be partners with their doctors. Medicine has always been a business, but today it is business with a capital B—a two-doctor practice may require a 10-person support staff. A nurse and a part-time bookkeeper won't do. Community hospitals once had relatively fixed service areas. Now they compete for market share, and staff specialists offer procedures once limited to urban medical centers.

Bill Fifield has been part of these changes as a family practitioner for nearly 30 years, chief of Porter Hospital's medical staff, and member of the hospital and medical center boards.

I can remember when I was a child my mother would take me to see the GP. There was no schedule, no nurse. The doctor was alone in the office. There would be a waiting room full of people, and you'd take your turn.

Your entire record was on a 5" by 7" card in his desk drawer. If you had a sore throat, he would go to his cabinet and take a big stock bottle of pills and pour some in an envelope and write "One pill

When he started practicing 30 years ago, patients rarely questioned his recommendations, today many patients want to be an active partner in decision-making, a positive change, says Bill Fifield.

four times a day."

This Norman Rockwell physician is really becoming a dinosaur. It's so much more complicated and stressful today to be a family doctor. If you are alone and don't have backup coverage then you don't have a life or a life you'd want for your wife and kids.

That visit was probably three bucks. I'd guess our standard office visit today is close to $40. We have a staff of two full-time nurses, two part-time nurses, a medical transcriptionist, a file clerk, two receptionists, and an office manager. That's pretty standard for a small family practice office—two physicians and a nurse practitioner.

When I started 30 years ago people were more interested in crisis intervention. Patients wanted relief from their cough or headache and rarely questioned your recommendations. They definitely do now and want to be part of the decision-making. Doctors were once placed on a pedestal. We certainly don't occupy that space any more and shouldn't.

Some of this change has come from doctors, but most of it came from the patients. Today, the public is much better educated and more aware of the importance of lifestyle choices and the modification or elimination of risk factors like high blood pressure, obesity, smoking, and diabetes.

Patients find information on the Internet and can be more up to date on some issues than I am. Patients will ask about new developments before I have had a chance to read the journal article. Or they see a drug advertisement and are told to "Ask your doctor about it."

Most of the Internet information explosion is very good. But some may not be and patients may choose treatments that are contrary to what I think is in their best interest. Treating breast cancer with herbal medicine, for example, may not be as helpful as conventional surgery, radiation, and chemotherapy. Obviously the choice is theirs but ultimately that choice might hurt them.

Overall, people are healthier today. If you look at life expectancy, people born in 1900 had a life expectancy of 45 to 50. A child born in 2002 has a life expectancy nearly two times that. Heart disease, cancer, and stroke are the three major causes of death, and we're making progress in those areas. Diabetes is being recognized earlier and treated more effectively.

People are getting their cholesterol down. Blood pressure is being treated. People aren't

Primary care doctors will have to concentrate on more complex problems and delegate routine health issues, like earaches and hypertension, in the future. These problems can be managed by nurses and nurse practitioners as long as they are supervised, says Fifield.

dying of heart attacks at the rate they used to.

But so much of the cost of health care gets back to lifestyle choices. So many of the "medical" problems that people come here to talk about are psychologically related, although they may not recognize or initially want to accept that.

If we could somehow convince members of our society to make healthy choices. Don't smoke. Get exercise. Eat a healthy diet.

And how do we instill in parents the impor-tance of spending quality time with their kids, read-ing to them and playing with them? Dad has dinner in front of the computer. Mom has dinner at a meet-ing. And the kids get a TV dinner in front of the TV.

Families don't talk about current events and issues. Kids don't play cowboys and Indians. They watch video games. Schools can certainly do a lot, but many parents expect the school to "fix" their kids and supply the attention that they should be providing.

I sometimes feel poorly prepared to help people deal with chronic alcoholism, smoking, and the stress in their lives. I think all family doctors do. These are real tough issues to get a handle on.

We try to open the door to a discussion of patients' broader concerns when they come in for physicals and when we think it is appropriate. In the last several years we have started asking people if they have guns in their houses. Some people were offended. "What's that have to do with my health?"

People have a right to bear arms, but we don't want their personal choices to present a risk to society. We don't want another Columbine where a 14-year-old steals a loaded rifle, takes it to school, and shoots his schoolmates and teachers.

We constantly deal with the "worried well" whose problems—headaches, chronic diarrhea, palpitations—are caused by the stress in their lives. I have common sense advice—talk with your family, your boss, and friends. And medication can help. But I'm not a psychologist or psychiatrist and will sometimes recommend counseling or therapy.

Thirty or 40 years ago if a family physician suggested that a patient see a therapist there was real resistance, "Oh, the doctor wants me to see a shrink. He thinks I'm crazy."

Now people are aware that most of us at some time in our lives can benefit from some counseling and therapy. Somebody from the outside can look at your situation, give you an objective view, and guide you through a difficult situation in your life.

~

There are three issues in health care—quality, access, and cost. You can have two but really not all three. We have pretty good quality and timely access, but we certainly don't have inexpensive health care.

There is some fraud and abuse, but they are a tiny part of why health care costs are increasing. Part is our aging population. These costs will only increase as our population ages.

Part is our use of technology. A number of years ago one county in California had more CAT scan machines than the entire country of Canada. And if you have the latest whatever you will want to use it, partly because you have to pay for it and

partly because patients want the latest.

I encourage patients to try conservative therapies initially when I'm certain that they are not in any medical danger. Lack of health insurance has virtually no affect on what I provide, but it certainly impacts their overall care. Take someone with terrible back pain who may have a slipped disc that requires back surgery. The only way to determine that can be an MRI, which can cost $1,000 to $1,200.

If the person has no health insurance that cost is a very, very major issue. In situations like that perhaps we are forced to try some therapies that we might not try if payment wasn't an issue. In other cases, we encourage patients whenever possible to use generic drugs, which often work as well as brand names, often at a fraction of the cost. Most people are pretty comfortable with generics.

Patients are affected by increasing insurance premiums and are beginning to realize that we just don't have a blank check to do everything anymore. But there still is the view, "Yes, we have to reduce the cost of health care, but I want everything for Aunt Tilly."

How do I counsel families facing costly but perhaps futile medical procedures? It is an individual thing. I talk with the family. Ultimately the decision has to be up to the patient, the family, and the person with durable power of attorney for people who can no longer make decisions.

Sometimes the insurance company says, "No. We're not going to pay for that." So to some extent it is between the patient and insurer. This can be a frustration for us.

At what point are we as a society going to have to make some tough decisions? Are we going to be able to or should we pay for certain technologies or drugs or procedures simply because people want them?

I don't know how many politicians are going to have the courage to tackle these questions.

I'm not a businessperson, never have been, and don't have any particular interest or expertise in business. I want to practice medicine and see patients. That's what I'm trained to do, do best, and like to do. When Tim (Tim Cope, his partner in Champlain Valley Family Health) and I first started practicing together in 1979 there were times when we took out loans at 22% interest to pay the staff and weren't sure that we could pay ourselves. It was pretty lean at times, and we had to borrow to keep the office going. It's even harder for residents with big medical school debts to start a private practice today.

Tim and I have long felt that one big advantage in being employed is that the hospital or health plan manages the business so we can concentrate on medicine. About 10 years ago, we talked about aligning with CHP (Community Health Plan). CHP was considering building a large office building in Middlebury with X-ray, lab, and possibly physical therapy and other ancillary services. They would have been a real threat to Porter if they had done that. CHP couldn't make any money and has since pulled out of Vermont.

About eight years ago, we sold our practice to Porter Hospital. Everything looks the same except the bills, which now come from Porter Practice Management rather than from Champlain Valley Family Health.

I can't think of any comments, either negative or positive, from patients. Most patients aren't even aware that we're employed by the hospital.

Most primary care practices do not make a lot of money for the hospital. Some lose money. It's the nature of our reimbursement. We admit people to the hospital, but surgeons do procedures,

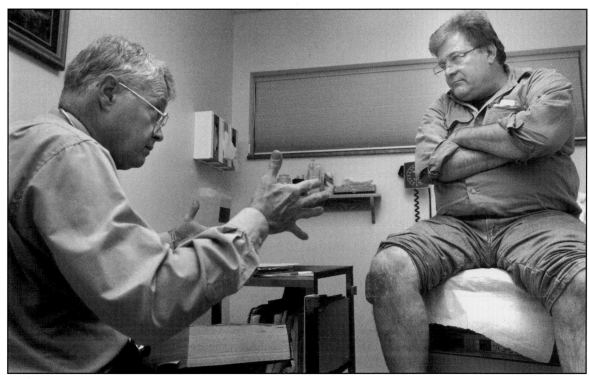

Today's Internet-savvy patients may be more current on the latest treatments and drugs than their doctors, but they still need help in evaluating the proven from the untested, says Fifield.

which generate more income for the hospital.

Many board members wondered if employed doctors were going to earn their keep. Jim Daily, our CEO, has been very good at persuading the board that these practices are a good investment, because primary care is what keeps Porter going. If the hospital wants to attract good people it has to have a good relationship with primary care physicians. So even though we may not directly make a lot of money for the hospital our overall impact is great.

No one has said, "You have to see this many patients per day, generate this many dollars." But Porter has to be a financially healthy institution—no margin, no mission is part of the strategic plan—so I can see that becoming an issue some day. I understand that we have to think about the bottom line, but my top priority as a physician is to advocate for my patients.

Since I have been on the Porter board, I have certainly become much more aware of the financial aspects of the hospital's operation. Much of the board discussion concerns financial issues, and most of the board members are businesspersons.

When I was medical staff president, I read the minutes of the hospital board very carefully and reported on them at quarterly medical staff meetings. What surprised me was how little interest some medical staff members have in the operation of the hospital.

Perhaps it's because our lives are just so full. Your practice may be 50 or 60 hours a week. You're up at night and are tired. You have family commitments so people think, "Gee, I really don't need to get involved. Everything seems to be going OK. It's a tight ship."

Porter is certainly financially viable and stable and on solid ground, but we don't have a tremendous endowment or operating margin. Our

Helping patients deal with stress and the attending health problems when there are no easy solutions is one of a primary care doctor's greatest challenges, says Fifield.

So the College is very much interested and supportive of Porter's long-term viability.

In the best case, Porter will expand its outpatient facilities—lab, X-ray, physical therapy—as all hospitals are doing. And I'd like to see more emphasis on women's health and on care of older folks, such as an assisted living facility linked to Porter.

While our inpatient population will drop, I would like to think that Porter will remain viable as an inpatient facility. We can take care of most cases of pneumonia every bit as well as Fletcher Allen. People in Middlebury or Cornwall or Weybridge want to come to Porter and don't want to be in a hospital an hour and half away in a snowstorm.

If we have someone with a really weird pneumonia that's not responding, we can transfer the patient or get infectious disease and pulmonary consultations at Fletcher Allen. But in terms of outcomes we do a very good job at what we do.

endowment is approximately $350,000 in unrestricted funds. That's not much of a cushion.

Health care is a business and Porter Hospital wants to capture as much of the market share in our area as it can. We compete for patients in Brandon and Vergennes with Rutland Regional Medical Center and Fletcher Allen Medical Center. Porter owns two family practices in Vergennes (2002) and one in Brandon to encourage people from those communities to think of Porter as their hospital.

To a large extent competition is good. When I came here, the obstetrics service at Porter was going great guns in part because it was the first area

hospital with classes to prepare parents for childbirth and child raising. That program improved the quality of care for everyone.

The downside is that competition can drive up costs. If you increase the supply of doctors and add technologies, the number of procedures and costs increases. The rate of procedures, like hysterectomies and c-sections, varies tremendously throughout the country. Why is that? Are too many being done in one area and not enough in another? Is it because of different approaches to treatment or because there are more doctors to do them?

All in all, I find it hard to foresee a time when Porter would close. The College owns the land we're sitting on and if Middlebury did not have a hospital what parents would send their kids here?

I started off in college as a physics major. Then I had a serious illness and came close to dying. That experience was largely what led me to change my major from physics to pre-med.

I've wanted to practice medicine since then. Overall, it has been gratifying. I still love taking care of patients even if I don't have as much time with patients as I'd like.

Some of my colleagues miss the "good old days" when there were far fewer regulations and can't wait to retire. Some of my colleagues think that we are practicing in a "golden age of medicine" today. I'm somewhere in between.

I'm looking forward to retirement and am frustrated that so much of my time is spent dealing with things other than patient care—paperwork, bureaucracy, forms to justify medications not on a preferred list, prior approval and referrals for managed care.

But on the other hand, there has been so much progress during the time I've been in Middlebury. The Porter Hospital of 2002 is a very different place from the Porter of 1979 when I came. Our physical plant is light years ahead of where we were. The staff was about 15 to 20 physicians when I came. We are now 60 to 65 and have very good specialty representation.

We had no full-time emergency room staff. If you were on call and one of your patients came into the emergency room at 3 o'clock in the morning with a sore throat you were expected to see them. Now we have full-time emergency room coverage. That is so basic to good-quality health care. We didn't have it when I came.

In so many ways we are better able to take care of our patients today, and the next 10 to 20 years are going to be extremely exciting. We can potentially cure diabetes through gene therapy. We may be able to identify the gene that programs some people toward alcoholism and alter it. Will we be able to alter the gene that programs us to age? If it is possible, is that good?

I don't think we're going to see some of these things in my lifetime, but we have the potential to cure or alleviate so many diseases today.

So I have found what I wanted in medicine. But there is always the pressure of moving on to the next patient, and the paperwork, dictation, insurance forms and phone calls that often keep me at the office until 7 or 7:30.

That's the part that frustrates me.

Patient care remains satisfying, says Fifield, but tight schedules, mounds of paperwork, insurance coverage hassles, and long days are driving doctors of his generation into early retirement.

Neil Gruber

Administrator, Helen Porter Healthcare and Rehabilitation Center

We're Going to End Up with a Crisis if This Continues

Helen Porter Nursing Home opened in 1970, part of the nationwide boom in nursing home services, following the passage of Medicaid and Medicare programs in the mid-1960s. By the late 1980s, Addison County had outgrown the 50 beds in Helen Porter and the 17 beds in a nursing home in Vergennes, causing a patient traffic jam. Recuperating hospital patients needed nursing home placement, but couldn't be discharged because the nursing homes were full. People needing elective surgery or other treatments couldn't be admitted because the hospital was full.

In 1991, a new 118-bed Helen Porter Nursing Home replaced the original home and was full within two years. But since the late 1990s, the census of many nursing homes has plummeted as services and payment for home and community-based care have expanded under the state's Act 160 plan. Some nursing homes have closed, and others, like Helen Porter, have been forced to eliminate beds and add new services, such as a dementia unit, in order to survive. (The interview was conducted in 2002.)

I've been in the business for 20-plus years and these last four years (1998-2002) have been the most challenging I've ever seen.

In 1998, my first full year as administrator here, the nursing home was 98% occupied, which is about as good as you can do. Since then our

Constant underfunding threatens nursing home quality and needed investment in training, programs, and infrastructure, Gruber believes.

average daily census has declined from 116 to 97, and we have downsized from 118 to 105 licensed beds to cut costs.

But the financial plan for this building was based on having close to 118 residents. In the 1999 fiscal year, with declining occupancy, the nursing home lost close to half a million dollars, and in 2000 we lost nearly a million dollars on a budget of $6 million. In the last three years we have had to cut costs and staff, reinvent ourselves with new programs, borrow heavily from Porter Medical Center, and get an extraordinary relief package from the state to help cover our deficits. Given our importance to the area, it was unlikely that we would have closed, but it wasn't out of the question.

For our first 25 years, we were mainly a long-term care facility with very little turnover of patients. But the business has changed, and now we're providing a great deal of short-term rehabilitative care. Our median length of stay used to be measured in months if not years; today it is 34 days. About one out of every five admissions will become a long-term resident. When I started here, perhaps a handful of residents went home in a year. Today, we may have that many discharges in a week.

In the past year, we have changed our name from Helen Porter Nursing Home to Helen Porter Healthcare and Rehabilitation Center to reflect our changing role. When this building opened there was a part-time physical therapist and a part-time aide. That was the extent of the rehabilitation staff.

Today, we have 11 or 12 on our rehab staff: a physical therapist, a physical therapy assistant, physical therapy aides, speech therapists, an occupational therapist and an occupational therapy aide. We couldn't have imagined several years ago that we would be taking care of a 16-year-old girl. But yesterday we admitted this girl, who was referred to us for rehabilitation by Fletcher Allen until she is ready to return home.

Insurance plans won't pay for lengthy, expensive hospitalization for rehabilitation today. But some people aren't well enough to go home immediately. They may need to learn how to use adaptive equipment, and their homes may need to be adapted. So we have now dedicated 21 beds to a rehabilitation and sub-acute care unit.

We are also developing a dementia unit that will have 36 beds. We have always had people with dementia, but by consolidating these residents in one wing we can offer new programs and better service with a specially trained staff. Many nursing homes will not take people with severe

Finding and keeping staff, especially licensed nursing assistants, in a tight labor market is an ongoing problem for nursing homes. In 2004, Helen Porter's 31% turnover among its 80 LNAs was less than half the average–64%–of the state's 40-plus nursing homes.

Alzheimer's so we think there will be a growing need for this service.

We will have another 8 or 10 beds dedicated to specialty care, like hospice and respite care. The remaining 30-plus beds will be our traditional long-term care population.

It's hard to calculate a break-even census with these changes, because reimbursements dif-fer in each category and depend on the needs of the patient. But if our census drops below 90 or is even in the lower 90s we may not be financially viable unless reimbursement rates are increased. And we don't anticipate that in the current budg-etary and regulatory regime.

But it appears that these changes are working and that the nursing home will be slightly in the black in fiscal year 2002. (The home was narrow-ly in the black in 2002 and 2003 but had a $265,000 deficit in 2004, as Medicaid reimburse-ments didn't cover costs.)

If you ask my peers in the 40-plus nursing homes around the state what their biggest problem is,

Helen Porter, faced with an abrupt decline in its traditional population of long-term care patients, has broadened its service with the development of an Alzheimer's unit and an expanded rehabilitation center. The center's expanded activity programs have included a ferry boat cruise for 40 residents on Lake Champlain, supported principally by a one-time $10,000 quality-of-life grant from the Vermont Department of Aging and Disabilities.

some would say staffing. Others would say reimbursement, but those would be the top two for everybody.

Most nursing homes probably don't face quite the same cost and staffing squeeze that we do. We're part of an organization (Porter Medical Center) that works hard to fairly compensate employees. And I have to compete with our hos-

pital—and hospitals traditionally pay more than nursing homes—for staff. Why would a nurse want to work at the nursing home if we paid significantly less or didn't provide the same benefits as the hospital, which is right next door?

I'm trying to cut costs without compromising quality, but this is more difficult to do than ever with the low unemployment rate in Addison and

Chittenden County and a shortage of nurses.

Back in 1999-2000 we faced a real Catch-22. Our census and reimbursement rates were both dropping. We needed revenue, but I had to restrict admissions when we were short staffed.

This nursing shortage will probably be worse than our last shortage in the late 1980s. The median age of nurses is now the mid-40s. There are many fewer people entering the profession. People would rather work in a Monday to Friday, 9 to 5 job, than weekends, evenings, and nights in a nursing home.

Many health care providers are feeling the shortage, not just nursing homes. My mother was scheduled for surgery at a major medical center, and she didn't know until the day of the surgery if the hospital would have the nursing staff for the operation. And this is a hospital that pays very, very well.

In the past, I've run ads all over Vermont and New York, posted jobs on the Internet, and haven't had a single RN nurse come to the door. The state's Blue Ribbon Nursing Commission had many suggestions two years ago to encourage more people to consider nursing and school enrollments are up, so that is a good sign.

And with the slowing of the economy it has become easier to hire LNAs. Our starting wage for a LNA is now more than $9 an hour ($10 in 2005), and we offer a generous benefits package that is probably better than three-quarters of the businesses in Addison County. We have a state-approved 80-hour training program for our own LNAs and then help them to move up the career ladder.

I lobbied the state Department of Aging and Disabilities, and we and nursing homes in Morrisville and Newport received state grants for local LPN training programs. Our program is offered by the Community College of Vermont here in Middlebury with interactive television programs offered through Vermont Technical College. We have one or two people who have gotten their associate's degree and another three or four who will be starting the program.

Many people leave the field because they don't feel appreciated and feel overworked, so we are also working hard on retention. I was in here this morning for our first staff appreciation breakfast and flipped pancakes for our staff. It was a small thing, but there were a lot of smiles that we were acknowledging the good work they do.

The state's policy under Act 160 is to reduce the number of nursing home beds and to provide more care in home and community-based settings. Officials say that Vermonters overwhelmingly want to remain in their homes, which is true. But part of the state's motivation is cost. There are going to be so many more elderly people that we won't be able to afford nursing home care under our current financing structure.

At the same time, it becomes cost prohibitive at some point to provide skilled, around-the-clock services in homes. Nursing homes have a cost advantage here with economies of scale in providing skilled care under one roof.

If the state wants fewer nursing home beds, they ought to have a plan for closings. Some communities have a surplus of beds, and there should be a plan to take some beds off line and compensate operators or help them provide new services. The state has given us a five-year, $100,000 interest-free loan to help us convert part of our East Wing to a dementia unit and for capital improvements in our rehabilitation and sub-acute unit. There should be more of that.

Helen Porter is now the only skilled nursing home facility in Addison County. The county has the second lowest number of nursing home beds per capita for people over 75 and is "significantly underbedded," according to the state's ratio.

We don't know how successful the state's emphasis on home and community-based care will be. If we close the doors on too many nursing homes, we may find that we need that infrastructure in the future.

What is most frustrating is the state and federal government's conscious underfunding of our care. Nursing home residents are sicker and needier than ever while reimbursements are being cut back. Our state Medicaid reimbursement in 1994 averaged $124 a day. In 2000, it averaged $123.

That 2000 rate was based on our costs in 1997 when the nursing home was being run by a for-profit nursing home chain. Those administrators reduced costs dramatically by cutting staff and programs and in so doing damaged staff morale and reduced services at Helen Porter. The board did not renew their contract, but state regulators used their costs to determine subsequent reimbursements.

Subsequently, the state adjusted the Medicaid day rate, after we ran large deficits, to nearly $160 per day in 2002. But this rate still does not cover our costs, and Medicaid provides two-thirds of our revenue. Private insurers are charged $195 to $200 a day for the same services. (In 2005, Medicaid's daily reimbursement of $190-plus continued to lag behind the room's cost of about $210 per day.)

Rate-setting officials say they have not seen an erosion in quality of care, and there is no need to improve reimbursement. Vermont's nursing homes are some of the best in the country, but we're going to end up with a crisis if this continues.

Today, nursing homes are under both financial and regulatory siege. We've always been a highly regulated industry, but the degree of that regulation has grown dramatically in the last five years.

But it's not clear to me that all this regulation has improved the quality of care. What is clear is that regulations have complicated our record keeping and increased our workloads.

Since the early 1990s we have had to complete a Minimum Data Set, which is a national database to monitor the quality of care in nursing homes. All my clinical staff fill out forms at admission and at various intervals describing in detail the resident's care.

These forms then determine reimbursement rates for Medicare patients receiving skilled care in our rehab and sub-acute care unit. We may then get reimbursed at four or five different per diem rates during a patient's 100-day stay, the maximum coverage of Medicare.

Medicare has one classification system with 48 different groups that determines its reimbursements. The state uses another formula for its Medicaid reimbursement rates with 44 classifications. So we need computer software that puts these residents into the proper category and a nurse whose only job is to fill out the Minimum Data Set.

Vermont has been ahead of most states in basing Medicaid reimbursements upon residents' care needs. The old reimbursement system in the 1980s and early 1990s paid you a flat rate, whether a patient needed a lot or a little care.

Some providers took advantage of the flat rate. If the rate was $100 a day, and one patient consumed $120 a day in resources and the another $90 a day, it was a no-brainer whom you served if you were a for-profit business.

So we now have this case-mix payment system that bases reimbursement on the medical needs of the resident. Theoretically, we are reimbursed based on need, but the state changed the case-mix classification system in the late 1990s to lower reimbursement rates and save money.

The prospective payment system was needed, but it needs to be done better. What was a fair system has now been subverted.

There are thousands of nursing homes in this country, and 95% are doing the best they can with limited resources. But there are some facilities that are more interested in the bottom line than in patient care. So some oversight is good.

But regulators are feeling pressured by the federal funding agencies to find more problems and deficiencies. Onerous regulations are placed on all nursing homes, not just those facilities that are frequently not in compliance.

There are 25 quality indicators in the Minimum Data Set. Take skin care. There's now a scope and severity scale from A, which is a very minor deficiency in a very isolated situation, to K or L. If there are negative findings, you're expected to correct them. Failure to correct them can lead to sanctions and ultimately to loss of your license.

In three of our last five state inspections we've been free of any major deficiencies. We're working diligently to maintain that level of quality, but it's getting harder and harder to do. We're getting paid less money, while we're being asked to provide higher-quality and more sophisticated care.

As a non-profit our mission is to serve the citizens of Addison County and we accept, unlike many for-profit nursing homes, residents based on need, not ability to pay.

We're not asking for a lot more money.

If we could get reimbursed by Medicaid at or near our true costs, another 10% to 15%, we could afford to provide the training, programs, and staffing that we can only dream about now.

Medicare patients are limited to 100 days of service in a nursing home. Staff evaluates their progress after 5, 14, 30, 60, and 90 days. Medicare reimbursement rates are adjusted after each review. When Medicare runs out, residents must qualify for Medicaid, pay privately, or have long-term care insurance.

Jim Daily
President, Porter Medical Center

Health Care Is a Challenging Set of Businesses

Community hospital CEOs, like other high-profile community leaders, often have tenures that can be counted on the fingers of one hand or two. Jim Daily came to Porter Hospital in the mid-1980s when he was in his late 20s and has now led the 45-bed hospital for nearly two decades, the second longest tenure among administrators of Vermont's 14 community hospitals. As head of the dominant health care institution and one of the largest employers in the county, Jim Daily's challenge is to be a good listener, collaborative partner, and community leader at a time when health care questions have no easy answers and there is little economic margin for error.

People expect that I will be accessible and that the hospital will have its finger on the pulse of the community. It's easy to concentrate on internal issues and assume that outside relations will take care of themselves. When you say, "We're great," you're in trouble.

We want a relationship with our neighbors. Meeting with them two weeks before we go before the planning board with a construction project is not a relationship. When we were going to build the 118-bed nursing home in the early 1990s, I could see that we were going to change some neighbors' views. So we made sure that the design was as flat as possible.

It's easier for a small community hospital to establish its importance than a several-hundred bed hospital in Rutland or Burlington. Your friends, neighbors, and other competent people are taking care of you. There is only one medical-surgery unit, one obstetrics unit, one intensive care unit. You don't need colored lines on the floor to find your way around the buildings.

I'm not saying that personal contact never happens in larger places, but it is easier to have it happen here.

Over the last five to seven years I've also created as many connections with Middlebury College as I can. The more important we are to Middlebury College the more confident I am that we will survive.

We lease the land we're on from the College for $1 a year with a 90-day cancellation. (A Middlebury native and College trustee gave the community $100,000 to construct a hospital in the early 1920s with the provision that the College own the land and hospital. The College retains ownership of the land, but a non-profit hospital corporation now owns the expanded hospital complex.) Porter is an integral part of the College's student health plan, and their medical director has been a Porter employee in the past.

When I came in the 1980s a few doctors questioned if Porter was the community's hospital or the College's. The College has three dedicated seats on the Porter Medical Center board, who serve at the pleasure of the College, but you can't tell who is from the College in our board meetings.

~

Porter's mission statement states that we should be a leader in determining the health needs of the community. This hasn't been easy work. There is a price to be paid for being the biggest fish in the pond. No matter what we do, some people think we can do more.

Health care has been a challenging set of businesses to be in. The counseling service has gone through some very, very difficult financial times. Home health has been challenging. Our sister organization, the nursing home, has had brushes with insolvency.

I have always thought that our mission statement meant we should be communicating with other organizations and working together when it served our patients or clients. But if this threatens us financially then all bets are off. We will only do that which guarantees our financial survival.

The recent community proposal to build an assisted living facility next to our nursing home is a case in point. Community and church members thought the county needed an assisted living facility, especially for lower income people. I was pretty sure that an assisted living facility would hurt our nursing home. The nursing home board also had many questions on its economic impact, which the developers didn't answer.

Now that the state has issued its regulations on the services that an assisted living facility must provide, it is clear that their assisted living facility wasn't in our interest. State regulations require that an assisted living facility must provide nursing home services if residents' conditions deteriorate and they want to remain there. In essence, the facility would become a nursing home and siphon off our volume.

Everyone supports the state's policy to have people age in place in the least restrictive setting. Addison County health care providers have done this better than anyone else in the state. But there is a limit. You can't keep stacking the deck against nursing homes.

Jim Daily is the public face of Porter Hospital, such as at this meeting with the state's Public Oversight Commission, which reviewed the hospital's proposed $14 million North Project expansion. After a multi-year planning and review process, Porter broke ground for a new birthing center, in- and out-patient operating and recovery rooms, and a relocated pharmacy in the spring of 2005.

The long-term care system simply can't take the shock of having $20 million pulled out of nursing homes and redirected to community and home care as the state has done. Two years ago (2001) the nursing home lost nearly $900,000, largely because of state policies. We have restructured programs at the nursing home and cut our losses, but we need higher Medicaid reimbursement rates to sustain the nursing home long term.

The economic impact of the nursing home and hospital on this community is probably north of $30 to $40 million. So wipe these institutions out, put some college dorms here, and the economic impact would be felt.

In the end it is hard to serve two masters. My job is to make sure that this place in toto is protected.

I decided early on that I didn't want the hospital's survival to be at risk from the policies of Burlington and Rutland hospitals. One of my first priorities was to create a primary care network in and beyond Addison County with primary care physicians, nurse practitioners, and internists.

When I came in the mid-1980s I was too inexperienced to see this big picture and thoroughly evaluate the hospital's needs. I found that there was a daunting list of physical issues—making sure that the toilets flushed, that we had

Porter employs 20 doctors of the 70-member medical staff at Porter Hospital and now owns and operates three specialty and five primary care practices as fewer and fewer doctors, especially those just out of medical school with debts to pay off, want to run their own practices. Creating a level playing field for the entire medical staff when it comes to access to new patients and the use of hospital facilities and technology is an ongoing challenge.

enough electrical capacity, that the roof didn't fall in—before we did strategic things.

We got that straightened around. And then I'm looking at CHP (Community Health Plan), which was employing physicians and was acting like an insurer and a provider. I didn't want them to come in and control 50% to 60% of the primary care market and give me the deal for Porter Hospital or they would send their patients somewhere else.

At the same time physicians were coming to me who were tired of running a practice and who were spending less and less time with patients and more and more time on paperwork and making

payroll. So CHP is on the horizon, and doctors are saying they have had it.

I wasn't sure that Porter would be a great employer, and most physicians don't make great employees. But I said, "We will use our strengths to combine with your strengths to be all winners."

In 1992 we bought our first practice and have acquired about one a year since. At one point, we owned and operated 11 practices, four specialty and seven primary care practices. We have strong outposts in the halfway zones in Brandon, Vergennes, and Bristol, where we compete with Rutland and Burlington. We have now cut back to

three specialty and five primary care practices.

We employ roughly 20 out of the 70 doctors on the staff. That is a good mix, but as we go through our next medical staff development plan we will be analyzing what would happen if doctors retire, leave, or get hit by a bus on the way to work.

There is some sensitivity among doctors that the hospital is a 600-pound gorilla. So we are all going to agree on what happens when doctors retire. Who is going to hire someone to replace them?

I have interviewed many physicians over the last 10 to 12 years and have met very few who are willing to take the risk of setting up their own practice. We have gone for long periods with overworked, self-employed specialists unable to hire partners. This lack of depth and breadth has hurt hospital revenues, so we have stepped in at times and hired specialists in obstetrics/gynecology and orthopedics. A private group provides our urology service. So I hope that we have proven that we don't have to own and operate every practice.

There is a lot of angst in the boardroom about the losses of some of our primary care physician practices. But it is important that we have a strong primary care base and that we control our destiny. And I look at the broader derivative income they generate for the hospital.

But there aren't significant economies of scale in employing these doctors. We pay our physicians a little more than the average self-employed primary care physician and have higher benefit costs.

I'd like to break even in primary care, and it appears that we will cut our losses from $900,000 to $250,000 this year (2003). But once a small hospital employs practices, getting rid of them is a real bear.

You can't assume that we'd eliminate our losses if we divested. One, doctors would be very angry.

Two, they'd defend their incomes doing X-rays, lab work, and other procedures the hospital does.

Whatever you do, you're not going to make a lot of money in primary care. What you have to do is make sure that your network creates a force field to compete with any predator in Brandon or Bristol or Vergennes. So we try to have a solid primary care network with well-trained physicians who are good at things beyond just "doctoring." We want quality people who are involved in the community.

I met with pediatricians the other night and said, "Here is where we have to get the numbers. What ideas do you have?" They are in charge of choices, but they have to land in this zone. They will either have to work longer, harder, or they'll have to give away some of the icing.

I'm pretty sure that they're not going to say, "I want to go back in business for myself." They have been weaned from that for too long. And most of them are realists enough to know that printing money is not one of our options.

From the mid-1980s into the early 1990s, we had to focus on improvements that weren't very glitzy. It's hard to do capital campaigns for things like heating systems.

I didn't know if the board and staff would be patient enough to wait until the early 1990s before we could start big bricks-and-mortar projects, first a new nursing home and then the South Project, which added a new emergency department, lab, and X-ray space.

What has not changed between the mid-1980s and today is the need for patience. We have been talking about and planning the North Project for seven or eight years. We are talking about a lot of money, $14 million, and I take every reasonable

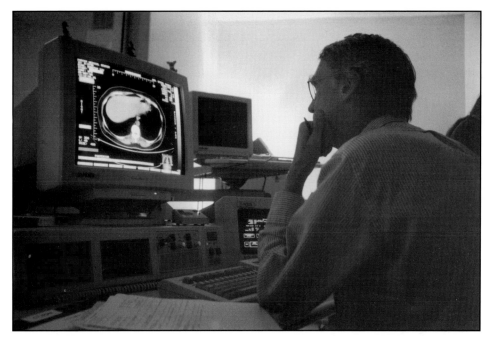

How much high-tech equipment should a community hospital have? What can the system afford? Porter has its own $600,000-plus CT scanner, above. Porter contracts with a for-profit imaging firm, which serves community hospitals in Vermont and New Hampshire with a mobile unit, to provide the more costly MRI testing two days a week.

opportunity to tell the physicians that the project is a priority but that they have to be patient.

The medical staff's expectations are high, but we have consistently kept our technology and equipment current. We don't have the extremely sophisticated equipment of a tertiary center or bigger hospitals, but our operating room for what we do is as well equipped as any hospital in Vermont and probably New England.

Looking at the environment in 1984 and today, there are still expectations that probably can't be met and shouldn't be met. During planning for the South Project, we considered having our own MRI, but we quickly became convinced

that a mobile service could more easily stay on the cutting edge of technology. So we have a trailer with a MRI that comes to Porter two days a week.

More recently, we had to tell some community members that it wasn't economically or medically feasible to provide dialysis services at Porter. Area residents will have to continue to go to Rutland or Fletcher Allen for this sophisticated service.

New technology drives costs up, but the real cost driver has been inflation in wages and salaries, especially in benefits like health insurance, pensions, and malpractice insurance.

Whoever sits in this office gets more credit than they deserve when things go well and more blame than they deserve when they don't go well. I was hired after the hospital board had fired the last two chief executive officers. There had been a vacuum in leadership, and a new person could come in, take stock of things, and generate some positive momentum.

My job day to day is still working on the micro level—budgets, staffing, facilities. That is what I like to do and am more comfortable doing than in opining on broad health care policy questions.

Next year (2004) our budget goal is to make $600,000 out of a net revenue of approximately $40 million. Hospitals are a narrow margin business, which reflects our high costs and government underpayment.

Getting squeezed by insurers is a constant concern. What do I do if an insurer tells us that they'll only pay $2,700 rather than our normal $3,000 for a procedure? If we don't meet their price, they will go elsewhere. I'd say if you send us everyone in our catch basin, we will give you $2,700. If our volume goes up, we can charge less.

If we still can't meet their price, then we have to talk about how important it is to have basic services in a community hospital. Is it worth it to turn this community hospital into an emergency room, ambulatory care and low-intensity care facility and have the rest go elsewhere? Certainly, it is less convenient.

When it appears there is not enough money, regulators and politicians say, "Oh, we must have too many hospitals." But I believe Vermont's community non-profit hospitals provide good geographic coverage with a minimum of overlap.

If I try to be unbiased and not be the CEO of Porter, I'd vote for a network of 12 or 13 solid community hospitals. I'd take the model where you concentrated more sophisticated procedures in area medical centers like Dartmouth Hitchcock or Fletcher Allen and did the most sophisticated procedures only in regional major medical centers in Portland and Boston. This would be the best long-term investment but would require that we broaden our definition of regional care.

By consolidating community hospitals, you'd redistribute but not necessarily save money. Some people wouldn't get care or would postpone care or have to travel for care. I doubt that would be cheaper in the long run.

I do not see any change in our independence in the near future. My former Fletcher Allen counterpart thought we should explore an affiliation at some level. But our land lease arrangement with the College would make it difficult, if not impossible, to have a formal affiliation. And as long as the hospital continues to be reasonably successful financially, I don't see affiliation in the works.

If the future of the hospital were in doubt then the board would explore all alternatives. But I have always assumed that I'd get fired for poor performance long before the board would consider merging with Fletcher Allen.

The average tenure for a hospital CEO today is around five years. I told the board when I came that I didn't plan to move to a bigger hospital after three to five years. But I was 29, and I wanted to stop short of saying that I wanted to retire here.

I view myself as a caretaker and don't want to get too involved in a sense of ownership. It's not mine. It's not my business. I'm privileged to be invited to be the leader, and I want to leave it better off.

One of my irrational side goals is one day to be the longest-serving hospital CEO in the state. I have been here just about 20 years; there's one CEO who has six months on me. But when you're frustrated, it's tempting to think about going somewhere else and starting totally new. But I can't remember when someone called about a job that described a better place to live than here. There are bigger places and places where you can make more money. And there are a lot of places with bigger problems. There are many hospitals in Massachusetts that are losing money hand over fist and aren't long for the world.

My job is still primarily to convince people of the path that we need to follow. It's a little easier now than when I was the new guy with no track record.

For a number of years I have been working to get the board to be more active and to take a more central role in areas like holding the medical staff accountable for the quality of clinical care in the hospital. That is one of their biggest challenges.

Frankly, the board has become too reliant on me: "Jim will take care of it." That is fine if we have discussed the issue, and I'm the best person to follow through.

Sometimes issues are uniquely their responsibility. So I have been pushing back and saying that you are the governing body. I'm accountable to you. I work for you. But health care is complicated, and hospital trustees spend only three or four hours a month being a trustee.

It's easy to say let the CEO do it.

Larry Goetschius

Executive Director,
Addison County Home Health
and Hospice

Could We Do It Better?

Appropriate health care serves community residents at the right time in the right place by the right people. One of Larry Goetschius's responsibilities as head of the area's home health agency is to help create and maintain this seamless web. But creating a system among many providers where the sum of services is greater than its parts has proved elusive in the past and will be an ever-greater challenge in the future, Goetschius believes.

Cooperating for the greater good of the health care system is difficult for traditionally independent, protect-our-own health care organizations, Goetschius believes.

Health care grew up as a cottage industry. We haven't gone beyond that.

The hospital acts independently. Doctors act independently. The pharmacy acts independently. We in home health act independently. That is the way health care has grown.

There are advantages to this approach. Organizations can provide a level of service that might not be possible in a "system." If I start a program, it's mine and I protect it. But that perspective doesn't lend itself to looking at the larger picture and continuity of care from organization to organization.

What you don't want is a system with lots of hand-offs. Errors take place in the hand-offs, and we have a system that's fraught with hand-offs.

Since becoming executive director 14 months ago (December 2000), I have been talking to people and trying to learn how home health care works. My background is program administration

in large hospitals and academic medical centers where all departments came together under the medical center umbrella. In the home health community there is no umbrella. We don't report to anyone and aren't forced to integrate with other organizations beyond our mutual interests in maintaining and improving patient care.

So I have been asking how we as agencies—home health, elderly services, mental health, the hospital, the nursing home—work together and what is our incentive to work together. A reimbursement pie that isn't getting any bigger is not a catalyst for people coming together. Instead everyone wants to protect their agency or organization as the pie shrinks.

And if the pie is shrinking, where should the money be taken from? Acute care where the people are sicker? Or out of home health where people are in theory not as sick? So my biggest challenge has been to understand what other people do and how to best integrate our services.

I'm finding that many long-standing agency administrators see us as being more conservative in our approach to care. When I first arrived that was a fairly hot issue, and I tried to understand our differences with the Champlain Valley Area Agency on Aging (AAA) and, to some extent, Elderly Services, over treatment of the elderly.

We really have different models for looking at the same situation. Home health follows the medical model, which is do no harm. We don't want to put anyone at risk because the home isn't "safe." Wires might be exposed. There might be holes in the floors and no sanitary facilities. Some clients might have some dementia and not be totally able to maintain themselves.

There may also be financial concerns if the person is to go into a nursing home. Does the family have to spend down most of their assets before becoming eligible for Medicaid coverage?

AAA folks believe that if a patient understands the risks of living at home then they will work as hard as they can to provide the services to make that happen.

We haven't had a way of saying, "Let's talk about our disagreements so we both understand why the decision was made." One side backs away, and we end up with bad blood. It's, "Can you believe what they did with that patient?" That goes into the storage bank and gets brought out every time anything like that begins to happen.

This probably happens only three or four times a year, but it is a huge emotional commitment. Staff can name disputed patients going back 3, 4, and 5 years.

I don't sense that my fellow administrators feel a great need for this review. At this point, they don't feel that the "system" is totally broken. My question is, "Could we do it better if we were working together in a more integrated way?"

It may be pie in the sky, but I would like to develop an environment where we all put our heads together and figured out how to best use our resources. Having worked at large medical centers, I saw disciplines that did not traditionally communicate talk to each other to the benefit of the patient.

The boomers probably won't hit us for another 5 to 10 years, but we can't wait that long to decide what we need to do. Combine that with the continuing effort to push people out of hospitals faster, and we will be seeing sicker patients at home. We are all going to have more business than we know what to do with.

What's driving health care costs? Utilization, high-tech procedures, new drugs.

I was at a meeting several months ago and said the state should start a discussion about what health care we as Vermonters are willing to pay for. Someone very angrily said that is rationing.

I'm not talking about rationing. I'm saying we ought to have a discussion if we want to have rationing or not. We talk about how much health care costs, but we separate the benefits from the costs. If it is personal, it is the benefits. If it is society, it is the cost.

We have to bring those two views together in the same room and decide if we are going to do less of, say, health care and more of, say, education. Maybe Vermont will be willing to pay for everything. But let's make that decision consciously and agree that we will pay more taxes for that premature $500,000 baby or that 89-year-old who needs bypass surgery.

When the Certificate of Need bill was being debated in the Senate, some legislators wanted to put restrictions on hospitals to control the cost of care. I'm thinking, "Hospitals don't control costs. A hospital has never made an order on a patient. Doctors place orders."

Hospitals can help start the public dialogue, but having them be the police is crazy.

Asking the doctors to do it is also not going to work. Doctors see themselves as advocates for the patient and are working from a higher principle than saving a little money.

Home health is not going to solve this. We are a following agency. We don't set the rules. We accept what we are given and work within that.

We want to care for people in the places that are most appropriate. Some of our services make money. Some lose money. We are not trying to put money in the bank, but have enough at the end of the year to keep us viable.

The health care system is not going to solve this. And we can't solve this locally. It's a state and national question. Society has to agree that we will do this, we won't do that.

The governor should start to facilitate these conversations. But politically, no one wants to get near it. People don't want to think that their mother isn't going to get the care that she needs when she needs it.

Dr. John McPartland

Complementary Medicine
Advocate

There Is a Middle Way, Truly Integrative Medicine

John McPartland became interested in plants as food and medicines after Euell Gibbons, author of Stalking the Wild Asparagus, *visited his Boy Scout summer camp. McPartland, a doctor of osteopathy with a master's degree in botany and plant pathology, has written widely on the history and role of holistic and herbal medicine and was one of the organizers of the Vermont Holistic Health Directory. In the fall of 2001, he left his Middlebury practice to become the dean of the first college of osteopathy in New Zealand.*

Many people think the sky's the limit when it comes to health care. Unfortunately, it isn't. We have the best health care technology in the world here in Vermont, but we can't afford it. And we will never be able to afford it as high-tech costs spiral upward.

We might have to change this by legislative fiat, by changing the focus of medical research and grants, by putting more resources into preventive medicine and community health care and not into the latest high-tech machinery to maintain somebody's life an extra six months. Instead of paying for liver transplants and liver transplant research, we should be putting our money into research on alcohol reduction. The end result would be the same, reducing liver disease, but it would be a lot cheaper.

Otherwise, we're going to see a two-tiered

About three-quarters of our health care system's expenditures involves treatment, often with high-cost drugs, of chronic conditions. Complementary medicine can be effective and cheaper, McPartland believes.

medical system. People who can afford the sky's-the-limit will get the sky's-the-limit. Everyone else will be eliminated by the constraints of modern society. States like Oregon have established a rationing system. That's going to come around, because we just can't afford everything. So we might as well start changing our focus.

I'd also like to see more rapport between the alternative and traditional medical communities, because they have a lot to learn from each other. "Alternative" is perhaps a misnomer, because it's not really alternative but "complementary" care. The vast majority who use unconventional therapy for serious medical conditions also seek help from a MD.

There are closed minds on both sides. You have indoctrinated MDs who don't want to learn anything about alternatives. You have alternative practitioners who read stuff off the Internet and take it as gospel truth.

Western scientific or allopathic medicine is good for many acute diseases, severe trauma, medical emergencies, surgery, and infections. Many of these problems and conditions are beating a hasty retreat. We don't see people dying of scarlet fever or strep throat or appendicitis today.

We're left with many chronic diseases. People are dying from chronic cardiovascular problems. There's more pain and suffering from chronic arthritis and autoimmune diseases. Many allopathic arthritis medicines are toxic in the long term, so you need to find something else. That's where alternative therapies come in. They support the person's health rather than fight the disease.

A body worker would approach arthritis from a musculoskeletal point of view, trying to treat arthritis pain by balancing the musculoskeletal system. Acupuncturists would approach it from a different angle. An herbalist would treat arthritis with herbs that are gentle on the system.

I define osteopaths, like me, who use manipulation on more than 75% of their patients to be in the alternative camp. The osteopathic theory is that manipulation enhances the proper movement of fluids, such as lymphatic fluids out of an infected lung or sinus. Some osteopaths also believe that manipulation helps balance myofascia, the muscles and their connective tissues. Your whole body is really not 649 separate muscles but one interconnected muscle. If muscles are in balance, everything functions better.

Some alternative practitioners manipulate the body's energy field. Acupuncturists manipulate the body's energy or chi with their needles. You can also manipulate energy with hands-on manipulation.

Chiropractors talk about innate intelligence, which is energy that they are helping to move. Innate intelligence is the same concept as Chinese "chi" and Indian "prana." Both are poorly defined "life forces" that animate all living creatures. It's not a very well understood system, and it's patently rejected by most MDs.

I came out of osteopath school, where training is very similar to MD schools, extremely ambivalent about the whole idea of "life force energy." But I have listened to what patients have to say after they saw different practitioners.

I have a file full of articles predicting the end of alternative medicine. But alternative medicine, be it massage therapy, acupuncture, or allergists, is filling a niche, especially in chronic problems, and people keep coming.

When I did an inventory of the alternative medicine community with the UVM med school in the mid-1990s, there were about 900 alternative people. I'd estimate it's over 1,200 now, which is as many if not more than the number of MDs.

There was a 1990 Harvard national study that estimated that there are more visits each year to alternative medicine providers than to primary care doctors. The study of about 1,500 adults found that about a third used an unconventional therapy during the year and that about a third of those people visited an alternative medicine provider. The highest use of unconventional ther-

apies was by the following group: non-black persons from 25 to 49 who had relatively more education and higher incomes. The majority used unconventional therapy for chronic, as opposed to life-threatening medical conditions.

Part of the increased interest is just greater awareness. Alternative medicine has been in the news and that starts to create its own interest. Part of the increase in interest is frustration with traditional approaches to chronic diseases.

Physicians who were trained even 15 years ago were given a heavy dose of ideology. They learned that acupuncture is quackery and herbal medicine is something we left behind 100 years ago. Today, more than half the medical schools offer courses in alternative medicine. So younger physicians are learning what syndromes benefit from alternative approaches, and many younger physicians have actually had experience with alternatives. That can make a difference.

But most physicians haven't taken the time to look into it and so they can't make recommendations on something they don't know exists or understand.

Many physicians, for example, think herbs are toxic. Very few herbs are toxic and the ones that are toxic are not being prescribed by herbalists. Period.

With acupuncture there is the concern that if you put needles in the chest of someone with pneumonia, you might drop a lung. That concern comes up all the time, but there are only two cases of pneumothorax from acupuncture in the medical literature.

In chiropractic, there is concern that manipulation could cause a stroke or damage a spinal

nerve. But there are only 110 cases in the literature of serious side effects. That's it. Studies have estimated the odds at one in one million that a manipulation could cause a serious side effect.

The end result is that the MDs see the danger and not the benefits. It's all side effects and no benefits. So alternative practitioners need to make the first move toward the traditional medical community. One way is through education.

Charlie Mraz, who lived here in Middlebury, was probably the most famous alternative practitioner in Vermont in recent years. The theory behind his bee sting therapy was that it stimulated the body to produce its own healing forces, its own cortisol. Bee stings acted like immunizations.

Some people say that's a bunch of hooey. But there's something to be said for encouraging the body to heal itself. But besides bee sting therapy, Charlie was a true shaman. When I was in school, we were taught to support and enhance the placebo effect, which is a concept diametrically opposed to MD training. We were taught it's a "real" medical treatment, if it helps you. Charlie was a healer, because he combined the benefits of the placebo effect and of bee stings.

There is a middle way, truly integrative medicine. That is going to be in our future because we can't afford the high-tech solutions. We have to incorporate some of these alternative modalities and we need to be listening to each other. Economic reality is going to force traditional doctors and alternatives to talk to each other more.

David Napier

Professor of Anthropology and Sociology, Middlebury College

We View Health and Well-Being Much Too Narrowly

David Napier has taught at Middlebury College for the past 20 years and at Harvard Medical School. He has written widely on the need for broad social and cultural experiences in the undergraduate education and medical school training of doctors. His students annually shadow rural health care providers and have surveyed community attitudes on the availability of health care in Addison County and the concerns of primary care physicians in rural Vermont.

The key to the well-being of individuals and communities lies in understanding the social dimensions of people's lives and integrating health and social services, David Napier believes.

The World Health Organization (WHO) recently ranked health care systems around the world based on life expectancy, system responsiveness, and financial fairness. The United States ended up 37th. We spend the most by far—$4,200 per capita (2000) compared to about $2,400 in France and Japan and $900 in Singapore. We rank near the top in many health measures, but we distribute services and costs unequally, the report said.

Many critics would say that the report is just political crap. WHO is made up of a lot of special interest lobbies from Third World countries that are trying to do us down.

But what can we learn from the report and other studies? What stands out is that our notions of well-being are culture specific and aren't universal. We are far more enamored, for example, of technology that will make us healthy than other countries. Human interactions don't wow us like technology.

France was ranked number one, and they have

a very different view of health and the body. They are willing to put up with more chaos in the body, more bacteria, and let the body's own systems respond. In France people with breast cancer have the same outcomes as we do, but they do far less surgery.

In France, many MDs are also licensed homeopaths. The government will pay for a spa if your doctor thinks you would benefit. For the French complementary medicine has a place in health care. We generally consider it weird alternative practice.

We are much more aggressive in our surgical procedures, in ordering diagnostic tests, and in prescribing expensive cruise missile drugs. Most Americans don't think about health care services until they need them, and then they want everything.

Middlebury College has an internship pro-

gram in Scotland and London for undergraduate students interested in health care. They learn that the most important factor in a patient's clinical care is not necessarily technology or the doctor but the person at the front desk or whoever sees that health and social services are integrated. That's what makes community medicine work.

In the United Kingdom, doctors and their staffs see themselves as advocates for their patients in a system that has limited resources. There should be no mystery why the levels of satisfaction in managed care are so low in the United States. It's obvious. Doctors are seen as an advocate for a cost-cutting organization no matter how nice they are.

We view health and well being much too narrowly. It doesn't make any difference if it is an urban or rural setting; doctors who know their patients understand the subtle distinctions that improve their sense of well-being. That could be something as simple as helping someone with arthritis turn off the leaky tap.

It doesn't mean the doctors will do that, but that they will know someone who can help. To use social science lingo, social, psychological, and financial problems get somatized, become part of us, and end up on the doctor's doorstep as illness.

We are shooting ourselves in the foot when we don't acknowledge that. Studies show that 80% of all diagnoses can be made from a careful case history. But it took the HMOs forever to realize that spending 20 minutes with a patient was more effective and cheaper than spending five minutes and ordering lots of tests.

Unfortunately, medical school students actually get worse at listening during their medical training, because they spend all their time presenting to residents and working up complex cases to impress their peers. At medical centers the patient has become a chart, which filters out the social dimensions of that person's life and well-being.

People worry too much that we will have to ration care in the future. The bigger problem is that we aren't talking enough about the social dimensions of well-being. We say that we value these services, but many other countries have more extensive social services and provide the universal health coverage that we don't. That doesn't mean that Americans are disingenuous. We genuinely have those values, but we haven't done a very good job of developing the environments where they can flourish.

Today, we aren't disposed to think about the longevity of the community the way my grandparents who lived through the Depression did. My grandmother was a hairdresser and maintenance person yet she still baked 30 to 40 loaves of bread on Saturday and passed them around to people of the community. That was her recreation.

I grew up in a very poor neighborhood of Pittsburgh with steel mills around us. One of the largest buildings on the main street of our town was a boys' club, effectively a social center where kids who had little or nothing to do could go for healthy sports or game-related activity. It was like a shelter with a director who befriended the kids.

Compare that with Middlebury. We have plenty of initiatives to rebuild our town hall or to put up more beautiful buildings on the college campus, but all one hears about skateboarders is how do we get them off the street because they are a nuisance.

When I came here in the late 1970s, the county was more of an agricultural community. But since then, our economy has moved from agriculture to tourism and college-related businesses. Boutique industries and alumni with resources make the town work, but this lifestyle is relatively alien to the agricultural community we were only two decades ago.

There is a feeling now that we are a middle-class community where people with resources can provide for their kids autonomously—my kid goes to tennis camp or soccer camp. There is not a baseline that says every child in Middlebury should have an after school program because we know that their parents are working and that they are going home to empty houses.

Isn't it better that they go to a youth center than go home and get on the Internet? God knows what they are dealing with there. As affluent as we are, we can't say Middlebury has this wonderful facility for our kids.

And there's not a lot of discussion about making that happen. At a school board meeting, the budget talk is about cutting this, cutting that. The rhetoric is that the kids have too much, even though most of the money is going to fix the roof or eliminate asbestos in the boiler room.

There is no real public discourse now on how childhood and adolescent experiences determine whether kids will want to part of the community in 10 or 15 years. It doesn't place the fault on any one person's doorstep, but the problem is certainly there for all of us.

How do we decide who gets what health care and social services when we can't have it all? There have been thousands of people who have tried to answer that and failed. It's pretentious to think that I can.

I do think there are certain win-win situations, and we have to decide which of them we value most. Having a MRI in the back of a trailer that pulls up behind the hospital and does expensive procedures is a win-win for a certain group—surgeons, drug companies, the manufacturer, hospital revenues, and some patients. For me having a youth center in Middlebury would be a much better guarantee of creating the social dimensions that are essential in a healthy, sustainable community. But we can't quantify its impact now.

What keeps me up at night is how insulated and self-replicating contemporary institutions allow themselves to become. Institutions are like cell colonies—they die from the center.

You have to make the efforts, as painful and discomforting as they are, to get outside your institutions and decide where your larger societal allegiances should be.

Chapter 9

Health Care Reform

It's Going to Take a Real Squeaky Wheel

Reform Will Be A Gut-Wrenching Thing

In his 2001 State of the State Address, Governor Howard Dean announced the formation of the Governor's Commission on Health Care Availability and Affordability. The seven-member, bipartisan group of legislators and present and past state human services and health administrators was to "identify ways we can achieve the dual goals of controlling costs and guaranteeing universal health care access."

Eleven months later, the commission issued a report that reflected the complexity of health care economics and politics and the difficulty that even a small group had in reaching consensus.

"Health care in Vermont is near a state of crisis—some of us would say it is already in crisis—and all health care sectors are on edge," the commission, known as the Hogan Commission, reported in its introduction. Vermonters' health care now costs over $2 billion, more than the legislature budgeted for all state government services, $1.8 billion a year. "We are rapidly approaching the point at which these (health care) costs will directly conflict with our ability to do such things as to maintain roads and bridges, for example, or to provide cost-effective services to our infants and children, to promote agriculture and tourism, or to provide any other services our citizens have come to expect," the commission warned.

If it was any consolation, the report noted "that many of these problems are national or even global in scope and that our abilities to solve them at the state level are limited." Indeed, the commission sent letters to the state's Congressional delegation with 25 recommendations for federal action, ranging from multi-billion-dollar new programs, i.e., Medicare coverage of prescription drugs, to procedural changes, i.e., shorten the eligibility questionnaire for home care services.

The good news was that Vermont ranked among the highest in the nation in percentage of residents who have health care coverage and that with significant exceptions—such as lack of dentists and primary care doctors in some rural areas—Vermonters have enough health care facilities and personnel.

The bad news was that 26% of the uninsured had delayed or postponed medical care because of cost, that many employers couldn't find appropriate, affordable health insurance for their workers, and that the state's Certificate of Need process to evaluate and approve major capital health care expenditures lacked regulatory resources and meaningful sanctions to control costs.

After 16 meetings, hearings with major interest groups, commissioned background papers, briefings by public and private health care organizations, and an extensive electronic exchange of views with the public—180 individuals and organizations submitted testimony—deep philosophical differences remained among commission members.

Two members filed minority reports to register their concerns and nearly all members inserted footnotes questioning, clarifying or opposing attempts at "consensus" statements within the report. With some caveats, commission members agreed, in a dispiriting list of particulars, that Vermont had good health care for some but not a good health care system for all.

Vermont's problem was lack of accountability and control. No one organization was responsible for ensuring the adequacy of high-quality medical care or that medical charges were appropriate or paid in full.

At the individual level, most consumers with health insurance were shielded from the cost of the service. At the state level, there was no global budgeting or targeted growth planning for health care. Although administrative costs have reached an unacceptable level, no one has been able to control them, the commission concluded.

To deal with these problems, the commission suggested six broad initiatives: promote personal responsibility for health behaviors; curb excessive administrative costs; offer affordable health care by extending Vermont Health Access Plan coverage with minimal damage to the commercial insurance market; strengthen the insurance market and promote the possibility of more insurers offering health insurance; enhance education and critical thinking about health and related topics; and curb unnecessary health care utilization.

The commission did not address the high cost of long-term care, pleading lack of time and resources. And the commission did not recommend a single-payer system, though it noted a second study group, the Lewin Group, had recently reported to the Agency of Human Services that a single-payer system could cover all Vermonters, including 51,000 uninsured residents, for 5% less

---

PRECEDING PAGE: *Sen. Gerry Gossens and Rep. Betty Nuovo meet with staff of the Counseling Service of Addison County.*

than current costs. Aside from the lack of political consensus for such a system, commission members questioned government's ability to control health care costs and were also concerned that a payroll tax to support the system could harm small employers and employees.

Several months after the commission's report, a third group, the 10-member Commission on Public Health Care Values and Priorities, created by a legislative resolution in 1994, surveyed 400-plus Vermonters.

This commission's report, "Hard Choices in Health Care 2002 What Vermonters Are Thinking," largely mirrored the findings of its 1996 survey.

• Two-thirds in both surveys said they would pay higher taxes and more for health insurance to provide coverage for everyone.

• Support for taxpayer-funded health insurance remains "rock solid." 94% supported federal Medicare coverage of the elderly and 87% supported federal/state Medicaid coverage of the low income.

• 75% believed that those receiving taxpayer-funded health care should pay at least some of the cost of their health care.

Within a span of six months, Vermonters had three reports assessing the state of health care in Vermont.

What did these reports accomplish? Did the legislature take "decisive action" as it was urged? Faced with a slumping economy and declining tax revenues, the legislature in subsequent sessions could do little but attempt to maintain current health care programs and minimize the harm of cutbacks.

Fast forward to the 2005 legislative session, where the health care proposals of the Democratically controlled House and Senate and a Republican governor again reflected the deep philosophical divisions that have made reform so difficult. Again, the numbers were disturbing.

State health care costs now topped $3.5 billion annually and were increasing at 10% a year, a rate more than twice that of the growth in personal incomes and state budget revenues. Double-digit increases in the cost of health insurance had increased the number of uninsured to 63,000, with the number of underinsured estimated at 90,000. Especially troubling were the multi-million-dollar deficits that the state faced in the coming years in funding its 37% share of the Medicaid program. In short, superb health care for some was still not translating into an accessible, affordable health care system for all.

Against this backdrop, Vermonters reiterated their support for comprehensive health care reform. Twenty-one of 23 Vermont communities approved a resolution at town meeting urging the legislature "to actively work for the creation of a universal and comprehensive health insurance system which is publicly financed and accountable to the citizens of Vermont."

Coalition 21, a non-profit health care advocacy organization that included representatives from business, health care, and consumer groups, was formed in the summer of 2004. Its guiding principles included support for a state policy that would ensure universal access and coverage to essential health care services for all Vermonters.

After a session-long debate, the House and Senate passed bills that would be financed by new income and payroll taxes and would move the state at varying speeds toward universal health care. Following the session, the governor, whose less ambitious proposal retained much of the current funding structure, vetoed the legislature's compromise conference bill.

The governor promised to unveil a new health care plan for the 2006 legislative session that would not contain his proposed tax on insurance premiums to pay for expanded coverage, a provision that received very little legislative or health insurance company support. The legislature, in turn, appointed a 10-member study commission to study how best to finance a universal health care system and how a publicly financed system would affect the economic competitiveness of the state.

What we are left with is the decades-long challenge of meeting the day-to-day health care needs of Vermonters and the bigger question of defining who we are as a caring society.

Should health care be considered differently from other goods and services in the economy? Is it a human right? If so, who gets what? Who decides? What can we afford? Is incremental change the most productive approach? Is comprehensive reform the only solution? How do we start and sustain a broad societal discussion of what we want from our health care system? Where will the leadership come from?

In this concluding chapter, Addison County residents—a hospital CEO, a businessman, a consumer activist, a state legislator, and a pediatrician—grapple with these questions.

The largest piece of the health care pie, about a third, goes to hospitals. Hospitals are being unfairly asked to curb utilization without detailed guidelines, says Porter Hospital CEO Jim Daily. We need a broad societal discussion about core health benefits, but politicians, providers, and payers are putting off such a discussion because it is so "gut wrenching," says Daily.

Federal, state, and local taxes that support Medicare, Medicaid, and health insurance of public employees pay for about 60% of the country's health care expenses. The majority of Americans not covered by publicly financed programs are covered by health insurance through their employers. These plans cover about 20% of the cost of the nation's health care. The remaining 20% is covered by individuals' out-of-pocket payments.

Maynard McLaughlin, president of a medium-sized engineering and construction firm that self-insures and provides generous health care coverage, believes that Americans have unrealistic health care expectations—high quality, low cost, and complete access. Americans must accept limits and take more responsibility for their own health if we are to control costs, says McLaughlin.

Peg Martin has been involved in county health programs for more than 30 years. She was one of the co-founders of the local Head Start program, a state legislator for 10 years, past president of the board of Elderly Services, Inc., and a former consumer representative on the board of the Vermont Program for Quality in Health Care. The health care community must learn how to talk about and balance individual desires and larger societal goals, she believes.

No matter how the debate over health care access and reform plays out, the state legislature will be in the thick of it. Comprehensive health care reform failed in the legislature in the early 1990s, in part because of the complexity of the process. Since then, as noted, there have been numerous task forces, studies and incremental expansions of coverage. What is now needed, former state senator Gerry Gossens believes, is a sustained, high-profile conversation, begun by the governor, legislature, and the state's medical leadership, that engages and educates the public.

Pediatrician Jack Mayer practiced in hardscrabble eastern Franklin County for 10 years before coming to relatively affluent Addison County. We must rethink the delivery of rural health care beginning with medical school training; we must also understand the importance of a rural network of supportive services and colleagues. But most important, health care, he believes, should be a basic human right where families and children are not at the mercy of the marketplace.

Jim Daily

President, Porter Medical Center

Reform Will Be a Gut-Wrenching Thing

Any discussion of slowing the cost of health care often starts with hospitals, the largest piece, about a third, of our health care budget. Jim Daily, head of Porter Hospital for nearly 20 years, believes that reformers and regulators are unfairly asking hospitals to curb utilization without sufficient guidelines. What is needed, he suggests, is a comprehensive and sustained societal discussion of what we want from our health care system and what we can afford.

Health care costs are likely to increase from 13%, 14% to 16%, 17% of our economy in this decade. Some say, "So what if 20%, 22%, 23% of our economy goes to health care. It's money well spent."

But at some point we are going to have to unaddict ourselves to "this health care thing," because these dollars are coming from education, housing, and other social needs. That's not the basis of a sound economy. The fact that the economic pie has been growing so fast has hid this.

But health care is clearly different from other goods and services in the economy. We can't have people dying because they didn't have money to get medicine. We can't have increased illness and disease because we are rationing care based on ability to pay like any other commodity. That won't play.

To make major cuts implies that we will have a broad societal discussion. That discussion will be a gut-wrenching thing. Until there is real pain or a

NOTHING WE'VE EVER DONE BEFORE WILL BE GOOD ENOUGH TOMORROW.

ANON.

Reworking our current non-system of health care will be politically difficult because every provider of health will say they are underfunded. To bring down costs, everyone must receive a basic set of benefits, says Daily.

catastrophe or a real demonstrated need we will continue to put off the difficult discussions about who lives, who dies, who pays and core health benefits for everyone.

With entitlements, whether they are government programs like Medicaid and Medicare or private health insurance plans, there will always be more demand than the supply of dollars to pay reasonably for the care. If you give someone a health care credit card, what do you think will happen? Utilization will go up.

State regulators and the governor say hospitals have to curb utilization. But it's not for me to determine the proper level of MRI use or who gets hip replacements at what age. It's too late and not right to tell patients when they're in a doctor's office or at the hospital, "Sorry, you don't meet today's criteria."

Everyone should be pushing for this discussion. But almost no one is, because the incline is too steep and we're too addicted to the money. Politicians realize that talking about rationing is a good way to lose an election. Companies don't want to talk about cutting benefits because that gets them into the difficult negotiations with their employees over who is going to pay how much.

Corporate America is now telling their employees that they will have a lump sum, say $5,800, for all their health care costs. If you want a low deductible then you have to pay for your own dental and eye coverage. That's fine if you're corporate America, but most businesses in Addison County are small and can't afford double-digit health care increases each year.

Not far into Medicare and Medicaid, we realized that these entitlement programs were costing a lot more than we thought. In two or three years, costs and utilization busted through all the actuarial estimates. Ever since, policymakers and legislators have been trying to slow or ratchet down the cost of these programs.

In life you usually get what you pay for. The state, by expanding Medicaid coverage and paying hospitals 30 to 40 cents on the dollar for some procedures, ends up undermining the system. As

In an effort to control health care costs, the state requires that hospitals justify and get approval for rate increases. Daily and chief financial officer Duncan Brines, right, appear here before the Public Oversight Commission in Montpelier.

government has expanded Medicaid programs, hospitals have also had fewer and fewer higher-paying private insurance plans to cost shift to.

That is not sound policy. Erosion of the quality of care is going to be a side effect. That's the future of health care. Don't expect a lot. It's going to be at best mediocre-plus.

I don't know any substitute for paying a fairer amount if you're going to entitle people to care. I'm not saying pay all the charges, but pay reasonable costs. A reasonable number cruncher could walk through a hospital and come up with figures on fair compensation and whether the hospital is spending money willy nilly on BMWs instead of Chevys.

Some might argue that Porter's community health, smoking cessation, and education programs could be eliminated. Hospitals should be in the "sick" business not the "wellness" business. There'd be differences over what is reasonable, but you could come up with definitions that would be much better than what we have now.

I understand the politics of wanting to provide care to various categories of people, but out here in the real world when Medicaid pays 30 cents on the dollar for some procedures, there's nobody for us to say, "Here's the rest of the bill."

Obviously, it is not politically appetizing to talk about limiting care. But we are getting older and living longer, which is an invitation to more chronic disease. That means more pills, more therapies, more surgical procedures, and increasing cost.

The health care you're buying today is not like a car that you bought 30 years ago which hasn't changed a whole lot. Your car has four tires and an engine. You put gas in it. You turn it on and it gets you from A to B.

In health care, we have a far different product. We can keep people alive, even in a small community hospital, with clot busters for your heart attack that might have killed you 10 years ago.

Who's going to say, "No. Stop that. Enough is enough."

Leadership has to come from the governor, business, and health care leaders in any major reform. But in our current political cycle of two-year terms, reform is really difficult.

The governor is elected in November and takes the oath of office in January. Sixteen or 17 months later governors prepare a budget that might not be theirs. It's just too small a window for major change. We need longer terms where officials are held accountable. Maybe we ought to have four-year terms or one six-year term for governor.

The governor can then tackle reform without worrying about reelection. Reform might take the whole term, but we could have discussions in every county and in as many communities as is feasible about a basic package. Here is what everybody gets—immunizations for kids, preventive and basic health care. Peripheral services will be available if you can pay for them, which is how we ration care now. That's been done in some states, most notably Oregon, where through public discussion they have prioritized the services that will be covered.

Hospitals like Porter would have to keep the discussion on a constructive footing. Imagine the concern of people in their 70s or 80s who are struggling to pay for prescriptions and who read that some people won't get basic care. Hospitals don't make tons of money, but Porter would have to be cut back a lot for us to not be able to perform.

But unless there is a real change in the landscape, I'm not confident that we are going to have this discussion any time soon. There does not seem to be the ability for real political bipartisanship on major reform. Politicians want to be on the cutting edge of new ideas, but our political process encourages marginal approaches, being a little faster and appearing brighter than the opposition.

Back in the early 1990s, the state legislature grappled with comprehensive reform and it failed. At the same time the private sector was looking at managed care to squeeze costs out of the system. But managed care is a marginal approach that can't cut costs forever. The first year or two of a diet you may be able to lose 10, 12, 15 pounds. When you drop from 200 to 160, losing 15 pounds a year becomes not only dangerous but also ill advised.

The status quo has certainly won most battles at the federal and state level recently. Reforms failed but the economy was so vibrant that the growth of some indices relented and premium increases abated. We are now confronted with the same increase in costs and premium increases with no managed care fix or silver bullet in sight.

What remains is that the state is now tweaking Medicaid budgets and reducing entitlements. The result will be that uninsured people will get shoddier care than people with insurance.

Back in the 1980s, we had an Addison County Health Council, which was the idea of Ted Collier, a local internist who was ahead of his time in his thinking. Ted argued that we needed broad representation and balanced investment in our health care system, a global budget for health care.

We are not an integrated health care system today. We are a lot of little parts. So how do you get a net over all this? You need common governance so there is common decision making on a global budget.

This global budget forces you to make allocation decisions for the county on mental health care, long-term care, physical health care, drugs, the hospital, the whole thing, and would require broad societal discussions. You're not going to be able to give everybody everything they want, because you don't have enough money.

The health council with the right vision and leadership could have emerged as the umbrella health services organization. I couldn't believe how far ahead Addison County could have been. But the council didn't have broad enough representation or enough people who felt strongly about it.

I don't know if we could create a similar health council or have global budgeting today. It certainly would not be without huge challenges. Reworking our existing non-system is almost like political reapportionment. Immediately people are going to be leery of their ox getting gored.

Every segment of the health care business will say that they are underfunded. We have low hospitalization rates in Addison County so we could see a windfall of funding while counties with high utilization areas could be cut. Those counties and their political representatives wouldn't be happy.

What it comes down to is you can't get universal coverage on the cheap. If you are going to bring down costs, whether they are age, income, or technology driven, then you must have a basic set of benefits for everyone. That means increasing taxes, which would be extremely unpopular.

I think we are the kind of people who believe in a core of benefits, but I don't know if that is the case until it is time to stand up and be counted. There is no way around the fact that we have a finite amount of funds. When allocations get too out of whack, when you have to wait too long for a diagnostic test or surgical procedure or don't have access to services at all, then people will be in the streets.

Maynard McLaughlin

President,
Bread Loaf Corporation

I Get on a Soapbox When People Say They Don't Have Any Responsibility for Themselves

Most Vermonters not covered by Medicaid or Medicare receive health insurance through their employers. But employer coverage varies widely: only about a quarter of firms with fewer than five employees provide coverage compared to 90% of firms with over 50 employees. The ever increasing cost of health insurance has led many larger employers, such as Bread Loaf, to self-insure and has forced others to reduce coverage. In the late 1990s, McLaughlin was the chair of a Vermont Business Roundtable task force that produced several studies, among them, "Can We Have It All? Balancing Access, Quality, and Cost in Health Care."

Low cost, high quality, and unlimited access to health care services is an impossible combination. Everyone must understand that we have limited resources and take more responsibility for their health, Maynard McLaughlin believes.

I feel very strongly that it is not the government's responsibility to provide health care. It's the individual's responsibility. More and more, it's government should provide this, provide that.

I get on a soapbox when people say they don't have any responsibility for themselves and that someone has to take care of them.

I'm not saying we should never do anything for anyone. But I'm saying we are at a point where too many people want everything done for them for problems that they brought on themselves by not taking any personal responsibility.

Sure cigarettes are addictive. I smoked two packs a day for 15 years. I understand when people say they can't quit, but I don't agree with that. That means that you are weak and are choosing not to quit.

Some things happen that are not choices. Our health care system can take care of that. But the only way to control health care costs is by controlling use, and we are using it more and more.

Five or six years ago the Vermont Business Roundtable (a non-profit, non-partisan organization of business leaders) put together a health care task force that included a cross section of the health care community—providers, insurers, and business

people. As we looked at reports and talked with people we found that everyone wants to have complete access to the system. No one wants to pay very much, and the quality has to be high.

There is an analogy in building. We tell clients that there are three factors in building: size, cost, and quality. You get to choose two, because the third is determined by the other two.

There is a disconnect in health care. People want it all and the highest quality but don't want to pay more.

This mindset will never change while the government continues to expand benefits without fully paying for them and without telling people that they can't have them. I have a difficult time with the state of Vermont's expansion of health care coverage through Medicaid and VHAP (Vermont Health Access Plan). It's crazy when you get to a point where the government is covering health care costs for children of people who make 300% of the poverty level. That's $50,000 for a family of four.

The governor (Howard Dean) is now saying (2002) that the state has to cut back on the programs that he has been expanding for nine years as if there was never going to come this day when we didn't have the money. That's the difference between being a politician and a businessperson. A businessperson has to understand that today's decision is going to be out there for a long time.

From my perspective there is very little that is not being done for Vermonters who can't afford health care. When we talk about the people who are still uninsured, we should talk about those who could be insured if they wanted to. They have made choices and opt not to have insurance.

If you're talking about people below the poverty level, they are covered. How high above the poverty line should you go? That is where you can create real problems with our economy and state.

When people demand a pharmaceutical benefit, we have to say we can't afford it. Those programs just keep growing and growing once they start. Unfortunately we as a country are shortsighted and have to get ourselves into a very difficult situation before we think about these questions.

It will take a complete breakdown of the health care system to get people's attention. It's hard to tell how close we are to that point, but it's getting to be a crisis.

The goal of our reports is to start a public dialogue. We hold a news conference and send them to the legislators and other groups interested in health care. But we are not a lobbying organization, and there is not a lot of follow-up. They're available, but I can't see that they have much impact.

The only way you will start a public dialogue is by saying, "No." Then people sit up and then the dialogue can start.

In that respect I have been doing my employees no favors by not increasing their premiums. They have been shielded from the cost of any procedure because their deductible is so little. Our family plan (2002) costs the employee $11 a week or $550. It's giving it away. Unless you understand what health care costs you are not really forced to decide, do I really need this?

Vermonters do use the health care system less than the national average, but that does not mean that we are not overusing it. Our costs are less than they are in other New England states, but does that mean that our costs are not high? No.

Our incomes are less so percentage wise we are still paying as much.

If we had an unlimited supply of money there would be no problem. But if there is a limited amount of money we have to say, "We can't keep throwing money at it."

Government has to take the lead here, because government has allowed people to feel as though there is no limit to how much money we have and what services they can get. Oregon had public meetings and then said we can only pay for these procedures. Then doctors found problems in patients below the line of coverage and said there were things above the line so the patient could get care.

In Oregon, you had public meetings so everyone understood that something was going to happen. Will people still rail against it? Absolutely. Organizations will say it is all wrong. Some will say we should spend whatever is necessary. But if that is correct, why are we having discussions about health care being so expensive?

Some say that everyone should be in the same health care boat. If one person can get it, then everybody should be able to get it. But who said the world's fair?

People from Canada who can afford it come to the United States to get what they can't get in Canada. It won't work to tell people they can't have it even if they can afford it. People will get it.

People look at universal coverage in Canada, Great Britain, Germany, and ask why we can't do it. Fine. Provide their level of services and a lot of our medical benefits will go away. A lot of drugs and pharmaceutical companies will go away.

Americans wouldn't accept that. They want everything and universal coverage, too. People have to understand that they can't get everything. There are limits. And part of those limits is that each person has to take responsibility for his or her health.

Peg Martin

Community Activist

If We Thought Globally

Peg Martin has been involved in county health programs for more than 30 years. She was one of the co-founders of the local Head Start program, a state legislator for 10 years, past president of the board of the adult day care center, and a former consumer representative on the board of the Vermont Program for Quality in Health Care.

I strongly believe that as members of a community, each of us has to be prepared to give a little because at some point we will be taking. We're not very good at this, and I'm not sure that we ever will be.

You can argue that we should only be doing x, y, and z as a health care system. We can all agree that heroic measures at certain points are not warranted. But when it involves friends or family we want a silver bullet. We want to live forever. Nothing is too good.

Yin and yang is probably a pretty crude metaphor, but in some respects these elements cannot be balanced. We have a global view and a personal view and have not found a way to meld the two in a reasonably productive and respectful way.

Until you have everyone in the same leaky health care boat you are not going to have the impetus for making changes. Some people don't understand why there are people who go to the emergency room at 2 in the morning with mouths full of abscessed teeth. It's not part of their ken.

I don't know what the answer is, but former Colorado governor Lamm hits it on the head when he says that we will have to decide what marginal medicine we can morally leave undone if we are to maximize the health of the group. But this is not going to be possible in a comprehensive way until something happens around funding, and we control our medical arms war.

The Vermont Program for Quality in Health Care (VPQHC) has had an impact in areas they have studied—cesarean sections, otitis media, diabetes. These are important, but they are fringe areas in terms of cost. VPQHC has been successful, in part, because it has been very, very careful to involve doctors and hospitals in a non-threatening way that says that we are supporting you as doctors. We are looking at best practices.

VPQHC has not tackled big cost items, like the use of MRIs. Everyone has access to an MRI now, and you can't easily limit its use.

This is all part of our silver-bullet, instant-gratification mentality. I was talking to an obstetrician recently, and he said he had to get a sonogram five years ago because patients were demanding it. When he told an expectant mom that she was fine, that wasn't good enough. She wanted a sonogram. She wanted to see the outlines of her child and post it on her refrigerator.

So the doctor invested in a sonogram. I'd wager if you talked to any obstetrician that they would say exactly the same thing. They have become absolutely run-of-the-mill.

At this point, Porter Hospital is dependent to a significant degree on new services to generate money. Insurers and regulators tell them to cut the length of hospital stays, so what do they do? They bring in a traveling MRI and get their own CAT scanner. Both are important money makers, but you get a snowballing of costs, which is difficult to stop.

If we thought globally and each entity were given a fixed dollop of money to operate, how would they use it? I think there would be a greater inclination to say OK, it makes sense to put this here and do that there. But with fee for service, there is a basic paranoia about cooperating and sharing resources.

I'd like to see Porter Hospital become the umbrella and facilitator of health care and pull together the disparate organizations that sometimes work against each other. This facilitation would have to be with the understanding that all entities have to give up, trade, or split responsibilities and reimbursements.

We have been struggling at Project Independence to build bridges to Porter, to home health care, to individual doctors. It makes all kinds of sense, for example, to provide physical therapy where the folks are, such as at adult day care, and not in a doctor's office or the hospital.

The Vermont Ethics Network is pushing the right buttons in its community discussions on limits to health care, but it is hard to know if they will make a difference. Wanting it all is deeply ingrained in our society.

There will always be the haves and have nots. I'm not sharp enough or well informed enough to say "This is the path" or what the funding or mechanics will be, but we're going to be in trouble if we don't find a way.

I'm a floor scrubber. I work on little pieces and do what I can in the community.

We as a society will have to decide what marginal medicine we can morally leave undone if we are to maximize the health of the group, Peg Martin believes.

Gerry Gossens

State Senator, Addison County

It Is Going to Take a Real Squeaky Wheel

No matter how the debate over health care reform plays out, the state legislature will be in the thick of it. Comprehensive health care reform failed in the legislature in the early 1990s, in part because of the complexity of the process. Since then there have been numerous task forces, studies, and incremental expansions of coverage. What is now needed, Gossens believes, is a sustained, high-profile conversation that is begun by the governor, legislature, and the state's medical leadership and that engages and educates the public. Gossens has been part of the debate both as a state representative (1993-96) and senator (2001-04) and as a member of several local boards, Addison County Home Health and Hospice, the Parent/Child Center, and Porter Medical Center. The interviews were conducted in 2002.

People on the right say let market forces decide. People on the left say the market has no heart and government has to regulate health care. Reform will require a middle-ground approach that incorporates ideas from across the political spectrum, former state senator Gossens believes.

Constituents have several levels of concerns.

Businesses say, "We can't afford to continue to cover our people."

Individuals say, "I can't afford insurance. Can you help me find something?"

And there is a lot of generic complaining. "What are we going to do about health care costs?" "What is the matter with Vermont?"

My standard answer is that health care is not just a Vermont problem. It is a national problem. No one has a handle on it, but we're trying. If there were an easy answer people would have found it by now.

I hear the criticism that no politician ever wants to say no, and I don't believe it. In Vermont we don't have many politicians. We have citizens who are temporarily serving in the legislature. We have some very thoughtful people, but we have not had the leadership in either the Senate or the House or in the governor's office to make health care reform a sustained priority.

We need to have a discussion about what we want, what we can afford, who lives, who dies, who pays, who decides. The sooner we have this societal discussion the better off we will be.

Every health care organization wants to do more. The state government wants to do more. I'm

on the appropriations committee (2002), and we have advocates waiting outside the door who want to make sure that we understand the terrible harm that will be caused by any cut in their budgets.

The legislature doesn't want to underfund worthy programs, but we are constrained by our resources. You learn very quickly in state government that no matter how much money you have people will always want to spend more.

Our job as legislators is to fund agencies as well as we can and to use state money to leverage the most federal money. But here the federal government often does not pay what it says it will. In Vermont, the federal-state cost sharing ratio for

Medicaid bills is about 63-37. The problem is that Vermont hospitals have relatively low costs and as a result the federal government's Medicaid reimbursement rates for state hospitals are among the lowest in the country.

We're coming face to face with the fact that Vermont has one of the most generous Medicaid programs and one of the lowest levels of payments to providers in the country. Medicaid has a menu of 39 services that are supported by one state or another. The Vermont legislature funds 31 of them, among the highest in the nation.

People have said Vermont has world-class health and social services built on a Third World tax base. In the late 1990s, state tax revenues soared from the stock boom. That boom is not going to come back.

How we scale back now is going to be a huge debate.

Oregon in its health care reforms has gotten residents to accept that rationing is viable and essential in controlling costs. Vermont's health care planning is ahead of most states, but we haven't begun that public discussion yet on what we can afford.

Unfortunately, cutting across the health care debate is a tremendous amount of political ideology. On the right you have people who say that medical savings accounts and personal responsibility are the answer. On the left you have people who want a single-payer system now.

People on the right say let market forces decide. People on the left say the market has no heart and government has to regulate. People in the middle are saying that we have to draw from both left and right in order to pass something.

The governor appointed a Bipartisan Commission on Health Care Availability and Affordability last year (2001). The appointments were clearly politically balanced. One member was too far left. One was too far right. The best governance and legislation are in the middle. If you put the extremists on committees then you are going to discredit the committee.

And the report came out in the second year of the biennium, which is too late for legislative action. The report hasn't had any impact. None.

The last time we were really serious about health care reform was in 1994 after the House and Senate appointed a special health care reform committee with senior people from both parties. We came up with attempted health care reform, but couldn't build a majority around any of the options. The consensus was that the 1994 reforms failed because they were seen as too complex, too political, and too influenced by special interests.

It is time for leadership to say, "Let's have this conversation again." Don't appoint a commission and say, "Come back in 18 months."

It's going to take a real squeaky wheel to start this debate. And here the best case is the worst case. We're going to go broke if we don't do something. So we have to do something.

We know what the issues are. We have all the statistics, reports, facts that we need. I would like to see the medical leadership in this state, hospital CEOs, the governor and legislative leaders begin the conversation in a very high-profile way.

I hope the new governor, whoever he is, will have the courage and leadership ability to take this on. If I were governor I'd be talking about it every day. I'd be using the bully pulpit to galvanize public opinion, to educate the public. I'd enlist the media, the press, television. Three weeks of stories on problems in health care would get a lot of attention, too. But you have to sustain this conversation with the governor and the medical leadership constantly talking about the big picture.

Our legislature is us. Unlike any other place in this country, we are very approachable and we hear people's concerns. We have 180 people in the legislature who are going to have to do a lot of work and a lot of listening.

Dr. Jack Mayer

Pediatrician

Health Care Should Be a Basic Human Right Not a Commodity

For Jack Mayer, pediatrics is prevention and public health in action. Mayer, who was instrumental in the creation of the county's Open Door Clinic, believes that we must rethink the delivery of rural health care beginning with medical school training and continuing on with an understanding of the importance of a rural network of supportive services and colleagues. But most important, health care should be viewed as a basic human right where families and children are not at the mercy of the marketplace.

My goal ever since I started medical school has been to practice rural pediatrics. I grew up in the Bronx and came up here when I was a kid with my uncle. He would take me skiing, and I fell in love with Vermont.

I started in private practice in eastern Franklin County in 1976 and looked forward to the challenge of being the first pediatrician. There were a couple of older family practitioners when I came. One was in his 70s or 80s. The other was 90. That part of the county was and still is rural, farming, and sparsely populated.

When I came out of Stanford, I was not prepared to deal with the social issues in a rural practice. I could take care of kidney transplants and very premature babies, but that wasn't what I was seeing. Ninety-five percent of my patients were on Medicaid and much of what I was doing was social medicine.

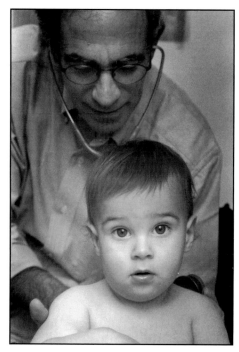

Dr. Dynasaur, which covers about half his patients, has been a great public health success story, Mayer believes.

At Stanford, if you were interested in primary care, it was almost like you were a failure. You weren't rising to your full potential. All my fellow residents are now at medical centers.

That attitude is less the case in Vermont because to UVM's credit they hold primary care in high esteem. And UVM's mission, much more than that of other medical centers, is to produce primary care providers.

A community health center had been set up in Enosburg Falls through a federal grant program that was establishing centers in high-need medical areas. The health center, which was in the old telephone building, provided office space, and I paid

the rent. My office was up a flight of stairs, which isn't a good place for mothers who are carrying babies, and it wasn't handicapped accessible.

My wife and I liked the challenge of homesteading. We lived in Bakersfield, a wonderful rural town, population 854, with lovely neighbors and friends. The psychic income more than made up for the loss of hard income.

Those were some of the best years of my life, but I was serving half of Franklin County and the practice was simply too big. Some days in the dead of winter when I was on call I would see 100 kids. From 8 in the morning until 10 at night, it was wall-to-wall, non-stop. Today, if I see 30 that is a busy day.

The medical need and the social and behavioral problems were huge. I was constantly looking for social service agencies to step in and help, but they were as poorly funded and overwhelmed as my practice. This was during the Reagan years and I was watching community health and social services go down the toilet with defunding. That only contributed to my sense of frustration and burn out.

And there was no way that I was going to get a partner. No one wanted to work for what I was working for. People coming out of residency with $100,000 in debt weren't interested.

After 10 years, feeling increasingly hopeless and burnt out, I said I had to get out. People were unhappy that I was leaving, but I found someone to take my place. A group pediatric practice in St. Albans that had offices in Swanton, Georgia, and Milton opened an office, so it was a smooth transition.

There is still one person there, but I believe he brought in a partner about two years ago. He was able to do that because he was part of the larger group. The year after I left, the center moved into a new facility where social, psychological, dental, and medical services were together. Those kinds of services and facilities attract and keep practitioners, because you feel that you are not alone in the wilderness.

In 1987, I came to Middlebury to work in Dr. Pete's (Dr. Wayne Peters) practice. He was the only pediatric practice in the area and worked with Jody Brakeley, just the two of them. He was looking for a part-time person to join them, because he wanted to cut down.

Coming to Middlebury with its comprehensive medical and social services and good schools was like dying and going to heaven.

We have set up a no-win situation in the way that we have structured medical education and training and in the way rural care is viewed and reimbursed. People coming out of medical school now are so burdened with debt that following their higher moral calling and working where they are not going to make a lot of money is very difficult. It would be lovely if we were like the Europeans and financed medical education and then didn't pay doctors such princely salaries.

This is obviously dreaming, because most physicians in the United States, unlike other countries, expect to be at the top of the economic pile right along with lawyers. It's a real barrier to our ability to distribute and provide care equitably.

If we as a nation decide that equity is important then we need to figure out another way of reimbursing physicians and financing medical education. If we decide that every physician is going to get paid $100,000, then let's pay the person in Enosburg Falls the same as the person in Scarsdale, New York. Most of my colleagues would probably laugh in my face and say, "What kind of socialist babble is this?"

Health care should be viewed as a basic human right, not as a commodity where families and children are at the mercy of the marketplace, Jack Mayer believes.

But over the last 20 years, medical educators have become more attentive to the social dimensions of care. It is certainly something that I stress when I'm teaching medical students and residents.

At least 50% of what I do is prevention and social medicine, which is just as important and maybe more important than dispensing antibiotics. Social medicine is really what medicine is. Medicine is a seamless fabric, and we have artificially tried to distinguish the scientific, evidence-based part of medical care from the social, psychological, and emotional aspects.

How do we convey this to students and residents?

In some sense the substrate has to be there. We have to stop admitting just biology and chemistry majors into medical school and start admitting English and psychology majors. We need people who understand that they are not going into a science-based profession but are going into a social service profession with scientific underpinnings. Science is just part of the larger social, environmental, emotional, and physical fabric.

I have always had a public health perspective on medicine. Pediatrics is public health in action. We immunize kids so we don't have to treat diphtheria. That is the basic premise in pediatrics.

I agree with the saying that politics is medicine writ large. The same principles that govern success or failure in medicine pertain to politics. Prevention is better than treatment. Social stresses cause disease.

What we do in public health affects society more than all our political machinations. Con-

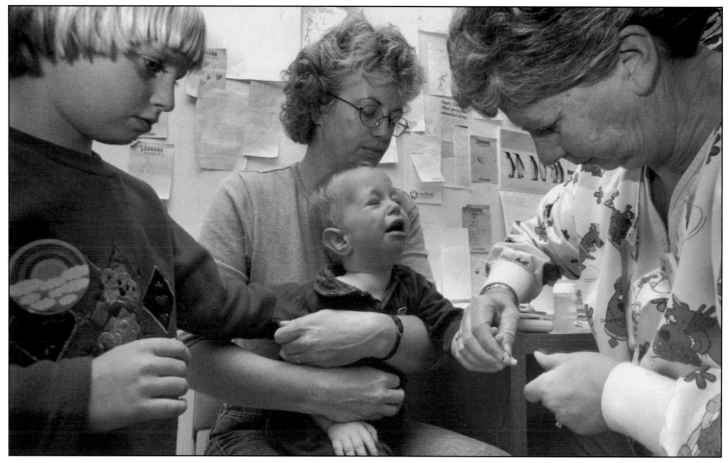

In tight-budget times, cutting children's prevention programs is short-sighted and will be more expensive in the long run, says Mayer.

versely, what we fail to do in public health and in our care of the elderly, children, and the poor is to the detriment of society.

We've come through a wonderful time in the last 8 to 10 years where the state has been very generous in meeting children's health care needs by expanding Dr. Dynasaur and Primary Care Plus. Dr. Dynasaur has made my life as a pediatri-cian immensely more satisfying, because I know people are not looking in their wallet or checking account before they decide to bring their kids in for care. I can provide care without wondering whether they are making decisions between food and health care.

Probably 50% of the kids that I see are cov-ered by Dr. Dynasaur. Dr. Dynasaur pays less than private insurance, but that's fine with me. It has helped me give better care. I can say to people, "You know what?. Maybe your kid doesn't need an antibiotic. Why don't I see you back in two days and see how things are going?"

Before, people would be thinking, "That's another $60. I can't do that."

I'm afraid now that with federal and state

budget deficits we are going to see programs and coverage slide. I'm starting to hear from people who are having difficulties. Their insurance has such a high deductible that they are paying out of pocket for most care or they have no health insurance at all for their kids. They make too much to qualify for Dr. Dynasaur but can't afford insurance.

I'm afraid we are going to repeat what happened in the Reagan years where good programs went down the drain. We are going to lose community health centers. We are going to lose Medicaid and Medicare funding. I have no doubt that some politicians who are making decisions about public health in Washington would be very happy to have Medicare and Medicaid disappear and to revert to a private-pay system.

So I fear for the public health of our county in 5 to 10 years. When you're in deficit, children's health care gets the short end of the stick.

There is a public health ethic in Vermont, but without federal funds our state programs will die. We can't run a deficit in the state. No matter how elevated our own philosophy, goals, and programs, we depend on federal funds for our health care programs.

I hope I am wrong. We are going to suffer unless we apply our public health principles to our political thinking. It is far more expensive and short-sighted to treat illness than it is to prevent it.

But it happened in the 1980s when Reagan cut public health budgets, and there was a huge increase in tuberculosis. Preventable diseases will reappear if people can't get their kids immunized because they can't afford to go to the doctor.

If the state can't afford to provide immunizations then we're not going to be 95% immunized and will see all these diseases come back. This isn't a scare story. This is history. Every time a nation's

immunization rate falls, disease reappears.

I don't know where the new governor (Jim Douglas) is going to get the money, but I hope he doesn't take it from kids' health care and from preventive health services. Making cuts across the board isn't equal sharing. Misery gets shared disproportionately by low-income people.

I've talked about the need for national health insurance for years. Why don't we have national health insurance like the rest of the developed world?

I have seen numbers where one-third of the costs in medical care are for administrative costs. My bookkeeper has billed 150 insurance plans in the past three years. These administrative costs are a nightmare and are only getting worse.

I'm not saying national health insurance is simple or there won't be any problems. It won't be nirvana, but at least there will be equity and we will have a better lifeboat if we all have to share it.

Maybe 10% of my colleagues would stand up and support national health insurance. The other 90% would look at me like some devil from the nether world.

They'd say the government screws up everything that it touches. I say social security and Medicare work. And they'd say I don't want the government telling me how much money I can charge or what I can make. I'm a businessman. This is my business.

But health care should be a basic human right not a commodity. Families and children should not be at the mercy of the marketplace.

People would complain, but it can't be as messy or as expensive as the system we have now. What we have now is such a waste of money and so unfair.

The impetus in medicine is toward more technological wizardry that is expensive and is not available unless you have the insurance to pay for it. Do we need more heart transplants or more community health centers? I'm not sure we can have both, which raises the question of rationing medical care.

We will have to set a budgetary cap on our health care expenses and say this is what we can spend. There will be hard decisions, but we're rationing care now through ability to pay, which is inherently unfair.

In pediatrics the ethical dimensions of these choices are clear. We're making decisions for children, who have no say or ability to pay, that will determine their health. Children don't decide to be born to parents without money or health insurance.

Acknowledgments

Listening to the community and its concerns for this portrait required the willing participation of many.

A first thank you must go to the Addison County residents in this portrait who sat down for one, two, and sometimes three interviews during the initial interviewing period, 2000-2002. Some participants patiently allowed me to shadow and photograph them for day-in-the-life photographs prior to the interviews.

These taped interviews, from one to two hours-plus, were edited and then returned, often with many follow-up questions, for the interviewee's review and approval. Interviews were excerpted in several formats prior to their collection in this book: a series of newspaper articles in *The Addison Independent* in 2003 and a more extensive collection for the advisory committee of the Department of Banking, Insurance, Securities and Health Care Administration developing the Health Resources Allocation Plan in 2004-2005.

Health care institutions, personnel, and programs are constantly evolving. For the most part, these interviews reflect conditions during 2000-2002. In some interviews, I have inserted in parentheses more recent figures and developments; I have also included an epilogue with several individuals. I have also added post-interview material in photo captions and in my introductions.

Other county residents, who do not appear in the book, shared their observations. Among them were Rita Andrews, Dr. Ray Collins, Dick Forman, Jeannie Harden, Ed Lieberman, Sandy Martin, Virginia Moser, Dr. Brad and Helen Patterson, Edi Poland, Jim Ross, and Naomi Tannen.

Beyond the residents in this portrait, many others shared their time and experience and helped arrange interviews.

At Porter Hospital, Ron Hallman was always helpful and prompt in providing historical and contemporary information, as were Jan Connors and Laurie Ahearn. Margaret Clerkin at Elderly Services, Inc. and David Andrews and Mary Pepe, at the Counseling Service of Addison County, were similarly helpful.

Hamilton Davis shared his knowledge of the Vermont hospital system and the role of community hospitals and was instrumental, in the early days, in shaping the project. David Napier at Middlebury College was similarly helpful throughout the project.

While this portrait is primarily an account of contemporary health care, our health care system is a continuum. Hans Raum at Middlebury College's Starr Library, Nancy Rucker and Suzanne Douglas at the Henry Sheldon Museum of Vermont History, and Bob Sekarak at the Dana Library of the College of Medicine at the University of Vermont were helpful in providing background material and searching their archives for the letters, records, and histories that are part of the chapter introductions. Bea Grause and Greg Farnum at the Vermont Association of Hospitals and Health Systems provided material on current conditions.

Many members of the Vermont Folklife Center in Middlebury have been helpful throughout the project: Jane Beck, executive director; Greg Sharrow, director of education; Christina Barr and Andy Kolovos, archivists. The Center, which gave me a grant to help transcribe interviews, will receive the full transcripts of the interviews, which run to 500,000 words, and the documentary photographs for its archives.

I have sought the advice of many about ways to share the Addison County experience. A special thanks must go to Angelo Lynn, publisher of *The Addison Independent*; John Campbell, executive director of the Vermont Ethics Network; John Crowley, Commissioner of the Department of Banking, Insurance, Securities and Health Care Administration; Ellen Oxfeld, Nancy Potak, Deb Richter, and Lynn Rothwell at Vermont Health Care for All; Dr. Mildred Reardon, associate dean for primary care at the College of Medicine at the University of Vermont; and Larissa Vigue at the Vermont Humanities Council.

This portrait has been a joint publishing production with United Way of Addison County. MaryEllen Mendl, executive director, has been generous in her time, support, and advice throughout the year-long publication process, as has been board member Liz Fitzsimmons. Thank you also to the board for its support.

Several community members read the initial manuscript and had valuable suggestions: Andy Kolovos, Peg and Sandy Martin, Dr. Jack Mayer, and Joshua Sherman. Bill Orr, as always, was a perceptive critic.

Publication of this portrait has been made possible by grants from several foundations and from generous community support. Many grant-wise people have been generous in their advice. Among them are Lydia Brownell, Julie Cadwallader-Staub, Mary Conlon, and Anne Jones-Weinstock at the Vermont Community Foundation.

Jan Albers, Catherine Bollinger, Gail Freidin, Charlie Kireker, Kate McGowan, Cheryl Mitchell, Spence Putnam, Maggie Quinn, Len Rowell, and

Joshua Sherman also shared their knowledge of community giving and the grant world. Adrienne Cohen provided invaluable constructive criticism on our grant applications.

The Fletcher Allen Community Health Foundation was the principal supporter of the project with a $10,000 community challenge grant. Penrose Jackson, chief staff person for the foundation, has been very helpful throughout the fund-raising process.

Many organizations and individuals have contributed toward the community match, among them: Addison County Home Health and Hospice, Chittenden Bank, Citizens Bank, Cooperative Insurance, Counseling Service of Addison County, MarbleWorks Pharmacy, Porter Hospital Auxiliary, Project Independence, Rotary Club of Middlebury, Shoreham Telephone, Twin Birches, United Way of Addison County, Vermont Federal Credit Union, Vermont Medical Society, and WomenSafe. The Cerf Community Fund and the Merchants Bank Foundation contributed generously toward the match.

The Lintilhac Foundation provided the initial support for the project. Director Nancy Brink was helpful throughout.

Many people have offered advice on book preparation and publication. Among them were John Crowl at Thistle Hill Publications and Phyllis Deutsch and Sarah Welsch at the University Press of New England. Book publisher Paul Eriksson was generous with his advice, as were Sally and Upton Brady.

Mason Singer had sound advice on book printers. A special thanks to Steve Alexander and Phyllis Bartling of Futura Design, who designed and prepared the book. Phyllis spent many late hours getting text and photographs to flow and fit.

Steve Jensen brought a careful eye to his proofreading of the galleys.

Don Patterson brought his years of thinking about the role of the documentary photojournalist in helping shape the project for the better.

David Moats brought a fair-minded perspective on the current health care reform debate in his foreword.

Finally, a heartfelt thank you to my wife Paula and daughter Anne for putting up with the mess in the study, the living room, and nearly every flat surface in the house. The boxes can now go to the basement.

This project began many years ago. My thanks to my father, a family doctor, and mother for caring about their communities.

About the Authors

George Bellerose, a freelance photojournalist, has lived in Addison County for the past 15 years. He has been a reporter at city dailies and rural weeklies and an editor and writer at three colleges. Among his previous books are *Facing the Open Sea: The People of Big Tancook Island* and *The Vermont Achievement Center: 40 Years of Service,* a history of handicapped services for Vermont children.

David Moats, a longtime resident of Addison County, won the 2001 Pulitzer Prize for the "even handed and influential" editorials that he wrote for *The Rutland Herald* (Vt.) on the passage of civil unions legislation. His book, *Civil Wars: A Battle for Gay Marriage,* covers the developments that led to the state's passage of the country's first civil unions legislation.